A Catalogue of The VanderPoel Dickens Collection
at The University of Texas

TOWER   BIBLIOGRAPHICAL   SERIES   NO.   1
Second Edition

A CATALOGUE OF

The VanderPoel Dickens Collection

AT THE UNIVERSITY OF TEXAS

Compiled by
Sister Lucile Carr, C.D.P.

THE UNIVERSITY OF TEXAS AT AUSTIN

PR
4580
.U65
1968

Published by
THE HUMANITIES RESEARCH CENTER
THE UNIVERSITY OF TEXAS AT AUSTIN

Distributed by
UNIVERSITY OF TEXAS PRESS
AUSTIN, TEXAS

Printed and bound in the United States of America

PREFACE TO THE NEW EDITION

The Dickens collection at The University of Texas, recently augmented by the fine collection of Mr. Halstead VanderPoel and renamed for him, is sufficiently enlarged to require this new catalogue.

Outstanding among the new acquisitions is the album of original water-color and pencil illustrations to *Pickwick* drawn for F. W. Cosens by "Phiz" (A157). A pre-publication copy of *A Christmas Carol* [B356(1)] with the text in a state antedating that of the inscribed presentation copies is, perhaps, the most exciting of the original editions in Mr. VanderPoel's collection. This little volume with green end papers and blue and red title page dated 1843, retains a spelling error and two other points that antedate the earliest recorded copies.

Numerous early American editions are testimony to Mr. VanderPoel's persevering zeal in assembling and preserving these early and too often fragile products of the first American publishing houses. Simple piracies, antedating the copyright law, are none the less interesting, for around them developed the concept of an author's legal right to his literary products. Dickens, who suffered perhaps more than his predecessors at the hands of literary pirates at home and abroad, in fighting for his own right became the benefactor of many who followed him in the business of writing books.

Perusing the VanderPoel Dickens collection has been a joy. To all in the Humanities Research Center and Miriam Lutcher Stark Library of The University of Texas who have added so much to that joy, many thanks. To Mr. Halstead VanderPoel, thanks in the name of all who come to share the fruits of many years of book collecting.

Austin, Texas, 22 April 1968   SISTER LUCILE CARR, C.D.P.

CONTENTS

ILLUSTRATIONS

INTRODUCTION

In the Humanities Research Center in The University of Texas is a unique unit of a fine collection of rare books to delight the heart of any bibliophile: first editions—in most instances first issues—of all major and secondary works of Charles Dickens. A gathering of Pickwick and Sam Weller; Micawber, Mr. Dick, and Betsy Trotwood; Sairy Gamp; Captain Cuttle; Scrooge and Tiny Tim as they came into this world is more than a collection of books. The unity of their world defies the disparate inhumanity of the word. Swinburne said "Sam Weller and Charles Dickens came to life together, immortal and twin born"; and Sam was but the first of many brethren to claim immortality from their great progenitor and confer it, in turn, on him who begot them.

Too seldom do we find this favored company together in pristine glory, as Dickens himself knew them—the original "green leaves" embellished with etchings by Cruikshank, Seymour, or "Phiz"; the first little gilt-edge Christmas book boasting John Leech's jolly illustrations of "Mr. Fezziwig's Ball" and "Scrooge's Third Visitor." Notices from author or publisher, telling of a tragic death or a broken plate, here account for missing illustrations, erasing the years since the sheets rolled from the press and these first copies reached the newsstands. Here, within the charmed circle, one slides on the very ice that bore the weight of Pickwick at Dingley Dell and hears that stroke of twelve which announced Scrooge's ghostly visitor.

The most remarkable feature of this collection, specifically as a collection, is probably its near approach to completeness. It is not lacking, however, in individual items in themselves worthy of notice—foremost among them an unrecorded "prime" *Pickwick* in parts. Monthly and, in the case of *Master Humphrey's Clock*, weekly parts of all subsequent works are here assembled, together with the original bound volume and many early American editions. Where the bound volume preceded the issue in parts, the original issue is invariably included in the collection. *Sketches by Boz*, for example, is represented by the two-volume first edition of the first series in original bindings and in remarkably fine condition; the first issue of the first edition of the second series is also in its original binding and in good condition, as is the first complete American edition. *Oliver Twist* is equally well represented in variant forms of the first issue of the first three-volume edition in the original brown cloth and the rare one-volume octavo edition in slate-colored cloth; in addition there are two American "firsts"—Carey, Lea and Blanchard's printing of the first two chapters, which antedated the first English edition in book form, and Colyer's first complete American edition, pirated from *Bentley's Miscellany*. Those rare early pieces—*A Sunday Under Three Heads, The Village Coquettes,* and *A Strange Gentleman*—are all present, two of them in varying states.

Association items are generously represented. Copies of *Pickwick* are inscribed to Sir James Emerson Tennent, to whom Dickens later dedicated *Our Mutual Friend,* and to Charles Kent, whom he claimed as his "most genial reader." A pre-publication set of *A Child's History of England* bears an inscription and a letter to Marcus Stone, who later illustrated *Our Mutual Friend.* There are two presentation sets of the original edition of *Great Expectations:* one from Dickens to the manager of his reading tours, Arthur Smith, and the second from Jane Carlyle.

Items of unusual interest in the following catalogue of the collection are indicated by daggers; those which we have not found recorded in standard bibliographies are marked with asterisks. Duplicates are included only in the few instances where there seemed special reason to mention them, cases where only a small number of other copies are known.

Collation of the issues in monthly numbers follows that in the standard works of Hatton and Cleaver and John Eckels. The word "lacking" in this catalogue, however, while it indicates the absence of an item mentioned in these bibliographies, does not necessarily imply that the issue described is of an inferior or later state. It seems reasonable to believe, particularly in cases where the absence of an advertisement is the more usual condition, that the earliest copies were bound without a certain pink or yellow slip.

The wealth of contemporary secondary material in the collection is relevant evidence of such capitalizing on Dickens's tremendous popularity. Some of it, as Cruikshank's charming original water-color illustrations to *Oliver Twist,* is of value in its own right. The collection includes a great many of the artistic and dramatic effusions, both bad and good, that followed the appearance of a new work by Dickens.

While no other collection, indeed not all other collections combined, could compete in original manuscripts with that bequeathed by John Forster—with subsequent acquisitions—to the Victoria and

Albert Museum, the Texas Collection has at least one manuscript, "The Ivy Green," written and signed by "Boz" in the album of Georgina Ross before he included it in Chapter VI of *Pickwick*, and more than 150 holograph letters, including sets of unpublished letters to Thomas Mitton and Lieutenant Frederick Tracey. There is also a complete MS. copy of H. B. Farnie's unpublished play, *The Golden Dustman*.

This delightful and imposing "world of Dickens" includes volumes in the collections of T. E. Hanley, Mrs. Miriam Lutcher Stark, John Henry Wrenn, "Ellery Queen," George A. Aitken, and, above all, the collection acquired by The University of Texas from Edwin Bachmann. Together they form a magnificent "whole."

With sincere gratitude, I acknowledge my indebtedness to President Harry H. Ransom of The University of Texas, who proposed the project and opened the doors of a delightful world to me, and to Mrs. Frances Hudspeth, his executive assistant, who in many ways has facilitated the work and increased the pleasure. Finally, my thanks are due to Dr. William B. Todd of the Humanities Research Center, who has read and reread the manuscript with infinite care and patience. His is the planning that has produced this first volume of a bibliographical series to be issued by the Research Center.

Austin, Texas, 20 July 1960　　　　SISTER MARY CALLISTA CARR

AUTOGRAPH MANUSCRIPTS AND OTHER

ORIGINAL WORK

1 : HOLOGRAPH POEM

A1

Poem, "The Ivy Green," in Dickens's holograph, signed, "Boz," in Georgina Ross's album [1836]. With one slight change ["stateliest building" for "proudest Edifice" in stanza III], the poem was later used in Chapter VI of *Pickwick Papers*.

A letter from Georgina Ross [a relative of the Barrows, distantly related to Dickens] to her niece, Janet Knox, states that this MS. antedates Dickens's use of the verses in *Pickwick*. It appears to be the only signed page of MS. extant for that work.

The album containing this MS. and a letter from Dickens to Miss Ross (A60) was valued by Ernest Maggs at £750 to £1000. He purchased it for the Count de Suzannet, in whose possession it remained until the dispersal of this collection in 1938.

A play by Mervyn Nelson, taking its title from this poem, opened on Broadway in April 1949, with a young actor from the Abbey Theatre, Daniel O'Herlily, as Charles Dickens. See illustration.

2 : LETTERS BY DICKENS

A2*

To Henry Austin: "11 Selwood Terrace, Queen's Elms, Monday Morning" [1834–1836]. Thanks for a critique printed in *The Chronicle*.

A3*

To Messrs. Chapman and Hall: "Petersham, Wednesday afternoon" [1836]. Enclosing copy for *Pickwick*, which Dickens characterizes as "a *very good bit* to finish with."

A4*

To E[dward] Lloyd: "48 Doughty Street, Monday Morning" [Nov., 1837]. A trip made possible by the conclusion of *Pickwick* prevents Dickens from "taking the chair at the Institution."

A5*

To Miss [Agnes] Strickland: "Twickenham Park Sunday Morning" [June–July 1838]. Concerning contributions for *Pic-Nic Papers*.

A6*

To Thomas Mitton: "Doughty Street, Monday Morning" [Nov., 1839]. Dickens decides, on the advice of W. C. Macready, not to take a house at 10 Kent Terrace because of the objectionable proximity of some stables.

Letter signed with initials only; with signed and addressed envelope.

A7°

To William Upcott: "Devonshire Terrace, Friday 6th March 1840." Fulfilling a request of Upcott's and mentioning Dickens's recent return from Bath.

Bound in *Memoirs of Joseph Grimaldi*, item B600, compiled by Upcott.

A8°

To Thomas Campbell: "1 Devonshire Terrace, York Gate Regents Park, 19th July 1840." Thanks for a letter and warm profession of admiration for Campbell's "genius."

A9

To George Cattermole: "Devonshire Terrace, Thursday August 13th" [1840]. Requesting a design and giving suggestions for a frontispiece for *The Old Curiosity Shop*.

Published in Nonesuch edition I, 268.

A10°

To Thomas Mitton: "Broadstairs, 6th October" [1840]. Request that funds be deposited at Coutts's.

Letter signed with initials only; with addressed envelope marked "Private," postmarked with the date.

A11°

To Thomas Mitton: "Christmas Eve 1840." Invitation to charades with the Smithsons. [Smithson was Mitton's senior partner.]

Letter signed with initials only.

A12°

To Mrs. Hurnall: "Devonshire Terrace, Saturday April The Seventeenth, 1841." Defers meeting because of press of work.

A13°

To Lieutenant Augustus Frederick Tracey: "1 Devonshire Terrace, York Gate Regents Park, Monday Mᵍ April The Twenty Sixth" [1841]. Sending money and offering cast-off clothing for a "(supposed) tailor" in jail [under Tracey's supervision at Tothill Fields]; expresses admiration for Tracey's humanitarian works.

A14°

To Lieutenant Tracey: "Devonshire Terrace, Wednesday The Twenty Eighth April, 1841." Following up the philanthropies mentioned in the previous letter and sending a donation to be given, at Tracey's discretion, to someone leaving the prison at Tothill Fields.

Signature excised.

A15*
To Lieutenant Tracey: "Devonshire Terrace, Tuesday May The Eighteenth 1841." Announcing that Dickens would bring three friends to view Tracey's "charge."

A16
To George Cattermole: "Devonshire Terrace, Wednesday Evening, July The Twenty Eighth 1841." Requesting illustrations for *Barnaby Rudge* and describing Dickens's idea of a riot scene in old John Willet's bar.
Published in Nonesuch edition I, 342.

A17*
To Thomas Mitton: "Devonshire Terrace, Friday October Twenty Nine" [1841]. About plans and necessary insurance for Dickens's trip to America.
Letter signed with initials only; with signed and addressed envelope.

A18*
To George Fletcher: "1 Devonshire Terrace, York Gate Regents Park, Second November, 1841." Refusing request for financial help.

A19*
To Justice [Joseph] Story: "Fuller's Hotel, Wednesday Ninth March 1842." Presenting Dickens's compliments and forwarding letters from England.
Formal note in third person.

A20*
To Thomas Mitton: "Broadstairs, Sunday" [August 1842]. ". . . I have nearly killed myself with laughing at what I have done on the American No.—though how much comicality may be in my knowledge of its Truth, I can't say. I seem to hear the people talking again. . . ."
Letter signed with initials only.

A21*
To Lieutenant Tracey: "Broadstairs, Kent, Sunday Eleventh September 1842." ". . . In my book on America, I purpose introducing this note. Please to inform me, in one line (directed here, where I am staying quietly, until the end of the month) whether there is anything in it, you would wish altered or omitted."

A22*
To Thomas Mitton: "Broadstairs, Twenty Eight September 1842. . . . I suppose it will be best to let him [Dickens's father?] have the cheque. . . ."
With signed and addressed envelope.

A23*

To Thomas Mitton: "Devonshire T., Monday afternoon" [1842]. "No. 18 of Parley's is out with this Inscription on the front 'that for reasons stated on the back, No. 17 will not be published until next week.' . . . The wording of the notice *may* serve our end."

Letter signed with initials only; with signed and addressed envelope.

A24*

To Thomas Mitton: "Devonshire Terrace, Thursday Morning" [Oct. 1842]. "I am paralyzed by having to tell you that the American Professor [Longfellow] whom I expected on the 10th suddenly made his appearance here, last night. Hence I'm captive today—. . ."

Letter signed with initials only; with signed and addressed envelope.

A25*

To Thomas Mitton: "In haste, Devonshire Terrace, Eighteenth November 1842." Deferring an appointment because of a postponed meeting at the Sanatorium.

With signed and addressed envelope.

A26*

To Thomas Mitton: "Saturday Mᵍ. Xmas Eve, 9 O'Clock" [1842]. Recalling a promise to attend the pantomime.

Letter signed with initials only.

A27*

To Thomas Mitton: "Devonshire Terrace, Tenth May, 1843." Making an appointment.

With addressed envelope.

A28*

To Lieutenant Tracey, addressed "Govornor": "1 Devonshire Terrace, York Gate Regents Park, Seventh June 1843." A facetious denial in Cockney dialect that Dickens had Tracey's umbrella, followed by a "Memorandum added by the chaplin" that it had been found in the unfortunate man's possession.

Letter signed "Villium Gibbuns, his mark."

A29*

To Lieutenant Tracey: "Devonshire Terrace, Ninth June 1843." Arranging to pick up Tracey for an engagement with Dr. Howe, ". . . a cold-blooded fellow . . . a regular American. . . ."

Signature excised.

A30*

To Captain [Frederick] Marryat: "Broadstairs, Kent, Sixth September 1843." Making plans for a trip to Langham and referring to *American Notes:* "It gives me great pleasure to find that you like the tickling. I shall go in again before I have done, and give the Eagle a final poke under his fifth rib."

A31*

To Thomas Mitton: "Twenty Fifth November 1843." Giving directions for handling some bills [contracted by Dickens's father ?].

Letter signed with initials only; with signed and addressed envelope.

A32

To John Overs: "Devonshire Terrace, Tenth May 1844 Friday." Suggesting Newby and Mortimer as prospective publishers [for *Evenings of a Working Man*.] Laid in copy of this book (B606).

Letter signed with initials only.

Published in Nonesuch edition I, 600.

A33*

To Thomas Curry: "Albaro. Saturday Thirty First August 1844." An invitation to dinner.

A34

To Mme. De la Rue: "Peschiere, Wednesday Morning" [1844]. ". . . with very bad grace, . . . I am obliged to deny myself the pleasure of coming to you this morning. . . ."

Bound together with a letter to J. S. Le Fanu (A131) in an octavo case of red levant morocco.

Published in Nonesuch edition I, 630.

A35*

To Lieutenant Tracey: "Devonshire Terrace, Fourth September 1845." Requesting Tracey to give to Dickens's father his opinion regarding a "curious case of Mysterious Disappearance."

A36*

To the Countess of Blessington: "Devonshire Terrace, Thursday Thirtieth October 1845." Offers to arrange for a box [repetition of the Amateur Theatricals at Miss Kelly's Theatre]; ". . . in the distraction of these great newspaper [The *Daily News*] arrangements, I find the little book [*The Chimes*] trots along—sometimes walks indeed—and sometimes stops altogether." See illustration.

A37*

To Lieutenant Tracey: "Devonshire Terrace, Monday Twenty Third March 1846." An amusing invitation to dinner.

A38*

To Mr. B^x: "1 Devonshire Terrace, Sixteenth Sept. 1846." Informing the correspondent that Dickens's "connexion with the *Daily News* does not extend to the acceptance or rejection of papers offered for publication," and that he had referred them to the editor [John Forster].

Formal note in third person.

A39*

To Lieutenant Tracey: "1 Chester Place, Regents Park Monday Morning March Eighth 1847." Dickens and Mrs. Dickens returned unexpectedly from Paris because Charley, who had been at King's College, had developed scarlet fever. An amusing letter inviting Tracey to call.

A40*

To Lady Lovelace: "1 Chester Place Regents Park, Thirty First March 1847." Requesting the address of Sir George Cranford.

A41*

To Lieutenant Tracey: "1 Chester Place Friday Ninth April 1847." Reminder of a dinner engagement.

Note signed "The Inimitable B."

A42*

To Lieutenant Tracey: "Chester Place Tenth June 1847." Dickens taking a gentleman from Lausanne, Switzerland, who had founded asylums for the blind, to observe Tracey's management of the prison at Tothill Fields.

Signature excised.

A43*

To Miss Biffin: "Devonshire Terrace, London, Twenty Seventh October 1847." Refusing to place his name on a subscription list.

Formal note in third person.

A44*

To Lieutenant Tracey: "Devonshire Terrace Thursday Night October Twenty Eighth 1847." Sending copies of an address and asking about the availability of Tracey's chaplain at Tothill Fields for Miss Coutts's "Home" at Shepherd's Bush.

A45*

To Alexander Ireland: "London, 1 Devonshire Terrace York Gate Regents Park Eighteenth November 1847." Explaining Dickens's inability to fulfill a promise to go to Manchester.

A46*

To Lieutenant Tracey: "Devonshire Terrace Twenty First November 1847." Arranging a meeting.

Letter incomplete; signature excised.

A47*
To Lieutenant Tracey: "Devonshire Terrace Monday Thirteenth December 1847." Setting Monday for committee meetings.

Letter incomplete; signature excised.

A48*
To Thomas Bowden: "1 Devonshire Terrace York Gate Regents Park Twenty Fourth December 1847." Sending check for advertising charges of the *Morning Herald* omitted from some previous statement.

A49*
To Lieutenant Tracey: "Edinburgh Thirty First December 1847." A New Year's greeting.

A50*
To [G. H.] Lewes: "Devonshire Terrace Twelfth April 1848." "Many thanks for your book, . . . I can't call a second farce for Saturday; having just got the Review, and fearing that I decry impracticabilities therein." Laid in a copy of *The Village Coquettes* [B525(1)].

Letter signed with initials only.

A51*
To Messrs. Reeve: "Devonshire Terrace, Tuesday Twenty Fifth April, 1848." Acknowledging receipt of a communication.

Formal note in third person.

A52*
To Lieutenant Tracey: "Devonshire Terrace. Thursday Twenty Fifth May 1848." Concerning amateur theatricals for the endowment of a curatorship of Shakespeare's house. Requesting advice about playing at Plymouth.

A53*
To Lieutenant Tracey: "Manchester, Tuesday 30th May 1848." Abandoning the idea of a performance at Plymouth.

A54*
To Lieutenant Tracey: "Broadstairs, Kent Twenty Sixth September 1948." Changing date of a meeting at Shepherd's Bush.

A55*
To William Sawyer: "Bedford Hotel, Brighton First December 1848." ". . . I thank you, very earnestly indeed for your unaffected assurance of interest and regard—. . ."

A56*
To Lieutenant Tracey: "Devonshire Terrace Wednesday" [1848]. Mentioning Dickens's intention to call to get information about some points in *Dombey.*
Signature excised.

A57*
To Mr. Mason: "Devonshire Terrace, Second April 1849." Concerning possible purchase of a gelding and sale of Dickens's "little mare."

A58*
To Lieutenant Tracey: "Devonshire Terrace Friday Night Fifteenth June 1849." Reminder of meeting at Shepherd's Bush.
Letter incomplete; signature excised.

A59*
To Lieutenant Tracey: "Devonshire Terrace Saturday Third November 1849." Refusing an invitation because of the arrival of friends.
Signature excised.

A60*
To Miss [Georgina] Ross: "Devonshire Terrace Twenty First January 1850." ". . . If you can suggest to me . . . any particular book or subject, Spanish or German, of which you could write a popular account, I will immediately tell you whether it would fit what I have in my mind. It should be interesting, of course; if somewhat romantic, so much the better; we can't be too wise, but we must be very agreeable. . . ." Laid in album containing MS. of "The Ivy Green" (A1).

A61*
To Miss [Georgina] Ross: "Devonshire Terrace, Twenty Ninth January 1850." About an article for *Household Words.*

A62*
To B[?]. Lang: "Devonshire Terrace Fourteenth June 1850 Friday Evening." Acknowledging complaint about an article and praising Lang's art. ". . . I think the fancy you have been instrumental in introducing into this country was much needed here."

A63*
To The Reverend I. Mould: "Broadstairs, Kent, Frid⁷ Evening Eighteenth October 1850." Sending money for a "benevolent object."

A64*
To Mrs. [Richard] Watson: "Office of *Household Words,* Saturday Twenty Sixth October 1850." "As Copperfield is *your* book, you know, it has occurred to me that you might possibly like to see the end of it

before the rest of the World does. . . . I sent you the sheets of the conclusion. Will you and Watson . . . kindly keep them to yourselves until publication-time?"

A65*
To Lord Denman: "Devonshire Terrace Monday Sixteenth December 1850." ". . . I have an inexpressible horror of slavery and all its atrocities; but I have avoided (as yet) any more distinct expression of opinion on the subject than is suggested by the article to which you refer, because I am *not* satisfied that the African Blockade advances the great end it is designed to promote. . . ."

A66*
To Lord John Russell: "Devonshire Terrace Twenty Fourth December 1850." Thanks for a pension granted John Poole, with a long description of Dickens's first meeting with the actor in Paris.

A67*
To Lieutenant Tracey: "Devonshire Terrace Twentieth February 1851." ". . . Supposing you have discovered nothing adverse to her story, we will take the little girl I saw. . . ."

A68*
To Lieutenant Tracey: "Devonshire Terrace Sunday Ninth March 1851." Requesting permission for [R. H.] Horne to visit Tracey's "boys" in preparation of an article for *Household Words.*

A69*
To Professor Owen: "Devonshire Terrace Seventeenth May 1851." ". . . A perfect storm of letters of introduction rising in all quarters of the Earth and bursting on my devoted head, oblige me to take a house at the seaside, and let this until the Exhibition is over. . . ."

A70*
To Mr. [T. J.?] Thompson: "Guild of Literature and Art, Saturday June 21st 1851." Regrets that a dinner engagement with Miss Coutts will prevent his accepting Thompson's invitation.
Letter signed with initials only.

A71*
To Lieutenant Tracey: "Broadstairs Kent Tenth July 1851." Concerning the transfer of a young woman "of the name of Jessup" from Tothill Fields to Miss Coutts's "Home" at Shepherd's Bush.

A72*
To Lieutenant Tracey: "Broadstairs Kent Friday Tenth October 1851." A complaint that "all the Nations of the Earth brought letters of introduction to me in London—and there was nothing for it but Flight."

A73*

To William Farren: "Athenaeum Club Saturday Evening Twenty Fourth Octr. 1851." Protesting an inconvenience suffered at Farren's theatre.

A74*

To Lieutenant Tracey: "Shepherd's Bush Tuesday Fourth November 1851." Concerning the discharge of a girl [Mary Anne Church ?] who had taken a "bonnet and gown" with an offer—if Tracey chose to intercede— to give her another chance.

Letter signed with initials only.

A75*

To Lieutenant Tracey: "Tavistock House Fifth February 1852." Requesting assistance in finding some interested person who might receive Mary Anne Church, who was giving trouble and must be sent from the "Home."

A76*

To Lovell Reeve: "28, Feb 1852." Thanking Reeve for a copy of the *Literary Gazette* and commending a paper on Shelley as "manly, generous, and gallant championship."

A77*

To Lieutenant Tracey: "Tavistock House Fourth March 1852." Reporting the death of John Forster's mother at Newcastle.

Letter signed with initials only.

A78*

To Lieutenant Tracey: "Tavistock House Sixth March 1852." A facetious note announcing that Dickens would be on hand for dinner.

Letter signed with initials only.

A79*

To William Howitt: "Tavistock House Tuesday Evg Eighteenth May 1852." ". . . I have reserved the religious credulity paper in the hope (having very great faith in the perpetual appearance of that class of maniac [?] before the public), that something might occur to render its publication particularly seasonable. . . ."

With signed and addressed envelope.

A80*

To Mrs. [Catherine Grace Frances] Gore: "Tavistock House. Twenty Seventh January 1853." Acknowledging receipt of a book and an "unexpected compliment" [a dedication to Dickens ?].

A81

To Richard Henry Horne: "*Household Words* Office, Wednesday, Second March 1853." Dickens's account of a performance of Bulwer-Lytton's comedy, "Not So Bad As We Seem," at the Haymarket, with references to articles contributed by Horne to *Household Words* and news from London for Horne, who was in Australia. With a postscript by W. H. Wills: ". . . The wholesale Literary pirates of America are at last to be brought within the pale of the law, a Treaty for International Copyright has been presented to the States Senate for formal confirmation, and will, there is no doubt, be ratified. . . ."

Bound together with a copy of T. J. Wise's privately issued pamphlet, [B657(2)], in a case of red levant morocco.

A82*

To Mr. Tidbury: "Tavistock House, Second April, 1853." Refusing invitation.

Formal letter in third person.

A83*

To Lieutenant Tracey: "Tavistock House Sunday Fifteenth May 1853." Requesting that Tracey have a guide take Professor Felton around Tothill Fields.

A84*

To Lieutenant Tracey: "Tavistock House Twenty Seventh May 1853." An invitation to dinner.

Letter signed with initials only.

A85*

To Lady Eastlake: "Pavilion, Folkestone Saturday Eleventh June 1853." An amusing account of Dickens's illness. ". . . Since Monday last, I have been shaving a man every morning—a stranger to me—with big gaunt eyes and a hollow cheek—whose appearance was rather irksome and offensive. I am happy to say he has at last retired from the looking-glass, and is replaced by the familiar personage whom I have lathered and scraped these twenty years. . . ."

A86*

Open letter: [Sept., 1853]. "William Cooper Domestique Anglais. Il va rester a Boulogne chez M. Charles Dickens. Chateau des Molineaux."

Note of identification, unsigned and undated.

A87*

To F. M. Evans: "Office of *Household Words*, Saturday Tenth September 1853." Regretting Dickens's inability to be with Evans on a "great family occasion."

A88°

To F. M. Evans: "Boulogne, Saturday Eighth October 1853." ". . . I do not think I can further abridge the *Child's History*, without doing it damage. I would decidedly give the public the benefit of the larger quantity. . . . I have corrected all the proofs for *Household Words*. For Press, I think you had best send them for revision *both* to *Wills and Forster*."

A89

To Marcus Stone: "Tavistock House Nineteenth December 1853." "You made an excellent sketch from a book of mine, which I received (and have preserved) with great pleasure. Will you accept from me, in remembrance of it, *this* little book [*A Child's History of England*]. I believe it to be true, though it may be sometimes not as genteel as History has a habit of being." Laid in Stone's copy [B499(1)] with transcript of his notes concerning the incident.

Published in Nonesuch edition II, 526. See illustration.

Marcus Stone recalled that, at the age of twelve, having "eagerly devoured" the fourth number of *Bleak House*, he was "at work upon an illustration of 'Jo' the sweeps & the gateway of the graveyard where his kind friend the poor law writer had just been buried." Dickens came into the room, looked over his shoulder, and commented: "That's very good. You must give it to me when it is done." In return, Stone received a proof of Phiz's illustration that he "might see how 'Phiz' had treated the same locality." A year and a half later he received a pre-publication presentation copy [B499(1)] of *A Child's History of England.*

A90°

To Lieutenant Tracey: "Tavistock House   Wednesday Night   First February 1854," Arranging to see a girl who was to be sent to Miss Coutts's "Home."

A91°

To Lieutenant Tracey: "Tavistock House   Thirtieth March   1854." "Thanks! Indiscretion itself, in capital letters forty feet high."

Letter signed with initials only.

A92°

To "Henry" [Austin]: "Tavistock House   Friday   Nineteenth May 1854   10 O'Clock a.m." Sending an enclosure with some added advice. ". . . It seems to me that your best course will be, immediately to address a short memorial to Lord Palmerston—though I fear the thing you want, will not be done. I don't know him well enough to address him privately on the subject. I may mention, between ourselves, that I *know* this Government do nothing for one another; and that what one man has to [word illegible] or give, another does not interfere with. Lord John himself shewed me this long ago, in a curious manner."

Letter signed with initials only.

A93*

To Lieutenant Tracey, addressed "My Dear Governor": "Tavistock House Twenty Fifth November 1854." Requesting that a note be forwarded to Dr. Davies.

A94*

To Lieutenant Tracey: "Tavistock House Twenty Fourth February 1855." Acknowledging a letter and mentioning that Dickens was "greatly prepossessed by Mr. Jeakes."

A95*

To Daniel Maclise: "Tavistock House Twenty Fourth April, 1855." Thanks for Maclise's "kind remembrance of the picture."

A96*

To Lieutenant Tracey, addressed "My Dear old Commodore": "Tavistock House Saturday May Twelfth 1855." Opening:

> Whom the rheumatiz—not gout—
> Has so sadly knocked about;
> Altho' he's a young 'un for to see—

assuring Tracey of his staunch friendship.

A97*

To Lieutenant Tracey: "Tavistock House Twenty Fifth May 1855." An invitation to dinner.

A98*

To "Henry" [Austin]: "Folkestone, Sundy August Nineteenth 1855." ". . . houses shaken yesterdy, by the firing at Boulogne—Camp at Shorn-cliffe composed, generally speaking, of the most hideous blackguards these eyes ever did rest upon. Out of Kink William Street Strand, I never beheld such Phrenology."

Letter signed with initials only.

A99

To Sir Edwin Landseer: "49 Champs Elysees, Paris Thursdy Tenth January 1856." ". . . What you say of Nos. 1 & 2 [Little Dorrit], is a real delight to me. For whenever I speak of men born by nature to be writers if they had not highly distinguished themselves in some other art (they are mighty few) I always instance you with your remarkable powers of observation and perception. . . ."

With signed and addressed envelope.

Published in Nonesuch edition II, 727.

A100*

To Lieutenant Tracey, addressed "My Dear Jack": "Paris, Champs Elysees 49 Sundy Twenty Seventh April, 1856." Agreeing to act as

sponsor for "Henry." "This is but a fag-end of a rope to heave overboard to an old salt floating about on the Hencoop of idleness; but if I were to pay out more, I should lose the post. So I won't yaw about like the dog-vane in a calm, but clap a stopper on and belay. . . ."
Letter signed "Edward Cuttle."

A101°
To Viscount Raynham: "30 April, 1856." Agreeing to preside at a hospital benefit dinner. [Dickens's speech on this occasion was published in pamphlet form.]

A102°
To "David E.": "Office of *Household Words* Saturday Third May 1856." Requesting copy of No. 6 of *Little Dorrit* and "a pull of No. 7."

A103
To Miss [Angela G. Burdett-] Coutts, addressed "My Dear": "Villa des Moulineaux, Boulogne. Saturday Fifth July, 1856." Referring to matters connected with the "Home" at Shepherd's Bush, with an amusing account in "VII Chapters" of a "state of amazing excitement about a robbery" on the Folkestone Pavilion, concluding with an account of the adventures of Dickens's raven ["Dick," second successor to the "Grip" of *Barnaby Rudge*. At his demise Dickens erected a small copper tombstone in the garden of Gad's Hill on which was inscribed: "This is the Grave of Dick The Best of Birds Born at Broadstairs Mids^r 1851 Died at Gad's Hill Place 14th Octr 1866."] with "two ferocious and extra-cunning French cats."
Letter signed with initials only.
Published in part in Nonesuch edition II, 788.

A104°
To Lieutenant Tracey: "Tavistock House Monday Twenty Seventh October 1856." Invitation to dine at *Household Words* office.
Signature excised.

A105°
To Lieutenant Tracey, addressed "My Dear Commodore": "H.M.S. Tavistock Port of London Thirty First October 1856." ". . . Whenever you come aboard, you shall have the best bottle of wine in the locker, and the best Irish stew in the caboose. . . ."
Letter signed "Harry Bluff."

A106°
To The Reverend George Wilkinson: "Tavistock House, London Nineteenth January 1857." ". . . I hear (as you do) on high and learned authority, that there need no longer be delays in chancery. Highly gratifying and convincing perhaps; but if that pestilent court cannot, or do not,

make its own agents do their duty, it is, in my poor opinion, body and soul a Humbug. Against such a dragon I know no remedy but a Saint George."

A107°
To John Dillon: "Tavistock House   Sunday Night   Eighth November, 1857." Regretting Dillon's absence from a dinner.

A108°
To Lieutenant Tracey: "Tavistock House   Twenty Eighth December, 1857." Accepting an invitation to dinner.

A109°
To W. Bridges Adams: "Tavistock House   Thirty First December 1857." Rejecting an article submitted to *Household Words* with the comment: ". . . I have feared that my mode of treating it would be too alarmingly surgical to be borne by any mortal parent of a pen-ink-and-paper child."

A110°
For Benjamin Cooper: "Tavistock House   Friday   Second April, 1858." A testimonial letter for Dickens's former coachman and groom.

A110a°
To Nelson Lee: "Tavistock House Friday Fourth June 1858." Referring to a MS. submitted by Lee which Dickens was returning with his comments.
Letter signed; framed together with portrait of Dickens.

A111°
To Lieutenant Tracey, addressed "My Dear Commodore": "Gad's Hill Place   Saturday   Twenty Fourth July, 1858." ". . . You know that if it were possible for me to come aboard o' the Windsor Terrace, I should answer your signals, joyfully, out of hand. But I *must* be at an Inn, and I myself, and *must* avoid engagements, under these circumstances [his public readings]."
Signature excised.

A112°
To E. Walford, M.A.: "Gad's Hill Place, Wednesday   Twenty Eighth July 1858." ". . . I would suggest to you that it is hardly well to rest any thing connected with the origin of the *Pickwick Papers*, on a vague "it is said"; when their origin has been for some years, exactly described by my own hand, and before the Public, in the Preface to the 'Cheap Edition' of that work. . . ."
With signed and addressed envelope.

A113*
To Mrs. [Frances] Trollope: "Tavistock House, Monday   Twentieth September 1858." A letter of introduction for Miss Fanny Ternan, who was travelling to Italy.

A114*
To George Fletcher: "Hen and Chickens, Birmingham. Wednesday Twentieth October 1858." Acknowledging receipt of a book and a letter.

A115*
To [Whitwell] Elwin: "Tavistock House, Frid^y Third June 1859." Concerning difficulty with the Committee of the General Theatrical Fund. ". . . I suppose we must in any case take some steps to bring Forster off with flying colors? He was here yesterd^y morning, smoking all over his head, and fuming exactly like a steamboat ready to start. He had ideas of our writing to the *Times*; and various rampant carriages and six were jostling each other in his mind. It was impossible to wonder at the dear fellow's being rendered very angry by a sense of his infamous treatment; but I felt that the only safe course was, to put everything by for a while. This I accordingly did, under various pretences—and I dare say he thought me a cold-blooded Villain for doing it."

A116*
To Andrew McEwen: "Office of All the Year Round. Tuesd^y   Thirty First July 1860." Rejecting some verses.
Bound in an octavo case of tan morocco.

A117*
To Mr. [W. W. ?] Vaughan: "Office of *All the Year Round* Friday Thirteenth September 1861." Acknowledging a communication.
Formal note in third person.

A118*
To Messrs. Dalziel Brothers: "Office of *All the Year Round* Friday Fourth October 1861." Acknowledging receipt of India proofs of illustrations to *Reprinted Pieces*, described as "very satisfactory indeed" in conception and execution.

A119*
To Captain Mayson: "Liverpool   Monday   Sixteenth December 1861." Refusing request, but expressing gratitude for his enrollment in the Third Manchester Rifles.

A120*
To Lieutenant Tracey: "Gad's Hill Place   Thursday   Twenty Sixth December 1861." Plans to go to Plymouth in fulfillment of arrangements made by Arthur Smith, "who is never to be replaced," and to visit Macready at Cheltenham.

A121*
To Edward Dove: "Tuesday Eighteenth February 1862." Returning
a letter from a clergyman and promising to give "the reverend gentleman
a large audience for his composition." Laid in *An Enlightened Clergyman* (B582). [Dickens fulfilled his promise in the article, "A Strange
Story," in *All the Year Round*, 8 March 1862.]

A122
To E. S. Dallas: "Paris, Rue du Faubourg St. Honoré, 27 Sunday,
Seventh December 1862." Acknowledging communication with plans
to assist Dr. Elliotson.
Bound in octavo case of rust-colored crushed morocco.
Published in Nonesuch edition III, 324–326.

A123
To The Rev. W. C. Sawyer: "Friday Nov. 6, 1863." Dickens's wish to
place his youngest son with Mr. Sawyer, headmaster of a school at Tun-
bridge Wells recommended by Mme. De la Rue.
Published in Nonesuch edition III, 370–371.

A124*
To Sir James Emerson Tennent: "Twenty Ninth October, 1864." Cited
under B25(2), a copy of *Pickwick Papers* inscribed to Tennent. [To the
recipient, who had been an old friend and schoolmate of John Forster's,
Dickens later dedicated *Our Mutual Friend*.]

A125*
To Thomas Hyde Hills: "Gad's Hill Place, New Year's Day 1865." Thanks
and praise of Hills's management of a "Fever Hospital."

A126*
To Lieutenant Tracey, addressed "My Dear Jack": "Gad's Hill Place,
Thursday Fifteenth June 1865." Concerning the railroad accident at
Staplehurst on 9 June.
Letter signed with initials only.

A127*
To Lady Harrington: "6 Southwick Place, Hyde Park Wednesday Seventh March 1866." Refusing an invitation because of previous engagements, "opposed to the strict injunction of my doctor," with the explanation, "I have been very unwell, and have 30 Readings before me or I
wouldn't mind him!"

A128*
To Frederick Chapman: "Gad's Hill Place Sunday Twenty Fifth November 1866." Introducing John Watkins, a portrait painter.

A129°
To T. H. Hills: "Gad's Hill Place Monday Sixth May 1867." "A thousand thanks!"

A130
To George Augustus Sala: "Queen's Hotel. Manchester Sunday Seventh March 1869." Concerning the use of Sala's name in an article for *All the Year Round.*
Published in Nonesuch edition III, 710.

A131
To J. S. Le Fanu: "Gad's Hill Place, Higham by Rochester, Kent. Wednesday Twenty Fourth November 1869." Praising a sketch for an article and discussing Dickens's use of "magnetism" to relieve the nervous disorder of an English lady in Genoa [Mme. De la Rue].
Bound together with a letter to Mme. De la Rue (A34) in an octavo case of red levant morocco.
Published in Nonesuch edition III, 752–753.

A132°
To Mr. Day [printer]: "Saturdy Twenty Eighth May 1870." A correction for page 75, No. III of *Edwin Drood.* "It stands: . . . [as printed on page mentioned]. It should stand. In the days when Cloisterham took offence at the existence of a railroad afar off, [*word deleted*] as menacing that sensitive Constitution, the property of us Britons, the odd fortune of which sacred institution it is to . . .*"

A133°
"Memorandum. Twenty Eighth May 1870. I have left Hyde Park Place; therefore please send proofs in future, either to Gad's Hill, or Wellington Street. I am at the latter place every Thursday."
Note signed with initials only. See illustration of this letter and A132.

3 : UNDATED LETTERS

A134°
To Thomas Mitton: "Thursday Morning." Making an appointment.
With signed and addressed envelope.

A135°
To Lieutenant Tracey: "Devonshire Terrace Saturday Fifteenth Oct^r." ". . . For Heaven's sake, put the virtuous boy between those dismal blinkers, instantly. . . .*"

A136°
To Mr. and Mrs. George Cruikshank: "Broadstairs, May 10." Thanks "for kind enquiries."
Formal note on black bordered card engraved with the names of Mr. and Mrs. Dickens.

A137°
To Lieutenant Tracey: [Incomplete, lacking address and date] Referring to Tracey's marriage. ". . . Timber also wheezes forth a congratulatory bark." Added to this letter is Tracey's note describing Timber as "one of the greatest curiosities you ever beheld."

A138°
To Sergeant T. N. Talfourd: "1 Devonshire Terrace. Thursday Morning." [1840 ?] Breaking an engagement and giving advice about a play of Talfourd's. ". . . It has occurred to me to suggest to you whether there *may* not be a reason for your not making the communication you thought of, until you are quite sure of Mrs. Talfourd. Would not your doing so now, and your declining to have it played after all, subject you again to all the past sorrows, annoyances and vexations of *The Athenian Captive* [1838]? I hope there is little chance of your preventing the representation of so noble a tragedy [*Glencoe* ?], but as you yourself touched on this point, I feel I should not do right if I refrained from saying what has occurred to [*word deleted*] me—especially as my genuine and heartfelt interest in your genius is my best excuse."
With signed and addressed envelope of different paper, stamped with the date 1849 or, possibly, 1840 [The last figure is incomplete.].

4:LETTERS BY OTHER WRITERS
REFERRING TO DICKENS

A139°
George Cruikshank, addressed "Sir": Undated [c. 1836]. Referring to illustrators and publishers of *Pickwick* as possessed of "too much respectability to be guilty of such a falsehood."
Pencil note with sketches.

A140
Thomas Carlyle to [James] Spedding: "Chelsea, Monday Morning—" Regretting Carlyle's inability to join in a celebration. ". . . One toast only I will beg of you on that festive occasion: 'The Memory of *Pickwick*,' drunk in solemn silence. . . ."

A141°
Robert and E. B. Browning jointly to Miss Bayley [12 pp. 3″ by 5″]:
"Sunday—Paris—Hotel de Londres Rue St. Hyacinthe St. Honoré [1858–
1859]." Referring to the separation, E.B.B. inquires:

> . . . What is this sad story about Dickens & his wife? Incompatibility
> of temper after twenty three years of married life!—What a plea!—brook
> then irregularity of the passions, it seems to me—"The wound is great
> because it is so small." Parents should endure more for the sake of their
> children, I do hold,—to avoid stripping off the leaves of natural house-
> hold joy from the green branches over their young heads,—taking the
> mother from one child & the father from another, & the sense of family
> love & union from all—Thinking only of my own peace & selfish
> pleasure, so, I would rather be beaten by my husband once a day than
> lose my child out of the house—yes, indeed—And the Dickens's have
> children younger than Penini—. Poor woman!—She must suffer bitterly—
> that is sure—. . .

A142°
John Forster to Lieutenant Tracey: Undated. Advising Tracey that
Forster had invited Clarkson Stanfield to accompany Dickens and him-
self to Tracey's for dinner.

A143°
Mr. Dickens Senr [Dickens's father] to [J. P.] Harley: "34 Edward Street
Portman Square Wednesday Morning." Requesting orders for a box at
the theatre.

A144°
Mamie Dickens to Thomas Hyde Hills: Undated. Expressing thanks.
Note written on black-bordered stationery.

A145°
Georgina Ross to Janet [Knox, her niece]: "6 Derby Street Durham Road
Sunderland September 3rd '74." Advising Miss Knox that she was sending
her album as a gift. "The piece ['The Ivy Green' (A1)] he [Dickens]
wrote in the album appeared there first—he afterwards inserted it in one
of his works [*Pickwick Papers*]."

A146°
Kate Perugini to unknown person, addressed "Dear Sir": "8th Oct 1902."
Stating that *The Life of Christ,* written by Dickens for his children, could
not be sold. [The work was finally issued in 1934 (B521).]

5 : OTHER MANUSCRIPTS

A147

"A LETTER FROM HOP-O'-MY-THUMB TO CHARLES DICKENS, ESQ., UPON 'FRAUDS ON THE FAIRIES'." BY GEORGE CRUIK-SHANK.

Bound in quarto case of red levant morocco, including: (1) pamphlet, 8 pp.; (2) Cruikshank's original MS. with 3 drafts of p. 1; (3) galley proofs of the pamphlet with Cruikshank's corrections and additions; (4) portrait of Cruikshank and Dickens.

Cruikshank's reply to Dickens's criticism of his abuse of the fairy tale in *Household Words*, 1 October 1853. Published in *George Cruikshank's Magazine*, February 1854, pp. 74–80, and reprinted in pamphlet form [(1) above] by D. Bogue [1854]. With two woodcuts by the author. See illustration.

A148

THE GOLDEN DUSTMAN. In Three Acts. Dated "London 20 June 1873."

Fair MS. copy, each act in separate brown paper wrapper, of the unpublished play by H. B. Farnie. "First played at Sadler's Wells Sat 16th June 1866. . . . Originally performed in 5 Acts." [based on *Our Mutual Friend*]

S. J. Adair FitzGerald [*Dickens and the Drama*] gives the cast of the original production in which Charles Warner played the lead as Bradley Headstone. The play was later performed at Astley's, the Britannia Theatre, and in the country with great success, so that it became "quite a stock play at the minor temples of the drama."

A149

THE HUMBUG OR THE SAVAGE AND THE MAIDEN. In One Act. Presented at the Tremont Theatre, 12 April 1842.

MS. of play based on *Nicholas Nickleby*, with cast and program "As performed at Mitchell's Olympic, N.Y. for upwards of 100 nights with unprecedented success."

A150

THE HEROES OF DICKENS. By John S. Barnet.

MS. written as a student in Brookline High School.

A151

MS. copy of Dickens's "Daily Remembrancer," 4 vols. 1838, 1839, 1840, 1841. [Original in the Forster Collection].

A152

MS. notes and materials gathered by F. G. Kitton for *Dickens and His Illustrators* and *The Minor Writings of Charles Dickens*.

A153

MS. of F. G. Kitton's "Introduction" to *Pickwick Papers.*

A154

Corrected galley proof of George Bernard Shaw's preface to *Great Expectations.*

Initialed and dated "12/12/36" by Shaw.

A155

Corrected page proof of George Bernard Shaw's preface to *Great Expectations,* Hamish Hamilton edition.

Initialed and dated "25/11/1946" by Shaw.

A156

Descriptive Catalogue of the Charles Dickens Collection of George Barr McCutcheon.

Original typescript in one-fourth green morocco binder. *Ex libris* George Barr McCutcheon.

6 : ILLUSTRATIONS AND PORTRAITS

A157*

Illustrations for *Pickwick Papers* by Hablot K. Browne ("Phiz").

F°. In full red calf.

A unique series of 43 original water-color and pencil illustrations on heavy paper. Illustrated holograph note by Browne certifies that he made these drawings expressly for F. W. Cosens, Esq. Dated "Oct. 1866." See illustration.

DRAWINGS AND SKETCHES BY CHARLES GREEN

A158

Pencil sketch, cover design for the Crown Edition of Dickens's *Works.*

A159

Two sheets of pencil sketches for cover of an edition of Dickens's *Works.*

A160

Water-color drawing, unfinished, "Sam Weller and the Pretty Housemaid."

A161
Pencil sketch, unfinished, "Pickwick, Wardle, and Sam at the White Hart."

A162
Pencil sketches, "Bailiff at Mantilini's," for *Nicholas Nickleby.*

A163
Two ink sketches for *The Old Curiosity Shop.*

A164
Ink and pencil sketches, "Miss Monflather's School," for *The Old Curiosity Shop.*

A165
Ink and pencil sketch, unfinished, "Mrs. Jarley and Nell," for *The Old Curiosity Shop.*

A166
Print, "Mrs. Jarley and Nell," etched by Dalziel.

A167
Ink drawing, "Death of Quilp," for *The Old Curiosity Shop.* See illustration.

A168
Print, "Death of Quilp," etched by Dalziel.

A169
Ink and pencil sketches, "Quilp" and "Soloman Brass," for *The Old Curiosity Shop.*

A170
Pencil sketch, "Quilp and Boy," for *The Old Curiosity Shop.*

A171
Pencil sketch, "Gabriel Varden armed by Dolly," for *Barnaby Rudge.*

A172
Pencil sketches, "Dolly Varden," for *Barnaby Rudge.*

A173
Pencil sketches, "Old Turveydrop," for *Bleak House.*

A174
Pencil sketches, "Prince Turveydrop," for *Bleak House.*

A175
Pencil sketches, "Pupils in Prince Turveydrop's Dancing Academy" and "Prince Turveydrop," for *Bleak House.*

A176
Water-color sketches, unfinished, "Pupils in the Dancing Academy," for *Bleak House.*

A177
Two plates of water-color drawings, "Esther Summerson," for *Bleak House.*

A178
Pencil sketch, unfinished, "Little Dorrit and Her Sister at the Theatre," for *Little Dorrit.*

A179
Two plates of pencil sketches for *Great Expectations.*

A180
Pencil sketches for *A Christmas Carol.*

A181
Pencil sketch, "Ghost," for *A Christmas Carol.*

A182
Two pencil sketches, "Mrs. Tetterby" and "Mrs. Tetterby and Her Boy," for *The Haunted Man.*

A183
Brush and ink drawing, unfinished, "Laboratory at King's Coll.," for *The Haunted Man.*

A184
Self-portrait, in pencil.

SKETCHES BY GEORGE CRUIKSHANK

A185
Pencil sketches, "Mr. Cooper's Introduction to Miss Billsmethi" and other sketches for *Sketches by Boz.* See illustration.

A186
Pencil sketch, "Quilp."

ILLUSTRATIONS BY "KYD" (J. CLAYTON CLARKE)

A187(1)
One hundred twenty-nine water-color character drawings, signed "Kyd." On water-color paper (8¾" by 11").
Sketches by Boz (12)
Pickwick Papers (24)
Oliver Twist (27 with title page and list of characters)
Barnaby Rudge (6)
Martin Chuzzlewit (12)
A Tale of Two Cities (12 with title page and list of characters)
David Copperfield (18)
Little Dorrit (12)
Edwin Drood (6 with title page and list of characters)

A187(2)
A second set of twelve character drawings from *Sketches by Boz*.

ILLUSTRATIONS BY F. W. PAILTHORPE

A188
Six water-color illustrations, unpublished, to *Memoirs of Joseph Grimaldi*. On plate paper (8¼" by 5").

ILLUSTRATIONS BY KENNY MEADOWS

A189
Twenty-four extra illustrations in pen and ink for *Nicholas Nickleby* "from drawings by Miss LaCreevy." London: 1839.

Bound in half red levant morocco, with marbled end papers. See illustration.

ILLUSTRATIONS BY WILLIAM SHARP

A190
Seventy-five original drawings in India ink (for zinc plates) for The Heritage Club Edition of *The Old Curiosity Shop*, on heavy paper, 7" by 11½". New York: 1941. Includes one drawing not used in that edition.

ILLUSTRATIONS BY EVERETT SHINN

A191
Two water-color illustrations for *Edwin Drood*, matted and framed, each 14¼" by 18". Signed and dated 1941.

1) "Jasper regains consciousness in Opium Sal's room in the company of 'a Chinaman, a Lascar, and a haggard woman'." (from Chap. 1) In light brown tones with shadings of blue and green. 2) "Jasper and Durdles in the crypt." (from Chap. 12) In blue tones with highlights of yellow and white. See illustration.

OTHER ILLUSTRATIONS

A192
Silhouettes of 17 characters from Dickens's works, on plate paper, 8½″ by 5¾″.

PORTRAITS AND OTHER ORIGINAL WORKS

A193
Brush and ink drawing by Walter Crane, "Mrs. Gamp," with remarque portraits of Dickens (6¼″ by 4″). See illustration.

A194
Portrait in oil by Augustus Egg, "Charles Dickens in Character," [from his larger painting, "Charles Dickens as Sir Charles Coldstream in *Used Up*," c. 1850]. Reproduced as frontispiece to this catalogue.

A195
Anonymous contemporary portrait in oil from a photograph of Dickens by Watkins (24″ by 20″).

A196
Anonymous contemporary bust portrait, oil on wood, framed. Panel size, 10″ by 8″. [c. 1860–1870].

A197
Original steel plate engraved by S. Hollyer: "Dickens in His Study at Gads Hill." Plate measures 18″ by 23¼″. Washington, D.C. 1875.

A198
Lithograph by T. H. Maguire from the painting, "Charles Dickens as Captain Bobadil," by C. R. Leslie.

A199
Large Royal Doulton jug. The spout is a bust of Dickens crowned with laurel. A brightly colored frieze in high relief of Dickens's characters surrounds the body of the jug. Height 10½″; diameter 8½″. No. 559 of 1,000, with seal.

A200
Five Royal Doulton figurines, 4″ high: The Fat Boy, Sergeant Buzfuz, Jingle, Fagin, and Sam Weller. Also Royal Doulton pitcher, 6″ high, with scenes from *Oliver Twist*.

A201
Circular bronze plaque, 7½″ in diameter; bust portrait in relief of Dickens at the age of 49. 1893.

A202
Marble bust of Dickens, 9" high; artist unknown.

A203
Portraits of Dickens printed on cloth by S. Lawrence, Ary Scheffer, W. P. Frith, and R. P. Lane.

A204
Photographs, mounted, 7⅞" by 10", of 16 localities associated with Dickens, by Catherine Weed Ward. From the library of Sir Henry Fielding Dickens.

A205
Thirteen additional photographs by Catherine Weed Ward. From the library of Sir Henry Fielding Dickens.

A206
"The Sixth Medal issued by the Circle of Friends of the Medallion in Manhattan." June, 1912.

MISCELLANEOUS ITEMS

A207
Ticket (Lieutenant F. Tracey's) to the Amateur Performance of *Every Man in His Humour* at Miss Kelly's Theatre, Saturday Evening, 20 September [1845].

A208
Two whiskey glasses with hand-painted pictures of Mr. Weller and Sam as they appeared in the court yard of the White Hart Inn.

A209
Ticket, Jos. Mayer, Esq., to the Soirée of the Liverpool Mechanics' Institution, Monday 26th February 1844. "Charles Dickens, Esq. in the Chair." Mounted on folio-sized paper.

A210
Ticket stub to Dickens's Reading, Friday 28 February 1868, at Tremont Temple [Boston]. Mounted on folio-size paper.

A211
Ticket stub to Dickens's Reading, Monday 30 March 1868. Unmounted.

A212
Ivory note book. Given to Dickens by Georgina Hogarth and used by him at Gad's Hill. With certificate of Georgina Hogarth. In olive green levant morocco case by Riviere.

A213
Collection of autographs, including the following:
1. Envelope, signed and addressed to Sebastian Schlesinger, Esq. by Dickens. Mounted with portrait of Dickens.
2. Dickens's signature and address: "Tremont House. Boston. Twenty-eighth January 1842."
3. Brief holograph note (torn) in Dickens's hand on Gad's Hill Place stationery.
4. ALS, dated 22 July 1841, from George Cattermole to Dickens.
5. Holograph note, signed "Joseph Grimaldi."
6. Typed copies of correspondence (6 letters) between Dickens and Robert Bonner, of the New York *Ledger* concerning publication of *Hunted Down.*
7. Notice of Novelties Club meeting, 29 January 1842, "for the purpose of receiving the answer of Charles Dickens, Esq. to the invitation of the Club."
8. ALS, dated 8 August 1871, from Charles Dickens, Jr.
9. ALS, dated 21 November 1885 from E. L. Blanchard to F. G. Kitton.
10. ALS, undated, from Hy Burnett to Mr. Kitton concerning a Dickens portrait.
11. ALS, dated 19 January 1912, from Kate Perugini to Robert Erskine, concerning Dickens Centenary.
12. ALS, undated, from Edward Bradley to his publishers concerning MS. of *Reminiscences of Charles Dickens.*
13. Holograph note, dated 12 October 1920, signed "John Galsworthy. 'When found make a note on.' Capen Cuttle."

A214†
Trial proofs from 935 original plates and woodcuts pulled in 1936 in preparation for the Nonesuch Edition [see B677(2)] with typewritten memoranda by Thomas Hatton.

I : "Dickens in Character." Portrait in oil by Augustus Egg (A194)

Oh a dainty Plant is the Ivy green,
That creepeth o'er ruins old:
Of right choice food, are his meals I ween,
In his Cell, so lone, and cold.
The Wall must be crumbled, the stone decayed,
To pleasure his dainty whim:
And the mouldering dust that years have made,
Is a merry meal for him.
    Creeping where no life is seen,
     A rare old Plant is the Ivy green!
Fast he stealeth on, though he wears no wings,
And a staunch old heart has he.
How closely he twineth, how tight he clings
To his friend the huge Oak Tree!
And slily he traileth along the ground,
And his leaves he gently waves,
As he joyously hugs, and crawleth round,
The rich mould of dead mens' Graves.
    Creeping where grim death has been,
     A rare old Plant is the Ivy green!
Whole ages have fled, and their works decayed,
And Nations have scattered been:
But the stout old Ivy shall never fade,
From its hale and hearty green.
The brave old Plant, in its lonely days,
Shall fatten upon the past:
For the proudest Edifice, man can raise,
Is the Ivy's food at last.
    Creeping on, where Time has been,
     A rare old Plant is the Ivy green.

           Boz.

II : "The Ivy Green" (A1)

III : Cruikshank's pencil sketches for SKETCHES BY BOZ (A185)

IV and V : H. K. Browne. Extra illustrations for PICKWICK PAPERS
(A157)

I hereby certify, that these forty colour illustrations
to "Pickwick" — are made by me expressly
for F. W. Cosens Esq.re and that there are others.

Oct. 1886.   Hablot K. Browne.

NICHOLAS NICKLEBY.

VI : Kenny Meadows's illustration in pen and ink for NICHOLAS NICKLEBY (A189)

POSTHUMOUS PAPERS of the PICKWICK CLUB

PART I

INTRODUCTION BY

PERCY FITZGERALD, M.A., F.S.A.

AUTHOR OF "THE HISTORY OF PICKWICK," "PICKWICKIAN MANNERS
AND CUSTOMS," "PICKWICKIAN STUDIES," "BOZLAND," "THE TRIAL OF
BARDELL *versus* PICKWICK," AND FOUNDER OF THE LONDON "BOZ CLUB"

NEW YORK & LONDON
GEORGE D. SPROUL · *MCMII*

VII : Publisher's proof. St. Dunstan Illuminated Edition of PICK-
WICK PAPERS (B30)

PREFACE.

I HAVE endeavoured in this Ghostly little book, to raise the Ghost of an Idea, which shall not put my readers out of humour with themselves, with each other, with the season, or with me. May it haunt their houses pleasantly, and no one wish to lay it.

Their faithful Friend and Servant,

C. D.

December 1843.

near neighbour's house; where, wo upon the single man who saw them enter—artful witches: well they knew it—in a glow!

But if you had judged from the numbers of people on their way to friendly gatherings, you might have thought that no one was at home to give them welcome when they got there, instead of every house expecting company, and piling up its fires half-chimney high. Blessings on it, how the Ghost exulted! How it barred its breadth of breast, and

X : Cruikshank's extra illustration in water color for OLIVER TWIST (B105)

XI : Charles Green's "The Death of Quilp." OLD CURIOSITY SHOP
(A191)

XII : Walter Crane. Sairy Gamp with remarque portrait of Dickens
(A193)

Charles Dickens

1 : MAJOR WORKS

B1†

SKETCHES BY "BOZ," ILLUSTRATIVE OF EVERY-DAY LIFE, AND EVERY-DAY PEOPLE. London: John Macrone. MDCCCXXXVI.

12°. Two volumes in original green cloth with yellow end papers, uncut.

First edition of the first series.

Inscription on back flyleaf: "This book came from the library of my father, Eugene Field. Nov. 1—1931 Eugene Field II."

B2

SKETCHES BY "BOZ," ILLUSTRATIVE OF EVERY-DAY LIFE, AND EVERY-DAY PEOPLE. London: John Macrone. MDCCCXXXVI.

12°. Two volumes in embossed dark green cloth differing from that of the regular first and second editions; cream colored end papers. Gilt design with title on spine placed one inch lower than on the regular first and second editions resembles that of the second edition with the words, "second edition," carefully removed.

Text in these volumes is composite. The first four sheets of Vol. I, including title page (verso with printer's imprint), three-page preface, and table of contents, together with the final page of text (imprint, "Whiting, Beauford House, Strand") corresponds to the first edition. The body of the text corresponds to the second edition. The binding of Vol. II is identical with that of Vol. I. Text is that of the first edition slightly expanded; it does not correspond at all to the second edition, which was completely reset by another printer. Edges of both volumes have been trimmed slightly.

B3

SKETCHES BY BOZ: ILLUSTRATIVE OF EVERY-DAY LIFE, AND EVERY-DAY PEOPLE. THE SECOND EDITION. London: John Macrone. MDCCCXXXVI.

12°. Two volumes in original green cloth with yellow end papers, uncut.

Second edition of the first series. Type was completely reset for this edition which came out in November 1836. The new preface is dated "Furnival's Inn, 1st August, 1836."

B4(1)†

SKETCHES BY BOZ: ILLUSTRATIVE OF EVERY-DAY LIFE, AND EVERY-DAY PEOPLE. THE SECOND SERIES. COMPLETE IN ONE VOLUME. London: John Macrone. MDCCCXXXVI.

12°. In original pink cloth; title on spine in gilt on black background; yellow end papers; uncut.

First edition, first issue. Lower half of p. viii blank, no list of illustrations.

Frontispiece, "Seven Dials." All plates with imprint: "John Macrone, 1836." Pages 25, 32, 62 misnumbered 52, 23, 46 respectively. Page 60 correctly numbered; page 299 with final figure in open type. Illustrations by George Cruikshank include "The Free and Easy."

"Mr. Macrone's Select List of New Works" dated December 1836, 20 pages at end of text.

B4(2)

SKETCHES BY BOZ: ILLUSTRATIVE OF EVERY-DAY LIFE, AND EVERY-DAY PEOPLE. THE SECOND SERIES. COMPLETE IN ONE VOLUME. London: John Macrone. MDCCCXXXVI.

12°. In original pink cloth. Title on spine in gilt on black background; also black strip at base of spine with "second series" in gilt letters. Yellow end papers; uncut.

First edition, second issue, with list of illustrations on p. viii.

Nine plates include "The Free and Easy"; with imprint "John Macrone, 1836." "Vauxhall Gardens by Day" appears only as frontispiece. Errors in pagination on pages 25, 32, and 62; page 299 with final figure in open type.

"Mr. Macrone's Select List of New Works" dated December, 1836, 18 pp. at end of text (lacks pp. 8/9).

B5

SKETCHES BY BOZ: THE SECOND SERIES. SECOND EDITION. London: John Macrone. MDCCCXXXVII.

12°. In original pink cloth. Gilt title on spine; at base "second edition second series Macrone 1837." Yellow end papers; uncut.

Illustrations include "The Free and Easy" as well as the additional plates, "The Last Cab Driver" and "Mayday in the Evening." Text reset; 375 pages (377 in the first edition).

"Mr. Macrone's Select List of New Works" dated February, 1837, 12 pages following the text.

B6†

SKETCHES BY BOZ. Philadelphia: Carey, Lea & Blanchard. 1837.

12°. In original buff paper boards with pink cloth spine, uncut.

First complete American edition of the second series.

B7

SKETCHES BY BOZ. NEW EDITION, COMPLETE. London: Chapman and Hall. 1839.

8°. Bound in half green morocco with green marbled boards and end papers; top edge gilt; edges trimmed. This first complete edition of the two series in one volume was made up of unsold monthly parts.

This copy shows marks of early issue:
    p. 18:   "8" in pagination set lower than "1."
    p. 83:   figures in pagination set level in bold, black type.
    p. 515: numbered at top center.
    p. 526: at foot of page: "Whiting, Beauford House, Strand."
    Plates
    11-40: with imprint: "London: Chapman & Hall, 186, Strand."

B8

SKETCHES BY BOZ. NEW EDITION, COMPLETE. Philadelphia: Lea & Blanchard. 1839.

8°. Cheap 8° edition. In brown paper boards with green cloth spine and paper label.

First publication in book form of "The Pantomime of Life." With advertisement: "This American edition contains 'The Public Life of Mr. Tulrumble' and 'The Pantomime of Life' by Boz—Sketches published by the author since the above [English] edition was issued. Philadelphia: August, 1839."

B9

SKETCHES BY BOZ. WITH TWENTY ILLUSTRATIONS BY GEORGE CRUIKSHANK. NEW EDITION, COMPLETE. Philadelphia: Lea & Blanchard. 1839.

8°. In original brown cloth with gilt stamping on spine. Binding varies from that described by Wilkins. With advertisement as in B8.

B10

SKETCHES BY "BOZ." PETERSONS' CHEAP EDITION FOR THE MILLION. Philadelphia: T. B. Peterson & Brothers. [n.d.].

8°. In salmon-pink paper wrapper; printed in double columns; pages unopened.

B11

SKETCHES BY BOZ. WITH A FRONTISPIECE BY GEORGE CRUIK-SHANK. London: Chapman and Hall. 1854.

8°. In original green cloth, with yellow end papers.

EXTRA ILLUSTRATIONS TO *Sketches by Boz*

B12

Three Extra Plates by Cruikshank [Chapman and Hall. 1839].

8°. "A Pickpocket in Custody," "The Dancing Academy," and "London Recreations" removed from bound volumes, no imprint.

B13(1)†

THE POSTHUMOUS PAPERS OF THE PICKWICK CLUB. EDITED BY "BOZ." London: Chapman and Hall. MDCCCXXXVI [MDCCCXXX-VII].

> Nos. I & II: With Four Illustrations by Seymour
> No. III: With Illustrations by R. W. Buss
> Nos. IV-XIX/XX: With Illustrations

8°. In 19/20 monthly numbers, as issued, with green printed wrappers designed by Seymour and advertisements.

This set has all "eleven points" required of a "prime" *Pickwick*.

> (1) All covers dated MDCCCXXXVI.
> (2) Wrappers of Parts I and II: "With Four Illustrations | by Seymour."
> (3) Wrapper of Part III: "With Illustrations | by R. W. Buss." This number contains the two Buss plates.
> (4) Part I has 4 plates: three are signed faintly by Seymour; the fourth is unsigned (which is correct). "Dr. Slammer's defiance of Jingle" has only 10 boards in the floor.
> (5) Part II has 3 plates signed by Seymour.
> (6) Part III has 2 plates signed, "Drawn & Etch'd by R W Buss," with the page numbers.

(7) Part IV has 2 plates signed indistinctly, "N.E.M.O."

(8) Parts II, III, X, and XV have the addresses by the author.

(9) Parts XVII, XVIII, and XIX/XX have the addresses by the publishers.

(10) Plates in Parts I-XI have only page references with no captions; parts XII-XIX/XX have neither page reference nor caption.

(11) The name "Weller" on the vignette title is spelled with a "V." The signature "PHIZ fecit." surrounds the center shield.

All wrappers are correct, with that of Part VIII in the rare first state. (The advertisement, "John Horner, the Man with the Plums," replaces the imprint on the inside back wrapper, the outside being identical with No. VII except that the second line reads: "Early in November will be Published.")

All correct advertising material is included except the slip, "Phrenology Made Easy," in Part VII and "Pigot's Coloured Views" in Part XIII. The "Advertiser" for Part VI is entirely unopened.

No. IV. in earliest state without "17" before "Albemarle Street."

No. V. Back Advertisements, p. 4: "The Best Life of Napoleon | . . . | Bourrienne's | . . . | The Emperor Napoleon."

No. X. not the earliest issue. P. 10, at bottom: "New and appropriate present | . . . | The Poetic Wreath."

No. XIV. "Advertiser" leaves in order varying from usual collation, but all present. Back Advertisements include 2 copies of p. 1.

Plates and text in this set appear as follows:

No. I. "Mr. Pickwick addresses the Club": Pickwick's vest buttons are on his left side; picture frames lightly etched; signature legible. (1st plate, 1st state)

"The Pugnacious Cabman": (2 plates in different states)

(a) One window to left of lamppost; milkmaid not sharply defined; Pickwick's coat collar ⅛ inch deep with no white line; black line defining hat brim; soldier in background has moustache. Signature faint. (2nd plate, 1st state)

(b) Three windows to left of lamppost; milkmaid sharply defined; Pickwick's coat collar 1/16 inch deep, indicated by white line beneath; no defined curve to brim of hat; soldier in background has no moustache. Signature legible. (1st plate, 1st state)

"The Sagacious Dog": Gamekeeper's gun has both lock and trigger; a white curve separates his hair from barrel of gun. Signature, "Seymour del.," legible. (1st plate, 1st state)

"Dr. Slammer's defiance of Jingle": Ten (not 11) boards in floor; panelling not etched in behind Jingle's head; lines of panelling fragmentary between lamps. Unsigned. (1st plate, 1st state)

Text: all marks of first issue except signature "E" on p. 25. (Since this copy exhibits all other marks of first issue, it appears to lend support to Eckel's view that the presence of this signature is not necessarily a mark of the third issue.)

p. [1]: "O" in "Observations" perfect

p. 3: "d" in "ardour" perfect; "h" in "honorable" perfect

p. 9: has footnote

p. 14: "h" in "heavenly" perfect; "w" in "we" perfect

p. 17: "7" in pagination slightly raised

p. 23: "s" in "stared" perfect

p. 25: has signature "E"

p. 26: caption "Posthumous Papers, &c." with pagination

No. II. (Plates bound in reverse order)

"Mr. Winkle soothes the refractory Steed": Winkle's gaitor buttons on right side of line; horse in vehicle has only one rein showing. Signed, lower center, "Seymour Del." (1st plate)

"Mr. Pickwick in chase of his hat": Lady on right with parasol has two plumes in her bonnet. Signed, lower center, "Seymour Del." (1st plate)

"The Dying Clown": The listener's hat touches his foot. Signed, lower left corner, "Seymour Del." (1st plate)

Text: not in earliest state.

 p. 27: "Chapter III" repeated
 p. 28: "was draw out"
 p. 30: "murmurings"
 p. 33: "every man"
 p. 37: "7" in pagination intact (earliest state)

No. II. Variant. (Plates bound in correct order; otherwise plates and text as above.)

No. III. "The Cricket Match": Signed, lower left corner, "Drawn & Etch'd by R W Buss."

"The Arbour Scene": Signed, lower center, as above.

Page numbers on both plates disproportionately large.

Text: in earliest state.

 p. 51: misprinted semicolon after "family"
 p. 52: letter "s," line 14 up, perfect
 p. 53: "snuff" overlaps outer margin

No. IV. "The Breakdown": Wheel in roadway; lower spokes touch rim. Signed very faintly, lower left corner, "N.E.M.O." (1st plate, 2nd state)

"First appearance of Mr. Samuel Weller": Three top boots at left definitely outlined; Wardle's stick shows no break. Signed, lower right corner, faintly, "N.E.M.O." (1st plate, 2nd state)

Text: not in earliest state.

 p. 91: "whydon't" not spaced
 p. 93: caption correctly spaced
 p. 112: (earliest state) damaged "l" in "light"

No. V. "Mrs. Bardell faints in Mr. Pickwick's arms": Picture over mirror nebulous; top panels of door well defined; glass shade on mantel covers an ornament (not a clock); Sam's legs straight. Signed "Phiz del."

"The Election at Etanswill": The beadle's legs are straight and together. Signed faintly, left of center, "Phiz del."

Text: in earliest state.

 p. 121: "th" for "the"
 p. 133: misplaced comma

No. VI. (Plates in earliest state except that pagination has been corrected)

"Mrs. Leo Hunter's Fancy dress dejeune": The bird cage rests on the boughs of the tree. Signed "Phiz del." Page 154.

"The unexpected breaking up of the Seminary for young Ladies": Bell hangs to right of door; no bell on the door. Signed "Phiz del." Page 169.

Text: in earliest state.

 p. 148: "Expiring Frog" out of alignment with "On a log."
 p. 154: Two quad marks between "their mama"
 p. 157: "Te Count"
 p. 161: "Wellerthe" not spaced

No. VII. (Plates bound in reverse order)

"Mr. Pickwick and Sam in the attorneys' office": Sam's legs are together; the third clerk from left has no pen. (1st state)

"Mr. Pickwick in the Pound": Two donkeys in the pound; hind legs of larger donkey not shown; eave of house on left very faintly drawn. (1st state)

Text: in earliest state.

> p. 194: "b" dropped out in "bagginets"
> p. 202: "r" upside down in "for" date "Sep. 28" (not Aug.)

No. VIII. (Plates bound in reverse order)

"The middle-aged lady in the double-bedded Room": Garment on chair is black; chair shaded black with 3 vertical rails.

"The last visit of Heyling to the Old Man": The tops of Heyling's chair are visible.

Text: lacks some marks of earliest state.

> p. 225: "e" almost obliterated in "reg'larly"
> p. 233: no quad marks visible between "I ever"
> Measurements correct

No. IX. "Mr. Weller attacks the Executive of Ipswich": Pickwick's right thumb turned in; Mr. Snodgrass's vest striped (not checked); no face on signboard.

"Job Trotter encounters Sam in Mr. Muzzle's Kitchen": Clock shows ten minutes to twelve; top of stool in foreground not showing; third shelf of cupboard half empty; Mary's left hand rests on edge of her hip.

Text: lacks one point of earliest issue.

> p. 260: "hodling"
> p. 261: (not earliest form) signature "X2"
> p. 267: "7" in pagination raised above other figures
> Measurements correct

No. X. "Christmas Eve at Mr. Wardle's": Dog and cat in foreground. (1st plate, 1st state)

"The Goblin and the Sexton": Face in the tree trunk; bone far from the skull; no tombstone. (1st plate, 1st state)

Text: address by author not first issue (dash at end of 4th paragraph).

> Measurements correct

No. XI. "Mr. Pickwick slides": Four stumps in foreground; no flying birds; black dog; church spire very faint in background. (1st plate)

"The first interview with Mr. Serjeant Snubbin": Pickwick's glove close to hat; fragments of paper spread on floor; no floral decoration on top of wardrobe; roll of paper in center of floor. (1st plate)

No marks of textual priority; measurements correct

No. XII. "The Valentine": No page number; newspaper on floor. (2nd plate, 1st state)

"The Trial": No page number; hat on front bench. (2nd plate, 1st state)

Text: in earliest state.

> p. 341: "inde- licate"; "inscription"
> p. 342: "S. Veller"
> Measurements correct

No. XIII. (Plates bound in reverse order)

"Mr. Winkle's situation when the door blew to": No space between the hat and shadow. (2nd plate)

"The Card Room at Bath": Cards on table are distinct. (2nd plate)

Text: in earliest state.
 p. 389: "wi shI was"
 p. 397: "Ithink" unspaced
 p. 400: "this friends"
 Measurements correct

No. XIV. "Conviviality at Bob Sawyer's": One book lying flat on top of book rack right of window; books on first shelf standing irregularly; on lower shelf, lying down. (1st plate)
"Mr. Pickwick sits for his Portrait": No star in top center pane of window; clock shows one hand pointing to VI. (1st plate)

Text: in earliest state.
 p. 432: caption—"F" in "OF" imperfect
 Measurements correct

No. XV. "The Warden's Room": Loop on clothesline. Unsigned. (2nd plate)
"Discovery of Jingle in the Fleet": Signed irregularly "Phiz" with flourish from last letter. Basket shaded within handle; arms of girls in foreground shaded; diagonal shading on clothes draped over line. (1st plate)

No marks of textual priority; measurements correct.

No. XVI. "The Red-nosed man Discourseth": The legs of Sam's chair are turned (not square). (1st plate)
"Mrs. Bardell encounters Mr. Pickwick in the prison": Hand rail on each side of the steps; Sam's hat has a cockade. (1st plate)

No marks of textual priority; measurements correct.

No. XVII. "Mr. Winkle returns under extraordinary circumstances": Top shelf on right empty. (1st plate)
"The Ghostly passengers in the ghost of a mail": The bundle at right of lantern is corded. Signed "PHIZ" in caps. (2nd plate)

No marks of textual priority; measurements correct.

No. XVIII. "The Rival Editors": Signed "Phiz del" in very small letters to left of center; no toasting fork or jug on side of cupboard. (1st plate)
"Mr. Bob Sawyer's mode of travelling"; Signed "Phiz del" in very small letters to left of center; no bundle on the Irishman's stick. (1st plate)

No marks of textual priority; measurements correct.

No. XIX/XX. (Plates bound in irregular sequence)
"Mr. Weller and his friends drinking to Mr. Pell": Small bottle on left corner of table. (1st plate)
Frontispiece: Signed "Phiz fecit" in lower center surrounding the Tupman shield. Stool has 4 stripes. (1st plate)
Vignette title: Signed "PHIZ fecit." Inn sign reads "Tony Veller." (1st plate)
"Mary and the fat boy": Knife in the fat boy's hand points downward. (1st plate)

No marks of textual priority; measurements slightly less than Hatton and Cleaver's figures.
 p. 609: imprint: "London: | Bradbury and Evans, Printers, | White-
  friars.
 p. [610]: blank

Provenance was not provided with this set of *Pickwick Papers,* purchased through Brentano's in New York in 1925, and no records are now available. So far as we can determine this is not one of fourteen sets included by Eckel in his 1928 census of *Prime Pickwicks in Parts*. If this is true, it is, indeed, a "bibliographic recluse," no longer *"spurloss versunken,"* deserving a place in the catalogue of distinguished copies.

B13(2)

A second set in 19/20 monthly numbers as issued. All wrappers "With Illustrations."

Percy Fitzgerald's bookplate is attached to the cover of the first number.

The set conforms to the following "points" as listed for the preceding one. Other "points" are lacking.

> (1) All covers are dated MDCCCXXXVI except XVII, which, through faulty printing, shows only the tops of some letters.
> (5) Part II has 3 plates signed by Seymour.
> (6) Part III has 2 plates signed "Drawn & Etch'd by R W Buss with the page numbers. (This copy has also a second set of plates by Phiz.)
> (7) Part IV has 2 plates indistinctly signed N.E.M.O.
> (8) Part XV has the address of the author. (Addresses are lacking in II, III, and X.)
> (9) Parts XVII, XVIII, and XIX/XX have addresses by the publishers.

Wrappers for Parts XV-XIX/XX are correct; others are as follows:

> No. I. As reprinted in December, 1836:
> Front (outside) With Illustrations; MDCCCXXXVI
> Front & back (inside) blank
> Back (outside) Cheap and Entertaining Periodical | This day is published, | . . . | The Library of Fiction.

> No. II. As reprinted c. May, 1837:
> Front (outside) With Illustrations; MDCCCXXXVI
> Front (inside) The Pictorial Album, etc.
> Back (inside) Travelling and Hunting Maps, etc.
> Back (outside) Popular Juvenile Books, etc.

> Nos. III-XII, XIV. As reprinted c. May, 1837
> As No. II above with added imprint: Bradbury and Evans | Printers, Whitefriars.

> No. XIII. As Nos. III-XII above except:
> Front (inside) Important Invention in the Fine Arts. | Cowen & Waring's | . . . | Caoutchouc.

All advertisements as well as addresses by author or publishers are lacking in Parts I-XIV. Advertisements in other Parts appear as follows:

> No. XV. "Pickwick Advertiser" lacking.
> Back Advertisements (others lacking)
> (1) Allen Bell and Co., 8 pp.
> (2) The Popular Works of Mr. Peter Parley, 2 pp.

> No. XVI. "Pickwick Advertiser" lacking.
> Back Advertisements (irregular)
> Robert Cadell, dated "Edinburgh, September 1837. | Life of Sir Walter Scott, Bart. | by J. G. Lockhart, Esq.," 16 pp. numbered 4-15.

> No. XVII. "Pickwick Advertiser" lacks pp. 3-6
> Back Advertisements (others lacking)
> (2) John Amesbury's Patent Spine Supports, 8 pp.

Text: not in earliest state; errors corrected; measurements as much as 4 mm. less than maximum.

No. VIII. "The last visit of Heyling to the Old Man": The tops of Heyling's chair are visible.
"The middle-aged lady in the double-bedded Room": Garment on chair is black; chair shaded black with 3 vertical rails.

Text: not in earliest state.
    p. 225: "e" almost obliterated in "reg'larly"
    p. 233: no quad marks visible between "I ever"

No. IX. "Mr. Weller attacks the Executive of Ipswich": Pickwick's right thumb turned in; no face on signboard. (1st plate)
"Job Trotter encounters Sam in Mr. Muzzle's Kitchen": Clock shows ten minutes to twelve. (1st plate)

Text: not in earliest state; errors corrected; measurements about 2 mm. less than maximum.

No. X. "Christmas Eve at Mr. Wardle's": Dog and cat in foreground. (1st plate, 1st state)
"The Goblin and the Sexton": Face in the tree trunk; bone far from skull; no tombstone. (1st plate, 1st state)

No marks of textual priority; measurements 2-4 mm. less than maximum.

No. XI. "Mr. Pickwick slides": Four stumps in foreground; no flying birds; black dog; church spire very faint in background. (1st plate)
"The first interview with Mr. Serjeant Snubbin": No roll of paper in center of floor. (2nd plate)

No marks of textual priority; measurements 2-4 mm. less than maximum.

No. XII. "The Valentine": Page number 343; no newspaper on floor. (1st plate, 2nd state)
"The Trial": Page number 358; no hat on front bench. (1st plate, 2nd state)

Text: in earliest state.
    p. 341: "inde- licate"; "inscription"
    p. 342: "S. Veller"

Measurements slightly less than maximum, but p. 370 shows 147 mm. as compared with 150½ mm.

No. XIII. "The Card Room at Bath": Cards on table very faintly etched. (1st plate) "Mr. Winkle's situation when the door blew to": Clear space between hat on ground and shadow. (1st plate)

Text: not in earliest state; errors corrected.
    p. 389: "w ishI was"

No. XIV. "Conviviality at Bob Sawyer's": No book on top of book rack. (2nd plate) "Mr. Pickwick sits for his Portrait": No star in top center pane of window; clock shows one hand pointing to VI. (1st plate)

Text: not in earliest state; typographical imperfection corrected; measurements 4-5 mm. less than maximum.

No. XV. "The Warden's Room": No loop on clothesline. Signed "Phiz del." (1st plate)
"Discovery of Jingle in the Fleet": Signed irregularly "Phiz" with flourish from last letter. (1st plate)

No marks of textual priority; measurements correct.

No. XVIII. "Pickwick Advertiser" lacks pp. 3-14.
 Back Advertisements (others lacking)
  (1) Lashmar and Bellingham (prices in small type), 1 leaf.
  (3) Simpson's Herbal pills (variant 1: Simpson's in solid face; paragraph 4 in small type)

No. XIX/XX. "Pickwick Advertiser" lacks pp. 1-16.
 Back Advertisements correct.

Plates and text appear as follows:

No. I. (Bound in irregular sequence)
 "Mr. Pickwick addresses the Club": Picture frames darkened; Tupman's waistcoat closed with black line; signature faint. (1st plate, 2nd state)
 "Dr. Slammer's defiance of Jingle": Eleven floor boards (2nd plate)
 "The Pugnacious Cabman": Milkmaid very faint; soldier with moustache; heavy black lines and sharp contrasts. (2nd plate)
 "The Sagacious Dog": No trigger on gun. (2nd plate)

 Text: not in earliest state.
  p. 9: has footnote

No. II. "The Dying Clown": The listener's hat touches his foot. (1st plate)
 "Mr. Pickwick in chase of his hat": Lady on right with parasol has two plumes in her bonnet. (1st plate)
 "Mr. Winkle soothes the refractory Steed": Horse in the vehicle has only one rein showing. (1st plate)

 Text: not in earliest state.

No. III. (Two suppressed Buss plates bound between the two by Phiz.)

 Text: not in earliest state.

No. IV. "The Breakdown": Wheel in roadway; lower spokes touch rim. Signed very faintly "N.E.M.O." (1st plate, 2nd state)
 "First appearance of Mr. Samuel Weller": Three top boots definitely outlined; Wardle's stick shows no break. Signed faintly, "N.E.M.O." (1st plate, 2nd state)

 Text: not in earliest state, but p. 112 has damaged "l" in "light."

No. V. "Mrs. Bardell faints in Mr. Pickwick's arms": Picture over mirror nebulous; glass shade on mantel covers an ornament (not a clock); Sam's legs are straight. Signed "Phiz del." (1st plate)
 "The Election at Etanswill": The beadle's legs are straight and together. Signed faintly "Phiz del." (1st plate)

 Text: not in earliest state; errors corrected; measurement 2-3 mm. less than maximum.

No. VI. (Plates in earliest state except that pagination has been corrected)
 "Mrs. Leo Hunter's Fancy dress dejeune": The bird cage rests on the boughs of the tree. Signed "Phiz del." Page 154.
 "The unexpected breaking up of the Seminary for young Ladies": Bell hangs to right of door; no bell on the door. Signed "Phiz del." Page 169.

 Text: not in earliest state; errors corrected; measurements 3-4 mm. less than maximum.

No. VII. "Mr. Pickwick in the Pound": Hind leg of larger donkey is shown; additional work on eave of house. (2nd state)
 "Mr. Pickwick and Sam in the attorneys' office": Sam's legs are together; the third clerk from left has no pen. (1st state)

No. XVI. "The Red-nosed man Discourseth": The legs of Sam's chair are turned (not square). (1st plate)

"Mrs. Bardell encounters Mr. Pickwick in the prison": Hand rail on each side of the steps; Sam's hat has a cockade. (1st plate)

No marks of textual priority; measurements correct.

No. XVII. "Mr. Winkle returns under extraordinary circumstances": Signed 'Phiz del." Top shelf empty. (1st plate)

"The Ghostly passengers in the ghost of a mail": Signed "Phiz del." in small letters; bundle at right of lantern not corded. (1st plate)

No marks of textual priority; measurements correct.

No. XVIII. "Mr. Bob Sawyer's mode of travelling": Bundle on the Irishman's stick.

Signature in center of plate. (2nd plate)

"The Rival Editors": Toasting fork and jug on side of cupboard. Signature in center of plate. (2nd plate)

No marks of textual priority; measurements correct.

No. XIX/XX. "Mary and the fat boy": Knife in fat boy's hand points downward. (1st plate)

"Mr. Weller and his friends drinking to Mr. Pell": Small bottle on left corner of table. (1st plate)

Frontispiece: Stool has 6 stripes; signature is undivided on left of shield. (2nd plate)

Vignette title: Signed "Phiz fecit." Inn sign reads "Tony Weller." (2nd plate)

No marks of textual priority; measurements approximately correct.

B13(3)

A third set in 19/20 monthly numbers as issued. All wrappers "With Illustrations."

The set conforms to the following "points" given under B13(1); all others are lacking.

(1) Covers (except nos. XIV and XVIII) dated MDCCCXXXVI. [All except XV-XVII as reprinted between October 1836 and May 1837].

(4) Part I has 4 plates of which three are signed faintly by Seymour. ["Dr. Slammer's defiance of Jingle" in later state with 11 floor boards].

(5) Part II has 3 plates signed by Seymour.

(8) Part XV has address by the author. [Addresses lacking in Parts II, III, X].

(9) Parts XVII, XVIII, and XIX/XX have addresses by the publisher.

(10) Plates in Parts I-XII have only page numbers without captions; parts XIII-XIX/XX have neither page number nor caption.

(11) Vignette title with "Veller"; frontispiece with "PHIZ fecit" surrounding center shield.

Wrappers for Parts XV-XVII are correct; others are as follows:

Nos. I-III, V, VII, IX-XIII. As reprinted c. May 1837.

Front (outside) With Illustrations; MDCCCXXXVI.

Front (inside) The Pictorial Album, etc.

Back (inside) Travelling and Hunting Maps, etc.

Back (outside) Popular Juvenile Books, etc.

No. IV. As reprinted in October 1836.
Front (outside) With Illustrations; MDCCCXXXVI.
Front (inside) Cheap & Entertaining Periodical.
Back (inside) Library of Fiction.
Back (outside) New and Splendid Volume.

No. VI. As reprinted in October 1836.
As No. IV except inside covers blank.

No. VIII. As reprinted in November 1836.
Front (outside) With Illustrations; MDCCCXXXVI.
Front (inside) Blank.
Back (inside) Blank.
Back (outside) Cheap and Entertaining Periodical.

No. XIV. As reprinted c. May 1837.
As Nos. I-III, etc. except dated MDCCCXXXVII.

No. XVIII. Correct except dated MDCCCXXXVII.

No. XIX/XX. Front cover correct. Back as for Part XIII of original issue:
Back (inside) Manly Exercises.
Back (outside) New Works, printed for Longman, Rees, etc.

Parts I-XIV all of late issue. All advertisements lacking. All textual indications of early issue mentioned by Hatton and Cleaver lacking except Part XII, p. 342, "S. Veller" uncorrected. All measurements contracted from 1 to 4 mm. compared with those given by Hatton and Cleaver.

Plates for Parts I-XIV as follows:

No. I. "Mr. Pickwick addresses the Club": Pickwick's vest buttons are on his right side; middle picture with faint single cord; signed faintly "Seymour." (2nd plate, 1st state).
"The Pugnacious Cabman": Milkmaid faintly etched; Pickwick's coat collar ⅛ inch deep with no white line; soldier in background has moustache; signed faintly "Seymour." (2nd plate, 1st state).
"The Sagacious Dog": Gamekeeper's gun has no lock or trigger; signed lower center "Seymour del." (2nd plate, 1st state).
"Dr. Slammer's defiance of Jingle": Eleven boards in floor; unsigned. (2nd plate, 1st state).

No. II. "Mr. Pickwick in chase of his hat": Lady on right has two plumes in her hat; signed lower center "Seymour Del." (1st plate).
"Mr. Winkle soothes the refractory Steed": Winkle's gaitor buttons on right side of line; horse in vehicle has only one rein showing; signed lower center "Seymour Del." (1st plate).
"The Dying Clown": The listener's hat touches his foot. Signed lower left "Seymour Del." (1st plate).

No. III. With two plates etched by Phiz in October 1836 to substitute for the original plates by R. W. Buss.

No. IV. "The Breakdown": Wheel with lower spokes touching rim; no signature visible. (1st plate, 2nd state)
"First appearance of Mr. Samuel Weller": Wardle's stick shows no break; boots at left clearly outlined; no signature visible. (1st plate, 2nd state).

No. V. "Mrs. Bardell faints in Mr. Pickwick's arms": Glass shade covers an ornament; picture over mirror is nebulous; signed faintly left of center "Phiz del." (1st plate)
"The Election at Etanswill": The beadle's legs are straight and together; signed "Phiz del." (1st plate)

No. VI. "Mrs. Leo Hunter's Fancy dress dejeune": The bird cage rests in the boughs; pagination is corrected; signed "Phiz del." (1st plate, 2nd state) "The unexpected breaking up of the Seminary for young Ladies": No bell on door; pagination is corrected; signed "Phiz del." (1st plate, 2nd state)

No. VII. "Mr. Pickwick in the Pound": Eaves of house are clearly etched; larger donkey shows only front legs; signed "Phiz del." (1st plate, 2nd state) "Mr. Pickwick and Sam in the attorneys' office": Sam's legs are together; the third clerk from left has no pen; signed "Phiz del." (1st plate)

No. VIII. "The last visit of Heyling to the Old Man": The tops of Heyling's chair are visible; signed "Phiz del." (1st plate) "The middle-aged lady in the double-bedded room": Garment on chair is black; chair is shaded black with 3 vertical rails; signed "Phiz del." (1st plate)

No. IX. "Mr. Weller attacks the Executive of Ipswich": Pickwick's right thumb is turned in; Mr. Snodgrass's vest is striped (not checked); no face on signboard; signed "Phiz del." (1st plate) "Job Trotter encounters Sam in Mr. Muzzle's Kitchen": Clock shows 10 minutes to 12; top of stool in foreground not visible; third shelf of cupboard half empty; Mary's left hand rests on her hip; signed "Phiz del." (1st plate)

No. X. "Christmas Eve at Mr. Wardle's": Dog and kitten in foreground; signed "Phiz del." (1st plate) "The Goblin and the Sexton": No face in tree trunk; signed "Phiz del." (2nd plate)

No. XI. "Mr. Pickwick slides": Five stakes in the ice; signed "Phiz del." (2nd plate) "The first interview with Mr. Serjeant Snubbin": No roll of paper on the floor; signed "Phiz del." (2nd plate)

No. XII. "The Valentine": No newspaper on floor; with pagination; signed "Phiz del." (1st plate, 2nd state) "The Trial": No hat on front bench; with pagination; signed "Phiz del." (1st plate, 2nd state)

No. XIII. "The Card Room at Bath": Cards on table very faintly etched; no pagination; signed "Phiz del." (1st plate) "Mr. Winkle's situation when the door blew to": Clear space between hat and shadow; no pagination; signed "Phiz del." (1st plate)

No. XIV. "Conviviality at Bob Sawyer's": One book lying flat on top of shelf to right of window; no pagination; signed "Phiz del." (1st plate) "Mr. Pickwick sits for his Portrait": No star in top center pane of window; clock shows one hand pointing to VI; signed "Phiz del." (1st plate)

Parts XV-XIX/XX. No marks of textual priority are indicated for these numbers by Hatton and Cleaver. All measurements in this set are approximately correct. Plates and advertising material are as follows.

No. XV. Address by the author, 4 pages. Front advertiser lacking. Back advertiser lacks 2 slips: "Caledonian Illustrations" and "The Popular Works of Mr. Peter Parley." "The Warden's Room": No loop on clothesline; signed "Phiz del." (1st plate) "Discovery of Jingle in the Fleet": Signed "Phiz" with flourish from last letter. (1st plate)

No. XVI. Advertiser lacking.

"The Red-nosed man Discourseth": Legs of Sam's chair are turned (not square). (1st plate)

"Mrs. Bardell encounters Mr. Pickwick in the prison": Hand rail on left of steps; cockade in Sam's hat. (1st plate)

No. XVII. Address by the publishers, 1 page; verso "New Works preparing for publication." Front advertiser lacking. Back advertiser lacks (3) "Edinburgh, September 1837. Life of Sir Walter Scott."

"Mr. Winkle returns under extraordinary circumstances": Top shelf on right empty; signed "Phiz del." (1st plate)

"The Ghostly passengers in the ghost of a mail": Bundle not corded; signed "Phiz del." in small letters. (1st plate)

No. XVIII. Address by the publishers, 1 page; verso "Sketches by 'Boz,' complete in one volume." Front advertiser lacking. Back advertiser correct.

"Mr. Bob Sawyer's mode of travelling": Bundle on Irishman's stick; signed lower center "Phiz del." (2nd plate)

"The Rival Editors": Toasting fork and jug on side of dresser; signed lower center "Phiz del." (2nd plate)

No. XIX/XX. Front advertiser correct. Back advertiser lacks (2) "Simpson's Herbal Pills" and (3) "Neill on Diseases of the Eye."

"Mary and the fat boy": Knife in fat boy's hand points downward; signed lower center "Phiz del." (1st plate)

Frontispiece: Stool has 4 stripes; signed around center shield "Phiz fecit." (1st plate)

Vignette title: Inn sign reads "Tony Veller"; signed "PHIZ fecit." (1st plate)

"Mr. Weller and his friends drinking to Mr. Pell": No bottle on table; coachman has 4 buttons on his coat; signed "Phiz del." (2nd plate)

B13(4)

An incomplete fourth set of monthly numbers as issued. All wrappers "With Illustrations."

Parts II, III, XVII lacking.

Parts I, IV-X, XIV all of late issue:
    Wrappers reprinted
    All advertisers lacking
    Text lacking points of early issue; measurements 2 to 6 mm. less than that given by Hatton and Cleaver (indicating late issue).

Parts X-XIII, XV, XVI, XVIII, XIX/XX have points of early issue as follows:

No. XI. Wrapper as reprinted c. May 1837.
    Advertiser correct.
    Plates both 2nd plate.
    Text: measurements approximately correct.

No. XII. Wrapper correct.
    Front advertiser correct with additional slip:
        "Horne's Public and Subscription Library"; verso blank.
    Back advertiser, "Mechi's Catalogue," lacking.
    Plates both 1st plate, 1st state.
    Text: Has one point of early issue (p. 342, l. 5, "S. Veller"). Measurements 1 to 2 mm. less than that given by Hatton and Cleaver.

No. XIII. Wrapper correct.
> Front advertiser has only pp. 1-2 and 15-16; lacks pp. 3-14 and Pigot's
> Coloured Views, 4 pages.
>
> Back advertiser correct.
>
> Plates both 1st plate.
>
> Text: Has points of early issue (p. 389, l. 5, "I wishI was"; p. 397, l. 4 up,
> "Ithink"; p. 400, l. 21, "this friends.") Measurements correct or ex-
> ceeding that given by Hatton and Cleaver (indicative of early issue).

No. XV. Wrapper correct.
> Front advertiser correct except with first 6 pages torn out (fragments
> remain).
>
> Back advertiser lacking.
>
> Address of the author, 4 pages.
>
> Plates both 1st plate.
>
> Text: No marks of textual priority are known for Nos. XV-XIX/XX.
> Measurements correct or slightly above that given by Hatton and
> Cleaver.

No. XVI. Wrapper correct.
> Front advertiser correct.
>
> Back advertiser [none usually included in this issue] as follows:
> > (1) "The History of the French Revolution."
> > (2) "Thiers's History of the French Revolution."
> > (3) "Simpson's Herbal Pills."
> > (4) "To the Nobility, Families . . . The New Tea Warehouse." Prices
> > in blackface. Verso blank.
> > (5) "Established 1820. John James Rippon's," 4 pages on yellow
> > paper.
> > (6) "Prize Essay on Sailors."
> > (7) "To softer prospects . . . Artists' Portfolio."
> > (8) "Literary Novelties."
> > (9) "Allan Bell & Co's. Unique Illustrated Classical Library." Verso
> > "Diamond Pocket Editions," 4 pages.
> > (10) "Apsley Pellatt," 4 pages in blue type.
> > (11) "The Popular Works of Mr. Peter Parley."
> > (12) "Royal Beulah Spa & Gardens" on green paper.
>
> Plates one 1st plate and the other 2nd plate.
>
> Text: Measurements correct or slightly above that given by Hatton and
> Cleaver.

No. XVIII. Wrapper correct, except MDCCCXXXVII.
> Front advertiser lacking.
>
> Back advertiser correct with extra insert: "Works published by Joseph
> Thomas," 4 pages.
>
> Plates one 1st plate and the other 2nd plate.
>
> Address by publishers.
>
> Text: Measurements correct or slightly above that given by Hatton and
> Cleaver.

No. XIX/XX. Wrapper correct.
> Advertiser correct.
>
> Plates, including frontispiece and vignette title, all 1st plate.
>
> Address of publishers lacking.
>
> Text: Measurements approximately correct.

B14(1)

THE POSTHUMOUS PAPERS OF THE PICKWICK CLUB. Philadelphia: Carey, Lea & Blanchard. 1836 [–1837].

Titles

Vol. I: Perambulations, Perils, Travels, Adventures and | Sporting Transactions . . . 1836.

Vols. II-V: Perambulations, Perils, Adventures and Sporting | Transactions . . . 1837.

12°. Five volumes in original buff paper boards with pink cloth spine and paper labels. End papers and advertisements intact.

First American edition. Volume I, the first of Dickens's books published in America, antedated the English edition in book form.

B14(2)

A duplicate set of five volumes, with all end papers and advertisements intact.

B14(3)

A third set of five volumes, with all end papers and advertisements intact. Vol. II, variant issue.

Title, Vol. II: Perambulations, Perils, Adventures, and Sport- | ing Transactions . . . 1837.

Text completely reset.

B14(4)

Two copies of Vol. I, second and third editions. In original buff paper boards with pink cloth spine and paper labels.

Titles

Vol. I (2nd edition): . . . Adventures, and Sport- | ing Transactions . . . 1837.

Vol. I (3rd edition): . . . Adventures, and Sporting | Transactions . . . 1837.

B15(1)

THE POSTHUMOUS PAPERS OF THE PICKWICK CLUB. WITH FORTY-THREE ILLUSTRATIONS, BY R. SEYMOUR, AND PHIZ. London: Chapman and Hall. MDCCCXXXVII.

8°. Two volumes in full red levant by Riviere made up from the original parts, untrimmed. All wrappers and addresses by author and publishers bound in with some advertisements. Wrappers, except No. III, and most plates are in first state.

B15(2)

A second set of two volumes in original half old calf with green marbled paper boards. First English edition in book form made up from the parts. (Perhaps earlier than the better known single-volume edition.)

Preliminary leaves with frontispiece and vignette title, both in earliest state, bound in Vol. II. Buss plates and some others of early issue. Footnote on p. 9; "Chapter III" on pp. 25 and 27; misspelling of "Picwkick" on p. 375.

B15(3)

A third set of two volumes in original half green morocco with brown marbled paper boards and end papers; edges marbled.

Sophisticated copy. Frontispiece and vignette title in later state. Extra Onwhyn plates with others of early issue including the two Buss plates.

B16(1)†

THE POSTHUMOUS PAPERS OF THE PICKWICK CLUB. London: Chapman and Hall. MDCCCXXXVII.

8°. One volume bound in half dark red morocco; edges slightly trimmed; top edge gilt.

First English edition in book form. With the two Buss plates and some others of early issue; footnote on p. 9; "Chapter III" on pp. 25 and 27; misspelling of "Picwkick" on p. 375.

Autograph copy inscribed: "Charles Dickens very much wishes that he had given this book to Miss Louisa King. First July 1844."

B16(2)

A second copy bound in three-quarters green levant morocco by Morrell, uncut, top edge gilt.

Plates not first issue; footnote on p. 9; "Chapter III" on pp. 25 and 27.

B16(3)

A third copy bound with additional plates by Onwhyn (72 illustrations plus frontispiece and vignette title) in full tan morocco by Hatchard, edges slightly trimmed, top edge gilt.

Some of the original plates in early state; footnote on p. 9; "Chapter III" on pp. 25 and 27.

B17†

THE POSTHUMOUS PAPERS OF THE PICKWICK CLUB. Calcutta: William Rushton. 1837–1838.

8°. First Indian edition in 18 monthly parts arranged for two volumes (Nos. I/II and XIX/XX being double numbers) as issued, with green wrappers lithographed by T. Block after the original design by Seymour. Lacks No. VII, Vol. II. Includes 30 plates lithographed by T. Block after the original illustrations.

This apparently unique set is described by Charles J. Sawyer in *A Dickens Library*. 1936.

B18†

THE POSTHUMOUS PAPERS OF THE PICKWICK CLUB. V. D. Land: Henry Dowling. Launceston. MDCCCXXXVIII.

8°. In original plum-colored cloth with black label.

This Van Diemen's Land edition is "entirely the produce of colonial industry— the printing, engravings, and the binding." Illustrations are lithographed from the original plates.

Ex libris William Glyde Wilkins. This copy, in very fine condition, was procured from a member of the Publisher's family, apparently unused. Accompanying the book are a copy of the "Jubilee of the Launceston Examiner. 1842—March 12th —1892," describing conditions under which this edition of Pickwick was published, and Mr. Wilkins's MS. describing the book, which he believed to be "absolutely unique" in this condition. Since publication of the first edition of this catalogue, the existence of several copies in Australia and New Zealand has been brought to the attention of the compiler.

B19

THE POSTHUMOUS PAPERS OF THE PICKWICK CLUB. NEW EDITION. Philadelphia: Carey, Lea and Blanchard. 1838.

8°. Rebound in three-quarters crimson morocco, with original green cloth covers and spine preserved; edges slightly trimmed; top edge gilt. Illustrations engraved by J. Yeager, reproducing those of "Alfred Crowquill" and "Sam Weller." Eighteen pages of advertisements.

Second American edition.

B20

THE POSTHUMOUS PAPERS OF THE PICKWICK CLUB. New York: James Turney, Jr. MDCCCXXXVIII.

8°. Twenty-six parts in green wrappers identical in design with original English edition. Lacks Pt. XX.

B21

THE POSTHUMOUS PAPERS OF THE PICKWICK CLUB. WITH ILLUSTRATIONS, BY CROWQUILL. New York: James Turney, Jr. MDCCCXXXVIII.

8°. In original purple cloth binding (faded). One of several variants made up from the issue in parts.

B22(1)

THE POSTHUMOUS PAPERS OF THE PICKWICK CLUB. New York: William H. Colyer. 1842.

8°. Two volumes in original buff paper boards with black cloth spines and paper labels.

B22(2)

A variant set of two volumes with brown cloth spines. Each volume has a frontispiece and vignette title not included in the above set.

B23

THE POSTHUMOUS PAPERS OF THE PICKWICK CLUB. London: Chapman & Hall. 1847.

8°. Eight parts, 1 May—30 September 1847, in original green paper wrappers. (First Cheap Edition)

Part I lacks front wrapper; Part V lacks back wrapper; "Advertiser" lacking in Parts I, IV, and VII.

B24(1)

THE POSTHUMOUS PAPERS OF THE PICKWICK CLUB. WITH A FRONTISPIECE. FROM A DESIGN BY C. R. LESLIE, ESQ., R.A. ENGRAVED BY J. THOMPSON. London: Chapman and Hall. MD-CCCXLVII.

8°. Cheap edition in original green cloth binding, and white end papers.

B24(2)

A second copy of the cheap edition in original green cloth, with grey end papers. Twenty-two extra illustrations bound in.

B24(3)

A third copy rebound in full blue levant by Zaehnsdorf; marbled end papers, edges gilt. Thirty-two extra illustrations by Sir John Gilbert and six by Phiz bound in.

B25(1)†

THE POSTHUMOUS PAPERS OF THE PICKWICK CLUB. London: Chapman and Hall. 1861.

8°. Two volumes in original red cloth, uncut. (Library Edition)

Presentation copy to Charles Kent, inscribed on flyleaf of Vol. I: "To William Charles Kent This set of my books With kind remembrance and regard Charles Dickens August 1861."

B25(2)†

A second copy of Vol. I in original red cloth, uncut.

Presentation copy to Sir James Emerson Tennent, inscribed on flyleaf: "Charles Dickens To his friend Sir James Emerson Tennent With affectionate regard Twenty Ninth October, 1864."

Inserted in volume is Dickens's holograph letter (A124) as follows: "Twenty Ninth October, 1864 My Dear Tennent. I am heartily vexed that you got this set of my books, because I had hoped to send you one when your own book should be finished. For the [*word deleted*] present I stand committed to a white lie, in the inscription I have written; but means must be devised for making it a piece of truth. Very affectionately yours Charles Dickens."

B26

POSTHUMOUS PAPERS OF THE PICKWICK CLUB. London: Chapman and Hall. [1873–1874].

4°. Five monthly parts, November 1873–March 1874, in original blue paper wrappers, as issued. (Household Edition)

Printed in double columns, with 57 illustrations by Phiz.

B27

THE POSTHUMOUS PAPERS OF THE PICKWICK CLUB. London: Chapman and Hall. [1874].

4°. Twenty-six "Penny Parts" of 8 or 16 pages, as issued. (Household Edition)

Printed in double columns, with 57 illustrations by Phiz.

B28

THE POSTHUMOUS PAPERS OF THE PICKWICK CLUB. EDITED BY CHARLES DICKENS THE YOUNGER. London: Macmillan and Co. 1886.

8°. Two volumes in original green cloth. (Jubilee edition)

B29

THE POSTHUMOUS PAPERS OF THE PICKWICK CLUB. WITH ILLUSTRATIONS BY R. SEYMOUR, R. W. BUSS, HABLOT K. BROWNE ("PHIZ") AND J. LEECH. London: Chapman and Hall. 1887.

8°. Two volumes in half blue crushed levant. Although the name of R. W. Buss is included among the illustrators, the two Buss plates are not reproduced.

B30†

POSTHUMOUS PAPERS OF THE PICKWICK CLUB. PART I. INTRODUCTION BY PERCY FITZGERALD. New York, London: George D. Sproul. MCMII.

4°. Vol. I, St. Dunstan Illuminated Edition of the Complete Works of Charles Dickens. Printed on vellum and bound in richly decorated blue morocco.

Publisher's Proof (copy for H. T. Goodwin). Fifteen sets of 130 volumes were announced at a subscription price of $1,000; so far as we know the projected edition was never published. See illustration.

B31

THE POSTHUMOUS PAPERS OF THE PICKWICK CLUB. ILLUS-TRATED BY CECIL ALDIN. New York: E. P. Dutton & Company. [n.d.].

8°. Two volumes on large paper. Bound in buff buckram.

B32

MR. PICKWICK ILLUSTRATED IN COLOR BY FRANK REYNOLDS, R.I. New York, London: Hodder & Stoughton. [n.d.].

4°. In original red cloth.

B33

THE POSTHUMOUS PAPERS OF THE PICKWICK CLUB. London: Chapman & Hall. 1909.

4°. Two volumes in original blue cloth. (The Topical Edition)

B34

THE POSTHUMOUS PAPERS OF THE PICKWICK CLUB. Chapman & Hall, Ltd., Lawrence & Jellicoe, Ltd. 1910.

4°. Two volumes in white vellum.

No. 14 of 250 copies autographed by the illustrator, Cecil Aldin.

B35

THE LOMBARD STREET EDITION OF THE NOVELS OF CHARLES DICKENS. EDITED BY JOHN HARRISON STONE-HOUSE. *Pickwick*. London: Piccadilly Fountain Press. 1931.

8°. Facsimile in 19/20 parts of original edition.

No. 218 of the deluxe edition of 1,000 copies.

B36

THE POSTHUMOUS PAPERS OF THE PICKWICK CLUB. New York: For The Heritage Club. 1938.

8°. In original grey cloth decorated in red.

EXTRA ILLUSTRATIONS TO *Pickwick Papers*

B37

Extra plates by R. W. Buss [Chapman and Hall. 1836].

Two copies of "The Cricket Match" on plate paper, 9″ by 5¾″.

B38(1)

Pickwickian Illustrations by William Heath. London: Thomas McLean. 1837.

Twenty etchings in ornamental paper wrapper—gold design on yellow, title in gold on black.

B38(2)

A second, large paper, copy. Wrapper with gold design on blue.

B39

Illustrations by Sam Weller (Thomas Onwhyn). London: E. Grattan. 1837.

Thirty-two etchings with front cover (spine and back cover lacking).

B40

Extra Illustrations by Sam Weller (Thomas Onwhyn) and Alfred Crowquill (Alfred H. Forrester). [1837].

Extracted from bound volumes. Three of the plates colored.

B41(1)

Sketches of Expeditions, From the Pickwick Club. By T. Sibson. London: Sherwood, Gilbert and Piper. 1838.

Ten plates in original blue paper wrapper with title "Sibson's Racy Sketches."

B41(2)

A second copy bound with original wrapper in full dark red levant morocco. *Ex libris* Loren Griswold DuBois.

B42

Seven Extra Illustrations by "Phiz." [1847].

On plate paper, 8°, published contemporaneously with the Cheap Edition.

B43

Plates to Illustrate the Cheap Edition of Pickwick. London: J. Newman. [1847].

Twelve etchings (8 from set of 22, and 4 from set of 32 plates) in original green paper wrappers.

B44

Plates to Illustrate the Cheap Edition by [Sir] John Gilbert, Esq., engraved by Messrs. Greenaway and Wright. Part 3, *Pickwick*. London: E. Appleyard. [1847].

Four plates, 12°.

B45

Thirty-two illustrations by Thomas Onwhyn for the Cheap Edition. [1847].

B46

Illustrations by "Phiz" for Pickwick Club. London: [Chapman and Hall]. 1874.

Fifty-five illustrations for the "Penny Parts," mounted on plate paper, with engraved portrait of the artist.

B47(1)

Illustrations to The Pickwick Club by Frederick W. Pailthorpe. London: Robson & Kerslake. 1882.

Twenty-four proof-plates, mounted, 8°.

B47(2)

A second set, colored, on plate paper, in original green paper wrapper.

B47(3)

A third set, on plate paper, in original green paper wrapper.

B47(4)

A fourth set, on India paper, mounted, in original green paper wrapper.

Inserted in this copy: "Mr. Sam Weller," etched and colored by Pailthorpe, and "Pickwick in the Pound," an unpublished colored drawing by Pailthorpe.

B48

Twelve Illustrations to The Pickwick Club Drawn and Etched by T. Onwhyn, 1847. London: Albert Jackson. 1894.

Etchings executed in 1847, but issued only in 1894. This set is colored.

B49

PICTORIAL PICKWICKIANA. EDITED BY JOSEPH GREGO. London: Chapman and Hall. 1899.

8°. Two volumes in original green cloth with gilt illustration.

Reproductions of 350 drawings and engravings by Seymour, Buss, Browne, and others, including 8 by Joseph Grego never before published.

B50(1)

Portfolio of Twelve Original Illustrations by A. B. Frost. London: A. J. Slatter. 1908.

On plate paper.

B50(2)

A second set, on India paper.

B51

Twelve Extra Illustrations to *The Pickwick Papers* by Charles E. Brock. Leamington Spa: Arthur W. Waters. Birmingham: Holland Bros. 1921.

4°.

B52

Pickwick Pictures, A Series of Character Sketches from *Pickwick Papers* by H. M. Paget. London: Ernest Nister. New York: E. P. Dutton & Co. [n.d.].

In stiff paper cover with colored illustrations, 8°.

B53

Extra Illustrations to *Pickwick Abroad* by John Phillips. [1838].

Extracted from bound volume.

B54

"Twenty-Six Illustrations to 'Pickwick Papers'." Clippings mounted in a blank book.

PLAGIARISMS, PARODIES, DRAMATIZATIONS, AND TRANSLATIONS OF *Pickwick Papers*

B55

SAM WELLER. A DRAMA IN THREE ACTS. BY W. T. MONCRIEFF, ESQ. London: Printed for the author by T. Stagg. 1837.

8°. In unprinted blue paper wrapper; no title page.

The play was produced 17 July 1837.

B56

SAM WELLER'S BUDGET OF RECITATIONS. A SUPERIOR COLLECTION OF ALL THE MOST NEW AND POPULAR TALES, DRAMATIC SCENES, BURLESQUE PARODIES, &C. London: J. Clements. 1838.

8°. In original brown cloth with yellow end papers.

B57

THE PICKWICK SONGSTER. London: S. Robins. [1838].

8°. Parts 1-16, wanting 2 and 10; bound in original yellow paper wrapper for Part II, uncut; many pages unopened.

B58

PICKWICK ABROAD; OR THE TOUR IN FRANCE, BY G. W. M. REYNOLDS. ILLUSTRATED WITH TWO STEEL ENGRAVINGS BY ALFRED CROWQUILL. London: Sherwood & Co. [1838].

8°. Odd parts: II, III, and XIV complete in original buff paper wrappers; text only of IV and XV.

B59(1)

PICKWICK ABROAD: OR THE TOUR IN FRANCE. BY GEORGE W. M. REYNOLDS. ILLUSTRATED WITH FORTY-ONE STEEL ENGRAVINGS, BY ALFRED CROWQUILL AND JOHN PHILLIPS; AND WITH THIRTY-THREE WOOD CUTS, BY BONNER. London: Printed for Thomas Tegg. MDCCCXXXIX.

8°. Large paper issue in original blue cloth, uncut.

First edition.

B59(2)

A second copy of the regular issue of the first edition, rebound in half old calf, edges trimmed.

B59(3)

A variant set of two volumes, rebound in half green levant with marbled boards and end papers. First edition. Captions on plates vary from those in B59(1), (2), and (4). "Mr. Pickwick's triumphant Entry into Paris" appears here as frontispiece with the caption "Mr. Pickwick's triumphal Entry into Calais." "Crashem swindling Winkle" appears here as "Mr. Cashem instructing Mr. Winkle," etc.

B59(4)

A large-paper copy of the second edition in original pink cloth and yellow end papers. Gilt illustrations on spine.

B60

"Mr. Pickwick's Hat-Box." Edited by Henry Ross, Esq. In THE NEW MONTHLY BELLE ASSEMBLEE, XII-XIII. London: 1840.

8°. Two volumes in original marbled paper boards; covers loose and spines lacking.

B61

THE POST-HUMOROUS NOTES OF THE PICKWICKIAN CLUB, EDITED BY "BOS," ILLUSTRATED BY 120 ENGRAVINGS. London: E. Lloyd. [1842].

8°. Two volumes, rebound in elaborately stamped green polished calf, edges gilt.

B62

A PICKWICKIAN PILGRIMAGE. BY JOHN R. G. HASSARD. Boston: James R. Osgood and Company. 1881.

8°. In original olive drab cloth decorated in black with gilt lettering and flowered end papers.

B63

ON THE ORIGIN OF SAM WELLER, AND THE REAL CAUSE OF THE SUCCESS OF THE POSTHUMOUS PAPERS OF THE PICK-WICK CLUB, BY A LOVER OF CHARLES DICKENS'S WORKS. TOGETHER WITH A FACSIMILE REPRINT OF THE BEAUTIES OF PICKWICK. London: J. W. Jarvis & Son. 1883.

8°. In original grey paper wrapper; frontispiece by F. W. Pailthorpe.

B64

WELLERISMS FROM "PICKWICK" & "MASTER HUMPHREY'S CLOCK" SELECTED BY CHARLES F. RIDEAL AND EDITED WITH AN INTRODUCTION BY CHARLES KENT. London: George Redway. MDCCCLXXXVI.

16°. In original green cloth illustrated in black with yellow end papers.

B65

THE HISTORY OF PICKWICK. AN ACCOUNT OF ITS CHARAC-TERS, LOCALITIES, ALLUSIONS, AND ILLUSTRATIONS. WITH A BIBLIOGRAPHY. BY PERCY FITZGERALD. London: Chapman and Hall, Limited. 1891.

8°. In original dark green cloth with gilt design; matching green end papers.

B66

AN INDEX TO PICKWICK. BY C. M. NEALE. London: Printed for the author by J. Hitchcock, Streatham. 1897.

8°. In original green paper boards with cloth spine.

B67

PICKWICKIAN MANNERS AND CUSTOMS. BY PERCY FITZ-GERALD. London: The Roxburghe Press, Limited. [n.d.].

8°. In original green cloth with gilt decoration and black end papers.

B68

THE LAW AND LAWYERS OF PICKWICK. A LECTURE WITH AN ORIGINAL DRAWING OF "MR. SERJEANT BUZFUZ." BY FRANK LOCKWOOD. London: The Roxburghe Press. [n.d.].

12°. In original blue cloth with gilt decoration and lettering.

B69

BARDELL V. PICKWICK EDITED WITH NOTES AND COMMENTARIES BY PERCY FITZGERALD. London: Elliot Stock. 1902.

8°. In original green cloth binding.

Ex libris Rear-Admiral Marcus Lowther.

B70

BARDELL V. PICKWICK. (THE TRIAL SCENE FROM PICKWICK.) A FARCICAL SKETCH. IN ONE ACT. BY CHARLES DICKENS. ARRANGED FOR THE STAGE FROM THE AUTHOR'S SPECIAL READING COPY, BY JOHN HOLLINGSHEAD. New York: Robert M. DeWitt. [n.d.].

12°. In original white paper wrapper. (DeWitt's Acting Plays, No. 166)

B71

AN OMITTED PICKWICK PAPER RESTORED BY POZ REPRINTED FROM THE TOKEN OF 1841. Brooklyn, New York: Berwick Press. 1903.

12°. First page as wrapper, printed in black and orange.

Chapter CCXIV, "Showing Mr. Weller's Views relating to Matrimony, with a slight Touch at Widowhood." No. 6 of 28 copies printed.

B72

DAILY PICKINGS FROM PICKWICK. COMPILED AND ABRIDGED BY FLORENCE DALGLEISH. London: John Lond. 1904.

8°. In original blue cloth with gilt lettering.

B73(1)

MR. PICKWICK'S CHRISTMAS BEING AN ACCOUNT OF THE PICKWICKIANS' CHRISTMAS AT THE MANOR FARM, OF THE ADVENTURES THERE; THE TALE OF THE GOBLIN WHO STOLE A SEXTON, AND OF THE FAMOUS SPORTS ON THE ICE AS WRITTEN IN THE PICKWICK PAPERS BY CHARLES DICKENS WITH ILLUSTRATION IN COLOUR AND LINE BY GEORGE ALFRED WILLIAMS. New York: The Baker & Taylor Company. [1906].

8°. In original green cloth with colored illustration.

Inscribed: "With best wishes from the artist—George Alfred Williams December; 1906—"

B73(2)

A variant copy. New York: The Platt & Peck Co. 1906. In original blue cloth with colored illustration.

B74

CHRISTMAS WITH MR. PICKWICK BY CHARLES DICKENS BE-
ING CHAPTERS FROM THE PICKWICK PAPERS, ILLUSTRATED
BY FRITZ KREDEL. Mount Vernon, New York: The Peter Pauper
Press. [n.d.].

8°. In buff paper boards printed in red and green. Title page in black, red, and
green.

B75

CHARLES DICKENS LES PAPIERS POSTHUMES DU PICKWICK-
CLUB OUVRAGE ILLUSTRÉ DE 24 PLANCHES EN COULEURS
ET DE 98 GRAVURES EN NOIR PAR CECIL ALDIN. Paris: Librarie
Hachette & Cie. 1912.

4°. Bound in vellum.

B76

DOCUMENTS PICKWICKIENS. NOTICE SUR CHARLES DICKENS
ET SES OEUVRES. Fragment of 32 pages.

B77

WHEN MR. PICKWICK WENT FISHING BY SAMUEL W. LAM-
BERT WITH ELEVEN ILLUSTRATIONS BY ROBERT SEYMOUR.
New York: Edmund Byrne Hackett. The Brick Row Book Shop, Inc.
1924.

12°. In original drab green paper boards with cloth spine and paper label, and
original dust jacket.

First edition.

Ex libris George Barr McCutcheon.

B78

THE INNS & TAVERNS OF "PICKWICK" WITH SOME OBSERVA-
TIONS ON THEIR OTHER ASSOCIATIONS. BY B. W. MATZ. London: Cecil Palmer. 1922.

8°. In original red cloth.

Second edition.

B79

MR. PICKWICK'S SECOND TIME ON EARTH BY CHARLES G.
HARPER WITH DRAWINGS BY PAUL HARDY. London: Cecil Palmer.
[1927].

8°. In original orange paper boards with green cloth spine and paper labels.

Presentation copy from publisher.

B80(1)

"PICKWICK" A PLAY IN THREE ACTS BY COSMO HAMILTON AND FRANK C. REILLY FREELY BASED UPON THE PICKWICK PAPERS BY CHARLES DICKENS. New York, London: G. P. Putnam's Sons. 1927.

12°. In brown paper wrapper. (French's Standard Library Edition)

B80(2)

A second copy in original wine cloth with gilt decoration and lettering.

B81

THE DRY PICKWICK AND OTHER INCONGRUITIES. BY STEPHEN LEACOCK. London: John Lane. The Bodley Head, Limited. 1932.

8°. In original purple cloth.

B82

THE ORIGIN OF PICKWICK. BY WALTER DEXTER AND J. W. T. LEY. London: Chapman and Hall, Ltd. 1936.

8°. In original orange cloth with gilt decoration and lettering.

B83(1)

A PICKWICK PORTRAIT GALLERY FROM THE PENS OF DIVERS ADMIRERS OF THE ILLUSTRIOUS MEMBERS OF THE PICKWICK CLUB THEIR FRIENDS AND ENEMIES. London: Chapman & Hall, Ltd. New York: Charles Scribner's Sons. 1936.

8°. In orange cloth. Verso of title page: "Printed in Great Britain."

B83(2)

A variant issue. Verso of title page: "First Published March 1936. Printed in Great Britain by William Clowes and Sons, Limited, London and Beccles. And Bound by A. W. Bain and Co., Limited, London."

B84

THE BAGMAN'S STORY AND THE STORY OF THE BAGMAN'S UNCLE. London and Edinburgh: Brimley Johnson & Ince, Ltd. [n.d.].

8°. In original blue paper wrapper.

B85

PITMAN'S SHORTHAND LIBRARY. PICKWICK PAPERS. London: F. Pitman. [n.d.].

8°. In original brown cloth with gilt lettering.

B86

OLIVER TWIST: OR, THE PARISH BOY'S PROGRESS. BY BOZ.
WITH OTHER TALES AND SKETCHES. Philadelphia: Carey, Lea
and Blanchard. 1837.

12°. In original buff paper boards with pink cloth spine and paper labels, uncut.

First edition of the first two chapters of *Oliver Twist*. This antedates the English
edition.

B87(1)†

OLIVER TWIST. London: Richard Bentley. 1838.

8°. Three volumes in original brown cloth, uncut; in unusually fine condition.
First issue of the first complete edition. A superb copy with no list of illustra-
tions; the "fireside plate"; and "London | Bentley" omitted from binding.

Ex libris William Nash Skillicorne.

Eckel has recorded two copies, one from the MacGeorge collection, with the
printer's imprint omitted from the binding. The University of Texas collection
contains a duplicate set of this same issue, with "London | Bentley" omitted
from the binding.

B87(2)*

A second set of three vols. with the list of illustrations; the "fireside plate"; and
"London | Bentley" omitted from binding.

This is a curious copy, as the omission of the publisher's name from the binding—
a mark of the earliest issue—is coupled with inclusion of the list of illustrations.

B88

OLIVER TWIST; OR, THE PARISH BOY'S PROGRESS. WITH
TWELVE ILLUSTRATIONS, FROM DESIGNS BY GEORGE CRUIK-
SHANK. Philadelphia: Carey, Lea & Blanchard. 1838.

8°. In 6 parts: pt. 1 in brown boards, pts. 2-6 in brown wrappers. Pt. 1 from
Bentley's Miscellany, the remainder from the 1838 three-volume edition. Front
cover of pt. 1 lacking.

B89

OLIVER TWIST. BY CHARLES DICKENS, (BOZ!) AUTHOR OF
"PICKWICK PAPERS," "NICHOLAS NICKLEBY," "SKETCHES OF
EVERYDAY LIFE," &C, &C. Philadelphia: Lea and Blanchard, succes-
sors to Carey & Co. 1839.

12°. Two volumes in original paper boards with pink cloth spines and paper
labels. Antedates completion of the issue in parts "evidently . . . to forestall
the Colyer edition published in New York."

B90

OLIVER TWIST. BY CHARLES DICKENS, (BOZ,) AUTHOR OF
"PICKWICK PAPERS," "NICHOLAS NICKLEBY," "SKETCHES OF
EVERY-DAY LIFE," &C, &C, &C. Philadelphia: Lea & Blanchard,
successors to Carey & Co. 1839.

8°. Bound in green and black mottled paper boards with black leather spine
and pink end papers.

B91(1)

OLIVER TWIST. COMPLETE IN ONE VOLUME. New York: Wm. H. Colyer. 1839.

12°. In original blue paper boards with cloth spine. Title on spine: "Oliver | Twist | By | Dickens, | (Boz.) | In One Vol."

With four illustrations by Cruikshank. Text beginning "Among other public buildings in the town of Mudfog, . . ." from *Bentley's Miscellany*.

B91(2)

A second copy bound in half green morocco with marbled end papers, top edge gilt.

Title page measures 150 mm. from top of title to bottom of date compared with 146 mm. in B91(1); Table of Contents lacking; p. 17 with title intact. In B91(1) the O and L are broken and the I has dropped out completely.

B92

OLIVER TWIST. WITH ILLUSTRATIONS BY GEORGE CRUIKSHANK. New York: James Turney, Jr. MDCCCXXXIX.

12°. In buff paper boards with green cloth spine and paper label.

B93

OLIVER TWIST. London: Richard Bentley. 1840.

8°. Three volumes in original green cloth, uncut. With "The author's introduction to the third edition." Dated "Devonshire Terrace, April, 1841."

B94

OLIVER TWIST. THE THIRD EDITION, WITH AN INTRODUCTION BY THE AUTHOR. London: Chapman and Hall. MDCCCXLI.

8°. Three volumes in original green cloth and yellow end papers, uncut. Third edition, second printing. With "The author's introduction to the third edition." Dated "Devonshire Terrace, April 1841."

B95

OLIVER TWIST. COPYRIGHT EDITION. Leipzig: Bernhard Tauchnitz. 1843.

8°. Lacking cover. With "The author's introduction to the third edition." (Collection of British Authors. Vol. XXXVI)

B96

OLIVER TWIST. WITH ILLUSTRATIONS BY GEORGE CRUIKSHANK. FOURTH EDITION. Boston: Lewis & Samson. 1844.

8°. In original black cloth. Portrait of Dickens engraved after the Lawrence portrait.

B97(1)†

THE ADVENTURES OF OLIVER TWIST. A NEW EDITION, RE-
VISED AND CORRECTED. London: Published for the Author by Bradbury & Evans. MDCCCXLVI.

8°. Ten monthly parts in green paper wrappers, as issued; in very fine condition,
some pages unopened.

First 8° edition. Wrappers for Parts I and III omit brackets after the number
and before "Price." Collation agrees exactly with Hatton and Cleaver. Ex-
cessively rare in this condition.

B97(2)

A second set of monthly parts with brackets omitted on wrappers for Parts I and
II. Part X lacks yellow advertising leaf. An extra plate, "Rose Maylie and
Oliver," in the original state, showing Rose in white dress and bonnet, has been
inserted in this set.

In fine condition.

B98(1)†

THE ADVENTURES OF OLIVER TWIST. A NEW EDITION, RE-
VISED AND CORRECTED. London: Published for the Author by
Bradbury & Evans. MDCCCXLVI.

8°. One volume in original slate-colored cloth with yellow end papers, uncut;
in very fine condition. Plate, "Oliver asking for more," before title.

Eckel, mentioning the rarity of this item, questions whether a single copy could
be found.

B98(2)

A second copy in original slate-colored cloth with yellow end papers, uncut.
Plate, "Oliver claimed by his affectionate friends," bound as frontispiece.

B98(3)

A third, rebound copy in green polished calf. No frontispiece; all plates inter-
polated with the text.

B98(4)

A fourth copy rebound in full tan polished calf with extra illustrations bound
in. Extra illustrations include: first impressions of Cruikshank engravings from
Bentley's Miscellany, reproductions in color of his watercolor illustrations; Pailthorpe's illustrations, first proof of his frontispiece with autographed inscription.
Original cloth cover and front wrapper to Pt. 1 also bound in.

B99

THE ADVENTURES OF OLIVER TWIST. London: Chapman and
Hall. MDCCCL.

8°. Five parts, 1 December 1849–1 April 1850, in green paper wrappers, as
issued. (Cheap Edition)

Ex libris William Glyde Wilkins.

B100(1)
THE ADVENTURES OF OLIVER TWIST. London: Chapman and Hall. [1871].

4°. Three monthly parts, July–September 1871, in blue paper wrappers, as issued. Printed in double columns. (Household Edition of *The Works*)

Third part contains at end first 16 pages of *Martin Chuzzlewit*. Cf. B187(1).

B100(2)*
American issue with paste-on cancels for each part reading "Price 30 Cents" and "New York Book Concern . . . No. 7 Warren Street, (Room 29,) New York."

B101
THE ADVENTURES OF OLIVER TWIST OR THE PARISH BOY'S PROGRESS. ILLUSTRATED WITH TWENTY-SIX WATER-COLOUR DRAWINGS BY GEORGE CRUIKSHANK. London: Chapman and Hall, Ltd. 1895.

8°. In original half crushed red levant, edges gilt. Limited to 500 copies.

B102
OLIVER TWIST. T. B. PETERSON'S UNIFORM EDITION. Philadelphia: T. B. Peterson. [n.d.].

8°. In original black cloth with yellow end papers.

B103
OLIVER TWIST. PETERSON'S CHEAP EDITION FOR THE MILLION. Philadelphia: T. B. Peterson & Brothers. [n.d.].

8°. In salmon-pink paper wrapper, as issued.

EXTRA ILLUSTRATIONS TO *Oliver Twist*

B104
Twenty-four Illustrations by George Cruikshank to *Oliver Twist*. [1837-1838].

Earliest impression as issued in *Bentley's Miscellany*. This set is uncut.

B105
Twenty-six Water Color Drawings by George Cruikshank Illustrating *Oliver Twist*. [c. 1838].

Proof plates of original issue, on plate paper (11″ by 7¾″); with "Fireside Plate" and "Rose Maylie and Oliver." In cloth portfolio. See illustration.

B106
Illustrations to *Oliver Twist* by George Cruikshank. [1838].

Extracted from bound volume.

B107(1)

Twenty-one Illustrations to *Oliver Twist* by F. W. Pailthorpe. London: Robson & Kerslake. 1885.

4°. Portfolio with half-title and list of etchings.

India proofs in black and three colored plates of "Pickwick in the Pound."

B107(2)

A second set, no. 79, in bistre.

B107(3)

A third set, no. 112, in color.

PLAGIARISMS, PARODIES, DRAMATIZATIONS, AND TRANSLATIONS OF *Oliver Twist*

B108

THE LIFE AND ADVENTURES OF OLIVER TWISS THE WORK-HOUSE BOY. WITH NUMEROUS ILLUSTRATIONS. London: E. Lloyd for J. Graves, Printer. [1839].

8°. Bound in green polished calf, edges trimmed and gilt. (Originally issued in 79 numbers with buff paper wrappers)

B109(1)

POLLOCK'S JUVENILE DRAMA. OLIVER TWIST, OR THE PARISH BOY'S PROGRESS. A DRAMA, IN THREE ACTS. London: B. Pollock. [c. 1839].

16°. In original brown paper wrapper, as issued, with 23 colored plates.

First edition.

B109(2)

A variant issue of *Pollock's Juvenile Drama. Oliver Twist.* Leaflet of 16 pages with 23 colored plates bound together in marbled paper boards.

B110°

CHARACTERS AND SCENES IN OLIVER TWIST; OR THE PARISH BOY'S PROGRESS. A DRAMA, IN THREE ACTS. EXPRESSLY ADAPTED TO SUIT THE JUVENILE STAGE, AND THE ONLY DRAMATIC VERSION PUBLISHED IN THIS FORM FROM ANY OF DICKENS' CELEBRATED WORKS. [private printing, n.d.].

Reprinting, 12 copies only, of Pollock's Juvenile Drama, with plates. Bound in blue cloth with paper label.

With colored frontispiece, title page, and five additional plates; also verses, "To Fagin."

B111
OLIVER TWIST. A SERIO-COMIC BURLETTA IN THREE ACTS. BY GEORGE ALMAR, COMEDIAN. AS PERFORMED AT THE ROYAL SURREY THEATRE. CORRECTLY PRINTED FROM THE PROMPTERS COPY. EDITED BY B. WEBSTER, COMEDIAN. London: Chapman and Hall. [n.d.].

12°. In original pink wrapper.

B112
OLIVER TWIST. A SERIO-COMIC BURLETTA, IN FOUR ACTS. BY GEORGE ALMAR, COMEDIAN. AS PERFORMED AT THE WINTER GARDEN. New York, London: Samuel French. [n.d.].

12°. In original orange wrapper. (French's Standard Drama. No. CCXXVIII.)

B113
TWIST OLIVÉR. Pesten: Hartleben Konrád Adolf Sajátja. 1843.

12°. Three volumes in original brown paper boards with leather spine. Hungarian translation.

B114
TWIST OLIVER. Pesten: Emich Gustáv Sajátja. 1843.

8°. Incomplete set, volumes I and III only, in original brown paper boards with leather spine. Hungarian translation.

B115
THE STORY OF OLIVER TWIST BY CHARLES DICKENS. No. 1, One Penny: Complete in Itself. London: Henry Vickers. [n.d.].

4°. Sixteen pages printed in double columns. (The Penny Library of Popular Authors)

B116
SIKES AND NANCY A READING BY CHARLES DICKENS (REPRINTED FROM PRIVATE PRINTING, BY J. H. STONEHOUSE). London: Henry Sotheran & Co. 1921.

8°. In original grey paper boards.

With introduction and bibliography of the "Reading Editions" of Dickens's works by J. H. Stonehouse.

B117
THE STORY OF OLIVER TWIST CONDENSED FOR HOME AND SCHOOL READING. BY ELLA BOYCE KIRK. New York, London: D. Appleton and Company. 1921.

8°. In original tan cloth.

B118(1)
OLIVER AND THE JEW FAGIN FROM THE OLIVER TWIST OF
CHARLES DICKENS. [New York]: Redfield. [n.d.].

16°. Large paper issue in original tan cloth. (Dickens' Little Folk)

B118(2)
A second copy, regular issue, in original plum colored cloth.

B118(3)
A binding variant of the regular issue, in original blue-black cloth differing
in texture from B118(2).

B119
OLIVER TWIST, AND THE ARTFUL DODGER. BY CHARLES
DICKENS. London: A. Ritchie & Co. [n.d.].

4°. Sixteen pages printed in three columns. (No. 6 of the Paragon Library)

B120
THE ARTFUL DODGER. [no title page].

8°. Thirty-two pages compiled from the complete work.

B121
OLIVER TWIST. A DRAMA, IN FOUR ACTS BY GEORGE ALMAR,
COMEDIAN. AS PERFORMED AT THE WINTER GARDEN. New
York, London: Samuel French. [n.d.].

8°. In orange paper wrapper. (French's Standard Drama No. CCXXVIII)

B122
BUMBLE'S COURTSHIP. London, New York: Samuel French. [n.d.].

12°. In original peach-colored wrapper. [French's Acting Edition (Late
Lacy's)]

B123(1)
THE LIFE AND ADVENTURES OF NICHOLAS NICKLEBY. London:
Chapman and Hall. MDCCCXXXIX.

8°. In 19/20 monthly numbers, in original green wrappers, as issued.

First edition. Parts IV and V of earliest issue: Part IV with "visiter" for "sister"
on p. 123; Part V with "latter" for "letter" on p. 160. Part XV, Plate 29,
"Nicholas makes his first visit to Mr. Bray," second steel.

Deviations from Hatton and Cleaver:

   No. IV. Back Advertisements lack "Poor Man's Pill," 1 sheet.

   No. VIII. Back Advertisements lack "Heads of the People" (Robert
   Tyas), 1 sheet. This particular slip is lacking in all six sets owned by
   The University of Texas.

   No. XIX/XX. Portrait of Dickens does not have publisher's imprint.

B123(2)

A second set in green wrappers, as issued. Parts IV and V of earliest issue. Part XV, Plate 29, third steel.

Deviations from Hatton and Cleaver:

No. III. Back Advertisements lack "Joseph Amesbury's Patent Supports," 8 pp.

No. IV. Back Wrapper (outside), "Reform Your Tailors' Bills!" (at bottom) "The Premature Marriage."

No. VIII. Back Advertisements lack "Heads of the People," (Robert Tyas), 1 sheet.

No. X. Back Advertisements lack "Steel Pens. Joseph Gillott."

No. XIV. Back Advertisements lacking.

No. XVI. Back Advertisements lack "The Medical Casket," 16 pp.

No. XIX/XX. Back Advertisements lack "Hill's Seal Wafers," 1 leaf.

B123(3)

A third set in green wrappers, as issued. Two copies of Part IV—one with "visiter" and the second with "sister" on p. 123. Part V, first issue with "latter" error on p. 160. Part XV, Plate 29, second steel.

Deviations from Hatton and Cleaver:

No. III. Back Wrapper (outside), "Gilbert's New Map of England and Wales."
Back Advertisements lack "Joseph Amesbury's Patent Supports," 8 pp.

No. IV. Back Wrapper (inside), "This day is published . . . A Practical Treatise" (outside), "The Premature Marriage" (at top of page); "Reform Your Tailors' Bills!" (second issue)

No. VIII. Back Advertisements lack "Heads of the People" (Robert Tyas); Mechi's Catalogue has, irregularly, slip ad for Cumberland's British and Minor Theatre.

No. X. Front Advertiser lacks pp. 9-10.

No. XI. Front Advertiser lacks pp. 15-16.

No. XVI. Back Advertisements lack "The Medical Casket," 16 pp.

No. XVIII. Back Advertisements lack "Illustrated Beauties of the Ballet," 1 leaf.

No. XIX/XX. Front Advertiser lacks pp. 29-32.

B123(4-6)

Three additional sets in green wrappers, as issued. In two sets Parts IV and V are of second issue with errors corrected, and Part XV, Plate 29, of the second steel. The third set has Parts IV and V of the first issue, and Part XV, Plate 29, of the first steel, with the long title.

B124(1)

THE LIFE AND ADVENTURES OF NICHOLAS NICKLEBY. London: Chapman and Hall. MDCCCXXXIX.

8°. In original half morocco with impression of portrait by Maclise on cover. First edition in book form. Page 160, "latter" for "letter."

B124(2)

A second copy in original green cloth. Errors corrected.

B125(1)

THE LIFE AND ADVENTURES OF NICHOLAS NICKLEBY. Philadelphia: Lea & Blanchard, Successors to Carey & Co. 1839.

8°. In original buff paper boards with blue cloth spine and paper label.

First American edition in book form.

Imprint at lower left, verso of title page: "T. K. & P. G. Collins, Printers, No. 1 Lodge Alley." No List of Illustrations. Two illustrations only preceding title page, signed "Phiz Del." with imprint "Philada. Carey, Lea, & Blanchard." Text 404 pages with advertising leaflet of Lea & Blanchard, 6 pages, bound in.

B125(2)

A variant large-paper issue in original tan cloth, spine renewed. With slip entitling bearer to "authorized portrait of Mr. Dickens." Imprint at lower center, verso of title page: "Stereotyped by J. Fagin . . . Philadelphia. Printed by T. K. & P. G. Collins." List of Illustrations on verso of dedication. Text 403 pages. Introductory pages and text partially reset. Thirty-nine illustrations: 12 with publishers' imprint as above, remainder without imprint; variously signed "Phiz Del." and "J. Yeager, Sculp."

B126

TALES OF THE DAY. SELECTED FROM THE MOST DISTINGUISHED ENGLISH AUTHORS AS THEY ISSUE FROM THE PRESS. Vol. I. Boston: H. P. Nichols & Co. 1838.

8°. In original brown calf and marbled paper boards. Includes an early piracy of the first 10 chapters of "Nicholas Nickleby."

B127

THE LIFE AND ADVENTURES OF NICHOLAS NICKLEBY. WITH ILLUSTRATIONS BY "PHIZ." TWO VOLUMES IN ONE. New York: James Turney, Jr. MDCCCXXXIX.

8°. In marbled paper boards with red leather spine.

B128

THE LIFE AND ADVENTURES OF NICHOLAS NICKLEBY. WITH ILLUSTRATIONS. New York: Wm. H. Colyer. 1839.

12°. Two volumes in blue paper boards with brown cloth spine, trace of paper labels.

B129

THE LIFE AND ADVENTURES OF NICHOLAS NICKLEBY. London: Chapman and Hall. MDCCCXLVIII.

8°. Eight monthly parts, 30 Oct. 1847–1 June 1848, in original green paper wrappers, as issued. (Cheap Edition)

Ex libris William Glyde Wilkins.

B130

THE LIFE AND ADVENTURES OF NICHOLAS NICKLEBY. London: Chapman and Hall. [c. 1873].

4°. Bound with Great Expectations in one volume, marbled paper boards; printed in double columns. (Household Edition)

B131

NICHOLAS NICKLEBY. PETERSONS' CHEAP EDITION FOR THE MILLION. Philadelphia: T. B. Peterson & Brothers. [n.d.].

8°. In salmon-pink paper wrapper.

B132

THE LIFE AND ADVENTURES OF NICHOLAS NICKLEBY. ILLUSTRATED BY STEVEN SPURRIER. New York: The Heritage Press. 1940.

8°. In original brown cloth.

B133

NICHOLAS NICKLEBY. New York: A. L. Burt Company. [n.d.].

8°. In red cloth. (Burt's Library of the World's Best Books)

EXTRA ILLUSTRATIONS TO *Nicholas Nickleby*

B134*

Original Steel Plate: "Nicholas congratulates Arthur Gride on his Wedding Morning," engraved by H. K. Browne.

B135*

Original Steel Plate: "Mr. Linkinwater intimates his approval of Nicholas," engraved by H. K. Browne.

B136

Thirty-two Illustrations to *Nicholas Nickleby* by Onwhyn and other eminent Artists. London: J. Newman & Co. [1838–1839].

8°. In original green paper wrapper, as issued. (All illustrations by Onwhyn, some signed "Peter Palette.")

B137

Thirty-two Plates to Illustrate The Cheap Edition of *Nicholas Nickleby*; Engraved on Steel in the Best Manner, From Designs by Eminent Artists. London: J. Newman. [c. 1838].

8°. Four monthly parts only (four plates in each part), in original green paper wrappers.

PLAGIARISMS, PARODIES, DRAMATIZATIONS, AND TRANSLATIONS OF *Nicholas Nickleby*

B138

NICKELAS NICKELBERY. CONTAINING THE ADVENTURES, MISADVENTURES, CHANCES, MIS-CHANCES, FORTUNES, MIS-FORTUNES, MYS-TERIES, MIS-ERIES, AND MISCELLANEOUS MANOEUVRES OF THE FAMILY OF NICKELBERY. BY "BOS." EMBELLISHED WITH FORTY-TWO ENGRAVINGS. London: E. Lloyd. [1838].

8°. Bound in three-fourths red morocco. (Originally issued in weekly and monthly parts.)

B139

SCENES FROM THE LIFE OF NICKLEBY MARRIED. CONTAINING CERTAIN REMARKABLE PASSAGES, STRANGE ADVENTURES, AND EXTRAORDINARY OCCURRENCES, THAT BEFEL THE NICKLEBY FAMILY IN THEIR FURTHER CAREER: BEING A SE-QUEL TO THE "LIFE AND ADVENTURES OF NICHOLAS NICKLE-BY," EDITED BY "GUESS." WITH ILLUSTRATIONS BY "QUIZ." London: John Williams. 1840.

8°. Bound in three-fourths red morocco.

B140(1)

SMIKE FROM THE NICHOLAS NICKLEBY OF CHARLES DICK-ENS. New York: Redfield. [n.d.].

12°. In original green cloth. (Dickens' Little Folk)

B140(2)

A variant issue in orange cloth.

B140(3)

A third variant issue in original brown cloth.

B141

NICHOLAS NICKLEBY, OR THE FATE OF POOR SMIKE. London: A. Ritchie & Co. [n.d.].

4°. Sixteen pages. (No. 5 of the Paragon Library)

B142

THE STORY OF SMIKE. London: Henry Vickers. [n.d.].

4°. Sixteen pages, printed in double columns. (No. 2 of the Penny Library of Popular Authors. Edited by Charles H. Ross.)

B143

THE FORTUNES OF SMIKE, OR A SEQUEL TO NICHOLAS NICKLEBY. A DRAMA, IN TWO ACTS. BY EDWARD STIRLING, ESQ. AS PERFORMED AT THE THEATRE ROYAL, ADELPHI. CORRECTLY PRINTED FROM THE PROMPTER'S COPY. London: Sherwood, Gilbert, and Piper. [n.d.].

12°. Rebound together with nine plays by various authors and six etchings.

B144

NICHOLAS NICKLEBY, A FARCE, IN TWO ACTS. BY EDWARD STIRLING, ESQ. AS PERFORMED AT THE PRINCIPAL THEATRES. New York: Samuel French. [n.d.].

12°. In original yellow wrapper. (French's Minor Drama. Acting Edition. No. CCLXIV)

B145
VINCENT CRUMMLES HIS THEATRE AND HIS TIMES. AR-
RANGED BY F. J. HARVEY DARTON. FROM NICHOLAS NICKLE-
BY. London: Wells Gardner, Darton & Co., Ltd. 1926.

8°. In blue-grey cloth with grey spine and paper label. Limited edition of 400
copies with hand colored frontispiece.

B146
NICHOLAS NICKLEBY RETOLD FOR CHILDREN BY ALICE F.
JACKSON. ILLUSTRATED BY F. M. B. BLAIKIE. London, Edinburgh:
T.C. & E.C. Jack. [n.d.].

8°. In grey cloth with paper illustration in color.

B147(1)
MASTER HUMPHREY'S CLOCK. London: Chapman and Hall.
MDCCCXL [MDCCCXLI].

8°. In 88 weekly numbers (arranged for 3 volumes) in original white paper
wrappers, as issued, uncut. In unusually fine condition.

First edition.

A superb set without repairs of any kind; wrappers of all parts, including the
first and last, in fine condition.

B147(2)
A duplicate set in fine condition with all wrappers intact.

B147(3)
A third set in very good condition with all wrappers intact.

B148
MASTER HUMPHREY'S CLOCK. London: Chapman and Hall.
MDCCCXL [MDCCCXLI].

8°. In 20 monthly numbers, green paper wrappers, as issued.

Part XX has the advertisement of George Virtue. Deviations from the collation
of Hatton and Cleaver:

> No. I. Back Advertisements lack "Tyas's Popular Illustrated Publications,"
> 2 pp.

> No. III. Back Wrapper (inside), "West's Unique & Elegant Gold" in
> double columns, page headed, "Advertisements"; (outside), "Now
> publishing, in Weekly Numbers, . . . The Pictorial History of France,"
> page headed, "Advertisements."

> No. IV. Lacks advertisement, "Magazine of Domestic Economy," 8 pp.

> No. X. Back Wrapper differs: (inside), "In 8vo. cloth, price 8s. Wander-
> ings in Germany," headed "Advertisements." (outside), "Mechi . . .
> Leadenhall Street, London. Mechi's Bagatelle Tables." Has George
> Virtue's advertisement on lilac paper.

First edition, published concurrently with the weekly parts.

B149(1)

MASTER HUMPHREY'S CLOCK. London: Chapman and Hall. MDCCCXL [MDCCCXLI].

8°. Three volumes in original brown cloth, spines mended, end papers marbled in pale pink and blue-grey on cream background, edges marbled.

First edition in book form. Vol. I without dedication leaf.

B149(2)

A second set of three volumes from Dickens's library, each volume with Dickens's bookplate and library sales sticker. In original brown cloth, end papers marbled in heavy blue and red on white background, edges marbled. Vol. I without dedication leaf.

B149(3)

A third set of three volumes: I and III with white end papers, II with end papers marbled as B149(2). Dedication leaf follows preface.

Type generally contracted vertically 1 to 5 mm. compared with B149(1,2); occasional pages with expanded text. Text slightly contracted horizontally. Vol. II shows "I" on spine; vol. III shows "II" on spine. Covers loose and torn.

B150

MASTER HUMPHREY'S CLOCK. London: Chapman and Hall. MDCCCXL [MDCCCXLI].

8°. One volume bound in three-fourths polished calf with marbled edges. Dedication leaf precedes preface.

B151

MASTER HUMPHREY'S CLOCK. London: Chapman and Hall. MDCCCXL [MDCCCXLI].

8°. An incomplete set of two volumes in original blue (vol. I) and green (vol. II) marbled paper boards with one-fourth polished brown calf, black leather labels on spine.

Vol. I: Frontispiece, title page to vol. I, preface to vol. I, preface to vol. II (from Part 52), illustration from Part 88 facing page 1 of text. Text includes pp. 1-306 of vol. I and pp. 1-228 of vol. II.

Vol. II: "Nell and the Old Man resting," published by R. Tyas, Oct. 1840, as frontispiece, title page to vol. II, illustration from Part 52, preface to vol. II, dated March 1841. Text includes pp. 1-306 of vol. II.

B152

MASTER HUMPHREY'S CLOCK, EDITED BY BOZ. WITH NUMEROUS ILLUSTRATIONS BY GEORGE CATTERMOLE & HABLOT BROWNE, AND A PORTRAIT OF THE AUTHOR ENGRAVED ON STEEL BY WELSH, FROM A PAINTING BY MACLISE. Philadelphia: Lea & Blanchard. 1840.

8°. First four monthly parts. Part 1 with yellow wrapper; parts 2 to 4 in white wrappers. All dated 1840. Publisher's apology slip in part 4.

B153(1)

THE OLD CURIOSITY SHOP AND OTHER TALES. WITH NUMER-
OUS ILLUSTRATIONS BY CATTERMOLE AND BROWNE. [Second
title page: MASTER HUMPHREY'S CLOCK. WITH 91 ILLUSTRA-
TIONS BY GEORGE CATTERMOLE AND HABLOT BROWNE].
Philadelphia: Lea and Blanchard. 1841.

8°. One volume in original black cloth, spine lacking. Made up of monthly
parts, including pp. 1-362, to the conclusion of *The Old Curiosity Shop*.

B153(2)

A variant issue made up from parts in original tan cloth with gilt stamping
on spine. Pages 1-362, measurement of text varies 1 to 3 MM. from B153(1)
on some pages.

B154

THE OLD CURIOSITY SHOP. BY BOZ. WITH WOOD CUTS. [Lea
and Blanchard, c. 1841].

8°. In original buff paper boards with blue cloth spine and paper label. Title
pages and plates lacking. Cheap edition following issue in parts, 362 pages.

B155(1)

MASTER HUMPHREY'S CLOCK. New York: William H. Colyer. 1841.

12°. Two volumes in original blue-grey paper boards with cloth spine and
paper labels. Contains all material through completion of *The Old Curiosity
Shop*.

Second American edition.

B155(2)

A second set of two volumes in original binding.

B156

THE OLD CURIOSITY SHOP. [Incomplete] In THE MUSEUM OF
FOREIGN LITERATURE, SCIENCE, AND ART. Philadelphia: E.
Littell & Co. Extra volume, 1841.

8°. In original brown cloth with paper label, 138 pages.

B157

MASTER HUMPHREY'S CLOCK. New York: Richard Marsh. [n.d.].

8°. Vol. I of two volumes in original blue cloth. Includes material to conclusion
of *The Old Curiosity Shop*.

Ex libris William Glyde Wilkins.

B158

THE OLD CURIOSITY SHOP. London: Chapman and Hall. MDCCCXLVIII.

8°. Five monthly parts, June-Oct. 1848, in green wrappers, as issued. (Cheap Edition)

Ex libris William Glyde Wilkins.

B159

OLD CURIOSITY SHOP. PETERSON'S CHEAP EDITION FOR THE MILLION. Philadelphia: T. B. Peterson & Brothers. [n.d.].

8°. In salmon-pink wrapper.

B160

THE OLD CURIOSITY SHOP. ILLUSTRATED IN COLORS BY FRANK REYNOLDS, R.I. London, New York, Toronto: Hodder & Stoughton. [n.d.].

4°. Bound in full white vellum with gilt lettering and silhouette in black on gilt background.

B161

THE OLD CURIOSITY SHOP. ILLUSTRATED BY WILLIAM SHARP. New York: The Heritage Press. 1941.

8°. In original brown cloth. See A190 for original drawings for this edition.

B162

BARNABY RUDGE. BY BOZ. WITH ILLUSTRATIONS BY G. CAT-TERMOLE AND H. K. BROWNE. Philadelphia: Lea & Blanchard. 1841.

8°. Nineteen parts in white wrappers, as issued.

First American edition in parts.

B163(1)

BARNABY RUDGE. Philadelphia: Lea and Blanchard. 1842.

8°. One volume in original buff paper boards with cloth spine and paper label.

First American edition.

B163(2)

A duplicate copy of the first American edition, as issued.

B164

BARNABY RUDGE. Philadelphia: E. Littell & Co. At the office of the Museum of Foreign Literature. 1842.

8°. In original buff paper boards with brown cloth spine and paper label. Supplement to *The Museum of Foreign Literature*. 1842.

B165
BARNABY RUDGE. New York: William H. Colyer. 1842.

12°. Two volumes in original buff paper boards with blue cloth spines and paper labels.

B166
BARNABY RUDGE. London: Chapman and Hall. MDCCCXLIX.

8°. Six monthly parts, 1 November 1848–1 April 1849, in green paper wrappers, as issued. (Cheap Edition)

Ex libris William Glyde Wilkins.

B167
BARNABY RUDGE. PETERSON'S CHEAP EDITION FOR THE MILLION. Philadelphia: T. B. Peterson & Brothers. [n.d.].

8°. In salmon-pink paper wrapper.

B168
BARNABY RUDGE A TALE OF THE RIOTS OF '80. ILLUSTRATED BY JAMES DAUGHERTY. New York: The Heritage Press. 1941.

8°. In original brown cloth.

EXTRA ILLUSTRATIONS TO *Master Humphrey's Clock, The Old Curiosity Shop,* and *Barnaby Rudge*

B169
Fourteen Extra Illustrations for *The Old Curiosity Shop* and *Barnaby Rudge* by J. Sibson. London: Robert Tyas. 1841.

8°. On plate paper.

B170
Four Plates for the first Cheap Edition of *The Old Curiosity Shop,* engraved under the superintendence of Hablot K. Browne and Robert Young. Published with the approbation of Mr. Charles Dickens. London: Chapman and Hall. 1848.

8°. In green paper wrapper, as issued.

B171
Four Plates for the Cheap Edition of *Barnaby Rudge,* engraved under the superintendence of Hablot K. Browne and Robert Young. Published with the approbation of Mr. Charles Dickens. London: Chapman and Hall. 1849.

8°. In green paper wrapper, as issued.

B172

"Thirty-six Original Character Studies Illustrating *The Old Curiosity Shop*. Drawn in Colours by 'Kyd'." [J. C. Clark]. [n.d.].

4°. Original plates, mounted. Bound in half natural leather and parchment.

B173

Twenty Engravings by H. K. Browne. Illustrations for *The Old Curiosity Shop*, *Barnaby Rudge*, and *Dombey and Son*. London: J. T. Sabin. [c. 1890].

4°. In cloth portfolio. On India paper, mounted.

PLAGIARISMS, PARODIES, AND TRANSLATIONS OF *Master Humphrey's Clock*, *The Old Curiosity Shop*, and *Barnaby Rudge*.

B174

MISTER HUMFRIES' CLOCK. "BOS," MAKER. A MISCELLANY OF STRIKING INTEREST. ILLUSTRATED WITH NUMEROUS EN- GRAVINGS, BY AN EMINENT ARTIST. London: E. Lloyd. 1840.

12°. Rebound in three-fourths red morocco and marbled end papers.

B175

DOLLY VARDEN THE LITTLE COQUETTE FROM THE BARNABY RUDGE OF CHARLES DICKENS. New York: Redfield. [n.d.].

12°. In original green cloth with yellow end papers.

B176(1)

LITTLE NELL FROM THE OLD CURIOSITY-SHOP OF CHARLES DICKENS. New York: Redfield. [n.d.].

12°. In original dark green embossed cloth.

B176(2)

A variant issue in original dark green cloth; embossing and gilt design on spine varies from B176(1). No frontispiece. One page of advertisements for "Red- field's Publications" follows text.

B177

MRS. JARLEY'S FAR-FAMED COLLECTION OF WAXWORKS. London, New York: Samuel French. [n.d.].

12°. In original green illustrated wrapper.

B178

Playbill for the theatre, Crockherbtown, November 1858. Advertising *Master Humphrey's Clock* for Tuesday, 13 November 1858.

B179

BARNABY RUDGE. BY CHARLES SELBY & CHARLES MELVILLE. London: John Dicks. [n.d.].

12°. In original blue wrapper. (Dicks' Standard Plays)

B180
BARNABY RUDGE. Pest: Kiadja Ráth Mór. 1872.

12°. Three volumes in original blue cloth.

Hungarian translation.

B181(1)
THE LIFE AND ADVENTURES OF MARTIN CHUZZLEWIT. London: Chapman and Hall. MDCCCXLV.

8°. In 19/20 monthly numbers with green wrappers designed by Phiz, as issued.

First edition. Vignette title, first steel with transposed £ on signpost.

Deviations from Hatton and Cleaver:

    No. II. Back Advertisements lack "Prospectus . . . by Thomas Boys," 8 pp.

    No. IV. Back Advertisements lack "Corn Laws," 16 pp.

    No. V. Back Advertisements lack "Prospectus . . . by Thomas Boys," 8 pp.

    No. IX. Front Advertisements lack pp. 3-6. Also lacks slip, "On the First of October . . . The Baronial Halls" and Back Advertisement, "The Eighth Wonder," 32 page booklet.

    No. X. Back Advertisement lacking, "The Eighth Wonder," 32 page booklet.

    No. XIV. Back Advertisement lacking, "A Brief Glance at the Origin . . . of Clothing," 4 pp.

    No. XVI. Back Advertisement lacking, "The Temple of Fashion," 32 page booklet.

    No. XIX/XX. Back wrapper (inside) with additional lines: "A few copies in splendid scarlet binding . . ."

B181(2)
A second set of 19/20 monthly numbers, as issued. Vignette title, first steel with transposed £ on signpost.

Deviations from Hatton and Cleaver:

    No. II. Lacks "The Chuzzlewit Advertiser" and back advertisements; substitutes following slip ads (in front): "Dr. De Jongh's Cod Liver Oil," 1 leaf yellow paper; "Mutual Life Assurance . . . The Scottish Provident Institution," 2 leaves lavender paper; "Now Ready, Cassell's Magazine for April," and other publications of Cassell, Petter, and Galpin, 2 leaves white paper.

    No. III. Back Wrapper (inside), "The Illustrated London News"; (outside), Mechi—variant—top left corner: "Inventor of The Patent Castellated Tooth Brushes"; top right corner: "Inventor of the Twenty-five shilling Mechian Dressing-case." Back Advertisements lack "Dialogue on The Corn Laws," 8 pp.

    No. V. Back Advertisements lacking. "The Chuzzlewit Advertiser," pp. 5-9 not numbered; pp. 5-8 differ:

        p. 5: "Recently Published by Smith, Elder and Co."

        p. 6: "Nearly ready . . . Annual Biography."

        p. 7: "Annual Biography (continued)."

        p. 8: "Works Published by W. Strange."

No. VII. Slip ad lacking (to follow front wrapper) "Neatly bound in cloth . . ."

No. IX. Back Wrapper (inside), "On the 30th instant . . . The Fourth Volume of Punch"; (outside) Mechi—variant—as in No. VIII. "The Chuzzlewit Advertiser" differs:

  p. 3: "Recently published by Smith, Elder and Co., 65 Cornhill." Page headed "Advertisements."

  p. 4: "Nearly ready . . . Annual Biography."

  p. 5: "Annual Biography (continued)."

  p. 6: "Works Published by W. Strange"; headed "Advertisements."

Back Advertisement lacking, "The Eighth Wonder of the World."

No. X. Back Advertisements lacking.

No. XI. Back Wrapper (outside), Mechi—variant with "New Year's Gifts" as line 7. Back Advertisements differ:

  (1) "The New Year . . . To the World at Large" (E. Moses & Son) 4 pp.

  (2) "New Weekly Newspaper," 2 pp.

  (3) "Punch's Christmas Piece!" 2 pp.

  (4) "Hood's Magazine," 2 pp. (2 copies of this leaf).

  (5) "Eagle Life Assurance Company," 2 pp.

No. XIV. Slip Advertisement lacking (to follow plates) "Baronial Halls"; has "Third Edition . . . A Christmas Carol," 1 leaf, verso blank.

No. XIX/XX. Back Wrapper (inside) with additional lines: "A few copies in splendid binding . . ."

B181(3,4)

Two additional sets of 19/20 parts, as issued. One with vignette title from the first steel, the second from the third steel.

B182(1)*

THE LIFE AND ADVENTURES OF MARTIN CHUZZLEWIT. London: Chapman and Hall. MDCCCXLIV.

8°. One volume bound in full olive green levant by Riviere, richly ornamented, made up from original parts, uncut with one wrapper included. Bound in are four original illustrations by Phiz in water-color and pencil and 12 extra illustrations from later editions. See illustration.

B182(2)*

A second volume bound in full olive green levant made up from original parts. Bound in are two original illustrations in water-color and pencil by Phiz, a signed portrait of the artist, and a holograph letter signed H. K. Browne to Fred I. Follett, Esq., dated 17 Nov. 65 (?).

B183

THE LIFE AND ADVENTURES OF MARTIN CHUZZLEWIT. WITH ILLUSTRATIONS BY PHIZ. Philadelphia: Lea and Blanchard. 1844.

8°. Bound copy of pirated issue in parts. Illustrations by Yeager after Phiz. In original green paper boards, spine lacking.

B184
THE LIFE AND ADVENTURES OF MARTIN CHUZZLEWIT. New York: Harper & Brothers. [1844].

8°. Seven parts in original blue wrappers. Part 6 lacks wrapper.

B185
THE LIFE AND ADVENTURES OF MARTIN CHUZZLEWIT. London: Chapman and Hall. MDCCCL.

8°. Eight weekly parts, 1 May–1 November 1849, in green paper wrappers, as issued. (Cheap Edition)

Ex libris William Glyde Wilkins.

B186
THE LIFE AND ADVENTURES OF MARTIN CHUZZLEWIT. London: Chapman and Hall. 1857.

8°. In original green cloth. (Cheap Edition)

B187(1)
THE LIFE AND ADVENTURES OF MARTIN CHUZZLEWIT. London: Chapman and Hall. [1871–1872].

4°. Monthly issues, Parts 3-9, Sept. 1871–March 1872, in blue wrappers, as issued. See B100(1) (Household Edition of *The Works*).

B187(2)°
American issue, parts 3-4 only, with paste-on cancels as described in B100(2).

B188
MARTIN CHUZZLEWIT. PETERSON'S CHEAP EDITION FOR THE MILLION. Philadelphia: T. B. Peterson & Brothers. [n.d.].

8°. In salmon-pink paper wrapper.

EXTRA ILLUSTRATIONS TO *Martin Chuzzlewit*

B189
Seven Illustrations by Phiz for *Martin Chuzzlewit*. [c. 1850].

12°. Extracted from bound volume.

PLAGIARISMS AND ADAPTATIONS OF *Martin Chuzzlewit*

B190
MY OWN HOME AND FIRESIDE: BEING ILLUSTRATIVE OF THE SPECULATIONS OF MARTIN CHUZZLEWIT AND CO., AMONG THE "WENOM OF THE WALLEY OF EDEN." BY SYR. Philadelphia: John W. Moore. London: Wiley & Putnam. 1846.

8°. In original brown cloth.

B191(1)
THE TWO DAUGHTERS FROM THE MARTIN CHUZZLEWIT OF
CHARLES DICKENS. New York: Redfield. [n.d.].
12°. In original bright blue cloth with yellow end papers. (Dickens' Little Folk)

B191(2)
A variant issue from same type setting as B191(1) on large paper. New title
page, New York: John R. Anderson. 55 Beekman Street. 1878. Also vignette
title and advertisement following text, "The Safety Inkstand." In original brick-
red cloth. (Dickens' Little Folks)

B192
MR. PECKSNIFF'S PUPIL A COMEDY IN FIVE ACTS ADAPTED
BY I. M. PAGAN. London: J. M. Dent & Co. 1904.
8°. In original dark green wrapper.

B193
MARTIN CHUZZLEWIT: OR, HIS WILLS AND HIS WAYS, WHAT
HE DID, AND WHAT HE DIDN'T. A DOMESTIC DRAMA, IN
THREE ACTS. BY THOMAS HIGGIE AND THOMAS HAILES LACY.
London: Thomas Hailes Lacy. [n.d.].
12°. In original olive green wrapper. (Lacy's Acting edition)

B194(1)
DOMBEY AND SON. London: Bradbury and Evans. 1848.
8°. In 19/20 monthly numbers in green wrappers, as issued.

First edition, first issue. A perfect set with all marks of earliest issue: No. XI
with "capatin" on p. 324; No. XII, "October" at head of "Advertiser" in perfect state; No. XIV, "if" omitted on p. 426, l. 9, and pagination omitted on
431. No. XIX/XX with errata slip of two lines. Included are extra copies of
Nos. XI and XIV in later state: No. XIV has pagination on 431, "if" omitted
on p. 426.

B194(2)
A second set of 19/20 monthly numbers, as issued. Second issue throughout.
Deviations from Hatton and Cleaver:

> No. I. Back Wrapper (outside), "The Clothing Establishment" as for
> No. II. Front Advertisements lack pp. 3-14. [Correct copy of "Ad-
> vertiser" laid in] Includes November "Advertiser" with numeral
> altered to "I." Back Advertisements lacking.
>
> No. VI. Back Advertisements lack "Portrait of a Horse," 1 leaf.
>
> No. IX. Back Advertisements lack "Just Published . . . Gilbert's," 8 pp.
> [Copy of this advertisement lacking pp. 5/6 laid in]
>
> No. X. Back Advertisements lacking.
>
> No. XI. Back Advertisement lacking, "Letts, Son, & Steer," 1 leaf.
>
> No. XV. Lacks publishers' slips: "No Christmas Book by Mr. Dickens"
> and "New Story by Douglas Jerrold."

No. XVII. Lacks publishers' slip: "The Life and Adventures of Oliver Goldsmith." Back Advertisements lack "Mechi's Catalogue," 24 pp.

No. XVIII. Lacks publishers' slip: "The Four Portraits."

B194(3,4,5)

Three additional sets of 19/20 monthly numbers, as issued.

B195(1)

DOMBEY AND SON. London: Bradbury and Evans. 1848.

8°. Rebound in three-fourths polished calf with marbled paper boards and end papers.

First edition in book form, earliest issue. Errata—2 lines on whole page; p. 324 has error, "capatin."

B195(2)

A second copy bound in three-fourths green polished calf; edges trimmed.

First edition. Lacks twelve plates. Errata slip of 12 lines plus errata page of 8 lines. Error, "capatin," corrected.

B196

DOMBEY AND SON. WITH ILLUSTRATIONS BY H. K. BROWNE. Boston: Bradbury and Guild. 1848.

8°. One volume following issue in parts. In original red cloth, spine renewed, edges trimmed.

B197(1)

DEALINGS WITH THE FIRM OF DOMBEY AND SON. New York: Wiley & Putnam. 1847 [1846–1848].

8°. In 19/20 monthly numbers, in original brown paper wrappers, as issued.

Original American edition in parts. Part XIX/XX contains second title page with the imprint of John Wiley, dated 1848. (Illustrations for Nos. II, V, and VII brightly and badly colored)

Each part was issued as the corresponding number arrived from England, without allowing time for J. W. Orr to engrave the plates. Therefore each wrapper, with the exception of the last, carries the notice: "The Illustration for this Number will be given with the Next." On the last part the notice reads: "The Illustrations for these Numbers will be ready on the 15th of May, and may be had gratis of any bookseller." These last plates, as is almost invariably the case, are lacking in this set.

B197(2)

A second set of 19/20 monthly parts in original brown wrappers, as issued.

B198

DEALINGS WITH THE FIRM OF DOMBEY AND SONS. New York: Wiley & Putnam. 1847 [1848].

12°. Two volumes in original brown paper covers. Front of vol. 1 lacking. Made up from parts. Frontispiece from Lawrence portrait not included.

B199

DEALINGS WITH THE FIRM OF DOMBEY AND SON. New York: Burgess, Stringer & Co. 1847.

8°. Bound in marbled paper boards with leather spine, edges trimmed.

B200

DOMBEY AND SON. Philadelphia: Lea and Blanchard. 1848.

8°. In 19/20 numbers in yellow wrappers, except No. 1 in plain white wrapper, as issued.

American edition in parts, advertised as the only [American] edition with illustrations accompanying the text to which they refer. No. XIX/XX in wrapper for No. XI with numeral marked out and "19 & 20" written in ink.

B201

DOMBEY AND SON. Philadelphia: Lea and Blanchard. 1848.

8°. Bound volume following issue in parts. In red marbled paper boards and end papers, half polished calf; edges trimmed.

B202

DOMBEY AND SON. London: Bradbury and Evans. 1858.

8°. In original green cloth, edges trimmed. (Cheap Edition)

B203

DOMBEY AND SON. New York: Harper & Brothers. 1873.

8°. In original green cloth printed in black and gilt, and brown end papers. Printed in double columns.

B204

DOMBEY AND SON. New York: G. W. Dillingham, Successor to G. W. Carleton & Co. MDCCCLXXIX.

8°. In wine-colored cloth. (Carleton's New Illustrated Edition)

EXTRA ILLUSTRATIONS TO *Dombey and Son*

B205

Original Steel Plate: "Mr. Dombey and the world," engraved by H. K. Browne.

B206

Dombey and Son. The Four Portraits of Edith, Florence, Alice, and Little Paul, engraved under the Superintendence of R. Young and H. K. Browne, from Designs by Hablot K. Browne, and Published with the Sanction of Mr. Charles Dickens. London: Chapman and Hall. 1848.

In green paper wrapper, as issued.

B207

Dombey and Son. Full-length Portraits Designed and Etched by Hablot K. Browne, and Published with the Sanction of Mr. Charles Dickens. London: Chapman and Hall. 1848.

Eight plates in green paper wrapper, as issued.

PARODIES, DRAMATIZATIONS, AND ADAPTATIONS OF *Dombey and Son*

B208

DOMBEY AND DAUGHTER: A MORAL FICTION. BY RENTON NICHOLSON, LORD CHIEF BARON OF THE CELEBRATED JUDGE AND JURY SOCIETY, HELD AT THE GARRICK'S HEAD HOTEL, BOW-STREET. New York, Boston: Williams and Brothers. 1847.

8°. In original white paper wrapper, printed in double columns.

B209

DE FIRMA DOMBEY EN ZOON. HANDELAARS IN 'T GROOT EN KLEIN. Haarlem en Rotterdam: J. L. Van Der Vliet, A. C. Kruseman en H. Nijgh. 1847.

8°. Three volumes in original grey paper boards. First Dutch edition.

B210

"Dombey and Son Finished. Part the Best and Last." In THE MAN IN THE MOON. London: Clark. Feb. 1848.

24°. Nos. 1-30 (Jan. 1847-June 1849), a complete set of this curious little periodical in original buff wrappers.

Pp. 61-67, No. 14, a burlesque imitation of Dickens's work with illustration, "Captain Cuttle Rescues Dombey."

B211

THE STORY OF LITTLE DOMBEY. London: Bradbury & Evans. 1858.

8°. In flexible wine-red leather and marbled end papers. First reading edition.

B212

DOMBEY AND SON. DRAMATIZED FROM DICKENS' NOVEL. BY JOHN BROUGHAM, ESQ. IN THREE ACTS. New-York: Samuel French. [n.d.].

12°. In original buff paper wrapper. (French's American Drama No. 14) As performed at the New York theatres.

B213

LITTLE PAUL FROM THE DOMBEY AND SON OF CHARLES DICKENS. New York: Redfield. [n.d.].

12°. In original dark green cloth. (Dickens' Little Folk)

B214
LITTLE PAUL FROM THE DOMBEY AND SON OF CHARLES
DICKENS ILLUSTRATED BY DARLEY. New York: Clark, Austin,
Maynard & Co. 1861.

12°. In original red embossed cloth, with yellow end papers. (Dickens' Little
Folk)

B215(1)
FLORENCE DOMBEY FROM THE DOMBEY AND SON OF
CHARLES DICKENS. New York: Redfield. [n.d.].

12°. In original green embossed cloth. (Dickens' Little Folk)

B215(2)
Variant issue in original brown cloth.

B216
THE STORY OF LITTLE DOMBEY. BY CHARLES DICKENS. AS
CONDENSED BY HIMSELF, FOR HIS READINGS. Boston: Lee and
Shepard. New York: Charles T. Dillingham. 1879.

12°. In original orange wrapper; back wrapper detached.

B217(1)
PAUL DOMBEY. ABRIDGED FOR USE IN SCHOOLS. New York,
Boston, Chicago: Educational Publishing Company. 1895.

12°. In original buff cloth.

B217(2)
A variant issue in original purple cloth.

B218
LITTLE PAUL DOMBEY, ETC. ETC. (FROM "CHILDREN'S
STORIES FROM DICKENS") TOLD BY HIS GRAND-DAUGHTER
MARY ANGELA DICKENS AND EDRIC VREDENBURG, &C, &C.
ILLUSTRATED BY FRANCES BRUNDAGE, HAROLD COPPING,
&C. London, Paris, etc.: Raphael Tuck & Sons, Ltd. [n.d.].

12°. In original green cloth.

B219
THE GAY-DOMBEYS. BY SIR HARRY JOHNSON. New York: Macmillan Co. 1919.

8°. In original dark green cloth.

B220(1)
THE PERSONAL HISTORY OF DAVID COPPERFIELD. London:
Bradbury & Evans. 1850.

8°. In 19/20 monthly numbers, with original green paper wrappers and advertisements, as issued.

First edition.

Deviations from the collation of Hatton and Cleaver:

No. XII. Lacks slip ad (to follow plates) "Familiar in their Mouths as Household Words."

No. XV. Back Advertisements lack "Penny Maps," 1 leaf.

No. XVII. Back Advertisement lacking, "By Royal Letters Patent . . .," 2 pp.

No. XVIII. Back Advertisements lacking, (1) "Waterlow & Sons," 8 pp; (2) "Now Publishing, . . . Eliza Cook's Journal," 2 pp.

B220(2)

A second set, as issued. Deviations from the collation of Hatton and Cleaver:

No. IX. Lacks slip ad (to follow plates) "New Weekly Miscellany . . . Conducted by Charles Dickens."

No. XII. Lacks slip ad (to follow plates) "Familiar in their Mouths as Household Words."

No. XVII. Back Advertisement lacking, "By Royal Letters Patent . . .," 2 pp.

B220(3,4,5)

Three additional sets of monthly numbers in green wrappers. Some repairs and evidence of tampering with advertisements.

B221

THE PERSONAL HISTORY AND EXPERIENCE OF DAVID COPPERFIELD THE YOUNGER. ILLUSTRATED BY H. K. BROWNE. New York: John Wiley. 1849.

12°. In 19/20 parts as issued, in buff wrappers, with woodcuts by J. W. Orr. Parts XI-XVIII with imprint of G. P. Putnam. 155 Broadway. 1850.

B222

THE PERSONAL HISTORY OF DAVID COPPERFIELD. London: Bradbury & Evans. 1850.

8°. One volume rebound in full polished calf with marbled end papers, edges trimmed and gilt; original wrapper for Part I included.

First edition in book form. Vignette title has date, 1850, below publisher's imprint.

B223(1)

THE PERSONAL HISTORY AND EXPERIENCE OF DAVID COPPERFIELD. New York: John Wiley. [1850].

8°. Two volumes in original embossed black cloth; end papers advertising John Wiley's Publications, dated Nov. 1st, 1850, on pale green paper. Vignette title dated 1850.

B223(2)

A variant set of two volumes in dark blue cloth with same embossed design and end papers as B223 (1) except end papers on pale yellow paper. Half title precedes frontispiece. Vignette title dated 1851.

B224

THE PERSONAL HISTORY OF DAVID COPPERFIELD. Philadelphia: Lea and Blanchard. 1851.

8°. In original buff paper boards and cloth spine. With illustrations after Phiz by W. F. Gihon.

B225

THE PERSONAL HISTORY OF DAVID COPPERFIELD. WITH A FRONTISPIECE BY H. K. BROWNE. London: Bradbury and Evans. 1858.

8°. In original green cloth. Preface dated June 1858. (Cheap Edition)

B226

THE PERSONAL HISTORY OF DAVID COPPERFIELD. London: Chapman and Hall. 1872.

4°. Six of seven monthly parts (April-Oct. 1872) in original blue wrappers, as issued. (Household Edition, Parts 10-16, lacking 15)

B227

THE PERSONAL HISTORY OF DAVID COPPERFIELD. ILLUS-TRATED IN COLOUR BY FRANK REYNOLDS, R.I. London, New York, Toronto: Hodder & Stoughton. [n.d.].

4°. In original red cloth with gilt lettering and illustrative end papers.

B228

THE PERSONAL HISTORY OF DAVID COPPERFIELD. New York: Dodd, Mead and Company. 1921.

8°. In blue cloth binding.

B229

THE PERSONAL HISTORY OF DAVID COPPERFIELD. New York: The Heritage Press. 1935.

8°. In full natural calf.

PLAGIARISMS, PARODIES, DRAMATIZATIONS, AND ADAPTATIONS OF *David Copperfield*

B230(1)

THE CHILD-WIFE FROM THE DAVID COPPERFIELD OF CHARLES DICKENS. New York: Redfield. [n.d.].

12°. In original embossed purple cloth with yellow end papers, edges gilt. One leaf of advertisements for "Dickens' Little Folk" and "Redfield's Publications" follows text. (Dickens' Little Folk)

B230(2)

THE CHILD-WIFE FROM THE DAVID COPPERFIELD OF CHARLES DICKENS ILLUSTRATED BY DARLEY. New York: Clark, Austin, Maynard & Co. 1860.

12°. A variant issue on large paper. Vignette title (not included in B230(1)) follows frontispiece. Title page varies as indicated. (Dickens' Little Folk)

B231

DAVID COPPERFIELD. BY CHARLES DICKENS. AS CONDENSED BY HIMSELF, FOR HIS READINGS. WITH AN ILLUSTRATION BY S. EYTINGE, JR. Boston: Ticknor and Fields. 1868.

12°. In original blue paper wrapper.

Authorized American Edition of the Reading.

B232

DAVID COPPERFIELD. A DRAMA, IN THREE ACTS. ADAPTED FROM DICKENS' POPULAR WORK OF THE SAME NAME. BY JOHN BROUGHAM. London: John Dicks. [n.d.].

12°. In original green paper wrapper, as issued. (Dicks' Standard Plays No. 374)

B233(1)

DAVID COPPERFIELD, A DRAMA IN TWO ACTS. BY JOHN BROUGHAM, ESQ. New-York: Samuel French. [n.d.].

12°. In brown cloth. John Brougham's copy with extensive MS. notes and modifications, altering the play from two to five acts. Autographed "John Brougham New Version Sept. 1874."

B233(2)

A variant issue in brown wrapper. Front wrapper (inside) "French's Standard Drama" followed by 2 pp. of "English Plays for Sale." Back wrapper (inside) "Catalogue continued . . .," (outside) "French's Minor Drama."

B233(3)

A third variant in orange wrapper. New York and London. Front wrapper (inside) "Mrs. Wiggs of the Cabbage Patch." Back wrapper (inside) "Nothing but the Truth," (outside) "Come Out of the Kitchen."

B234

Playbill of Selwyn's Theater, Boston, advertising the "Very Last Time of the Highly Successful Drama of Little Em'ly" for Saturday, March 5. [no year].

B235

DAVID COPPERFIELD A READING, IN FIVE CHAPTERS, BY CHARLES DICKENS REPRINTED FROM THE PRIVATELY PRINTED EDITION OF 1866 WITH A NOTE ON THE ROMANTIC HISTORY OF CHARLES DICKENS AND MARIA BEADNELL BY JOHN HARRISON STONEHOUSE. London: Henry Sotheran & Co. 1921.

8°. In original grey paper boards.

B236(1)
BLEAK HOUSE. London: Bradbury and Evans. 1853.

8°. In 19/20 monthly numbers in original blue wrappers, as issued. First edition.

Deviations from Hatton and Cleaver:

No. I. Back Advertisements lack "W. Mott," 1 leaf, and "Norton's Camomile Pills," 4 pp. Has variant "C" of "Waterlow & Sons."

No. III. Correct. Has extra copy of "Norton's Camomile Pills," 4 pp, and variant "4" of "Crochet Cotton."

No. IV. Slip, *Household Words*, issue 2. Back Advertisements lack "Waterlow & Sons," 4 pp.

No. IX. Back Advertisements lack "W. Mott," 1 leaf.

No. XVI. Back Advertisements lack "Grace Aguilar's Works," 8 pp.

B236(2)
A second set in 19/20 monthly numbers, as issued.

Deviations from Hatton and Cleaver:

No. I. Wrapper incorrect: Back (inside) "Save Your Income Tax," (outside) "Mechi." Front Advertisements lacking. Back Advertisements lack "W. Mott," 1 leaf, "Norton's Camomile Pills," 4 pp.

No. V. Lacks slip *Household Words*.

No. VI. Slip *Household Words*, issue 2. Back Advertisements with "New Serial by Mr. Charles Lever" on dark blue paper torn off.

No. VIII. Lacks slip *Household Words*.

No. IX. Back Advertisements lack "Allsopp's Pale or Bitter Ale." Has three copies of "Cassell's Publications."

No. X. Lacks Bradbury and Evans Announcements, 4 pp.

No. XIII. Lacks slip "Handley Cross."

No. XVI. Back Advertisements lack "Grace Aguilar's Works," 8 pp.

No. XIX/XX. Lacks slip "New Periodical Work . . . 'The Newcomes'."

B236(3-6)
Four additional sets of 19/20 monthly numbers, as issued.

B237(1)†
BLEAK HOUSE. London: Bradbury and Evans. 1853.

8°. One volume specially bound for Dickens in half contemporary red morocco with marbled paper boards and end papers.

First edition in book form.

Presentation copy to Marguerite Power (niece of the Countess of Blessington and editor of *The Keepsake* in 1852, when Dickens contributed "To Be Read at Dusk"). Inscribed on dedication page: "Marguerite Power with the affectionate regard of Charles Dickens Fifth February, 1854."

This, apparently, is one of a few copies specially bound for Dickens. In a letter accompanying a similar presentation copy to W. C. Macready, Dickens wrote: "The red represents my blushes."

B237(2)
A second copy, in original green cloth and cream end papers, uncut.

B237(3)*
Variant issue, in original green cloth with yellow end papers, uncut—many pages unopened. Eight pages of Bradbury and Evans's advertisements at end.

Stamped at base of spine: "Sydney | W. R. Piddington."

B238(1)
BLEAK HOUSE. New York: Harper & Brothers. 1853.

12°. In 19/20 monthly numbers, in original buff paper wrappers, as issued. No. XIX/XX has 8 pp. of advertisements.

First American edition in parts. In exceptionally fine condition.

Numbers altered in ink on wrappers XII-XVII, XIX/XX.

First lines of back wrappers:

    No. I. New York, April, 1852
    No. II. Same
    No. III. Harper & Brothers
    No. IV. Choice Light Reading
    No. V. London Labor
    No. VI. The New Books of the Season
    No. VII. By Richard Hildreth
    No. VIII. New Books for November
    No. IX. Same
    No. X. Same
    No. XI. By Charles Dickens
    No. XII. Same
    No. XIII. Harper & Brothers (No. III)
    No. XIV. (As No. IV.)
    No. XV. Abbott's Franconia Series
    No. XVI. The New Books of the Season
    No. XVII. (As No. XI.)
    No. XVIII. (As No. XI.)
    No. XIX/XX. By W. M. Thackeray

B238(2)
A second set of 19/20 monthly numbers, as issued. Part 19/20 with 8 pages of advertisements. Back wrappers as in B238(1).

B239
BLEAK HOUSE. WITH ILLUSTRATIONS BY H. K. BROWNE. New York: Harper & Brothers. 1853.

12°. Two volumes made up from parts, in original bright blue cloth with yellow end papers.

B240
BLEAK HOUSE. Philadelphia: Getz & Buck. 1853.

8°. In green paper wrapper, rebound in black cloth, edges trimmed.

B241
BLEAK HOUSE. London: John Dicks. [n.d.].

8°. In original green paper wrapper, as issued; printed in double columns. (People's Edition)

B242
BLEAK HOUSE. London: Chapman and Hall. [1872–1873].

4°. Six of seven monthly parts, October 1872–April 1873, in original blue paper wrappers, as issued. (Household Edition, Parts 16-22, lacking 17)

B243
BLEAK HOUSE. London: Chapman and Hall. [1873].

4°. Bound together with *The Old Curiosity Shop* in half leather with marbled paper boards. (Household Edition)

EXTRA ILLUSTRATIONS TO *Bleak House*

B244°
A Set of "Dark Plates" by Phiz. [1852].

4°. Ten prints from the original plates on large sheets of plate paper, very fine.

PLAGIARISMS AND ADAPTATIONS OF *Bleak House*

B245(1)
DAME DURDEN LITTLE WOMAN FROM THE BLEAK HOUSE OF CHARLES DICKENS. New York: Redfield. [n.d.].

12°. In original embossed bright blue cloth. (Dickens' Little Folk)

B245(2)
DAME DURDEN LITTLE WOMAN FROM THE BLEAK HOUSE OF CHARLES DICKENS. ILLUSTRATED BY DARLEY. New York: John R. Anderson. 1878.

12°. In original green cloth decorated in gilt and black.

A variant issue on large paper. Title page as indicated, verso "Publisher's Notice." With vignette title not included in B245(1). Verso of p. 175 "The Safety Inkstand"; p. [177] "American Book Exchange."

B246
BLEAK HOUSE: OR, POOR "JO." ADAPTED BY GEORGE LANDER. London: John Dicks Press, Ltd. [n.d.].

12°. In original rose-colored wrapper.

B247(1)
LITTLE DORRIT. London: Bradbury and Evans. 1857.

8°. In 19/20 monthly numbers, in original blue paper wrappers, as issued.

First edition. A perfect set: errata slip in Part XVI; good "dark" plates; Part XI has plates in what appears to be the earlier state (inferior in workmanship); Part XVI, "Little Dorrit Advertiser" has p. 4 unnumbered.

B247(2)
A second set of 19/20 monthly numbers, as issued. A`perfect set. Part XI with plates in first state; part XV first state with "Rigaud" for "Blandois"; part XVI with errata slip, page 4 of "Little Dorrit Advertiser" unnumbered.

B247(3)
A third set of 19/20 monthly numbers, as issued. Parts XI, XV, and XVI as B247(2).

Deviations from Hatton and Cleaver:

No. VII. Back Advertisements include 3 extra slips: "Kaye's Worsdell's Pills," 1 leaf, 5″ by 7¼″; "Mott's New Silver Electro Plate," leaf on pink paper; "Cassell's Illustrated History of England," 1 leaf.

No. XVII. Front Advertisements: p. 3 "Medicine Chests"; p. 4 "The New Novels"; p. 5 "The Popular History of England"; p. 6 "Now Ready . . . Mudie's Select Library"; p. 7 "Metallic Pens"; p. 8 "The Best Food for Children"; p. 9 "New Label" (Rowlands).

B247(4-7)
Four additional sets of 19/20 monthly numbers, as issued.

B248
LITTLE DORRIT. London: Bradbury and Evans. 1857.

8°. Bound in half calf with marbled paper boards, edges trimmed.

First edition in book form.

B249
LITTLE DORRIT. London: Chapman and Hall. 1873.

4°. Six monthly numbers, May-October 1873, in original blue paper wrappers, as issued. (Household Edition)

B250(1)
A TALE OF TWO CITIES. London: Chapman and Hall. And at the Office of *All the Year Round*. MDCCCLIX.

8°. In 7/8 monthly numbers, in original blue paper wrappers, as issued. Page 213 misnumbered; with rust-colored leaflet advertising *Cornhill Magazine*.

First separate edition. (Original printing in *All the Year Round*)

Deviations from the collation of Hatton and Cleaver:

No. I. Back Advertisements substitute for (2) "General and Full Directions for the use of Morison's, The Hygeist," with cut of the College of Health (printed horizontally), 4 pp. (as for Part III).

No. III. Back Advertisements substitute for (2) "The Morisonian Monument, erected in front of the British College of Health" (as for Part I).

No. V. Has slip (preceding "Advertiser") on yellow paper: "193, Piccadilly, October 1, 1859 | New Serial, | . . . | 'One of Them.' | by | Charles Lever."

Except for reversal of these advertisements in Parts I and III, this is a perfect set. In very fine condition.

B250(2)

A second set. Page 213 misnumbered; with rust-colored leaflet advertising *Cornhill Magazine*. A perfect set except for the following substitution:

No. III. Back Advertisements substitute for (2) "The Morisonian Monument" (as for Part I).

In very fine condition.

B250(3)

A third set. Page 213 misnumbered; with rust-colored leaflet advertising *Cornhill Magazine*.

Deviations from Hatton and Cleaver:

No. III. Back Advertisements substitute "The Morisonian Monument" for "British College of Health"; as in B250(1, 2).

No. IV. Back Advertisement lacking, "Norton's . . . Pills," 4 pp.

No. VI. Back Advertisement, "Thomas De La Rue," lacks pp. 3/4.

Wrapper for No. I in B250 (1, 2) is Issue B as described in *The Book Collector*, Spring, 1958.
"T" in "The" below "NB" in "EDINBURGH."
Break in "r" of "right."
No colophon at foot of back wrapper.

Wrapper for No. I in B250(3) is Issue C.
"T" in "The" below "IN" of "EDINBURGH."
Break in "r" of "right."
Colophon at foot of back wrapper: "C Whiting, Beauford House, Strand."

B251
A TALE OF TWO CITIES. PETERSONS' UNIFORM EDITION OF DICKENS' WORKS. Philadelphia: T. B. Peterson and Brothers. [1859].

8°. In original brown cloth with yellow end papers, as issued; illustrations by John McLenan.

First American edition [December 1859], according to the editor's advertisement preceding the complete English edition.

B252
A TALE OF TWO CITIES. London: Chapman and Hall. [1874].

4°. Twelve "Penny Parts" with 25 illustrations by F. Barnard, as issued. (Household Edition)

B253

A TALE OF TWO CITIES. PRINTED ORIGINALLY, FROM AD-
VANCED PROOF-SHEETS PURCHASED FROM THE AUTHOR,
FOR WHICH EARLY PROOF-SHEETS, CHARLES DICKENS WAS
PAID IN CASH, AT THAT TIME, THE SUM OF ONE THOUSAND
POUNDS STERLING, IN GOLD. PETERSONS' CHEAP EDITION
FOR THE MILLION. Philadelphia: T. B. Peterson & Brothers. [n.d.].

8°. In original salmon-pink paper wrapper.

B254

A TALE OF TWO CITIES. ILLUSTRATED BY RENE BEN SUSSAN.
New York: The Heritage Press. 1938.

8°. In original brown cloth.

PLAGIARISMS, PARODIES, AND DRAMATIZATIONS OF *A Tale of Two Cities*

B255

A TALE OF TWO CITIES. A DRAMA IN TWO ACTS AND A
PROLOGUE. BY TOM TAYLOR, ESQ. London: Thomas Hailes Lacy.
[n.d.].

12°. In original pink wrapper, as issued. Wrapper advertises "French's Acting
Edition (Late Lacy's)."

B256(1)

A TALE OF TWO CITIES A DRAMA IN A PROLOGUE AND TWO
ACTS ADAPTED FROM THE STORY OF THAT NAME. BY TOM
TAYLOR. London, New York: Samuel French. [n.d.].

12°. In original brown wrapper (French's Acting Edition No. 166). Imprint on
title page gives addresses of Samuel French in London and New York. Back
Wrapper (outside) "Some Plays"; (inside) l. 4 ff. "The Oak Chamber Scene"
followed by 6 ll. of description in small type.

B256(2)

A variant issue in lighter brown wrapper. Imprint on title page includes ad-
dresses in London, Manchester, New York, Los Angeles, and Toronto. Back
Wrapper (outside) "Some London Productions"; (inside) l. 4 ff. "Two Oak
Chamber Scenes   A Grey Panel Scene . . . ."

B257

THE TALE OF TWO CITIES: A DRAMA IN THREE ACTS, AND A
PROLOGUE. ADAPTED BY HENRY J. RIVERS, WITH A LITHO-
GRAPHIC PORTRAIT OF MADAME CELESTE, AND REMARKS
BY D.–G. London: Davidson. [n.d.].

12°. In original white wrapper.

B258(1)†

GREAT EXPECTATIONS. London: Chapman and Hall. MDCCCLXI. [The right of translation is reserved.]

8°. Three volumes in original purple cloth with light cream end papers; advertisement for Chapman and Hall's publications, 32 pages, with date, May, 1861, on pp. 1, 2, and 5.

First separate edition, with all "points" of first issue; a very fine set. (Original printing in *All the Year Round*)

Misprints:

  Vol. II. p. 162: "their" for "her"

  Vol. III. p. 34: "raving" for "staving"

   p. 145: "but" for "was"

   p. 150: "led" for "lead."

Presentation copy to Arthur Smith. Inscription on Gad's Hill Place stationery attached to cover of Vol. I. "Thursday fourth July, 1861 Arthur Smith from Charles Dickens." In Vols. II and III are Arthur Smith's book plates. (Eckel mentions a set bound in green cloth presented to Arthur Smith. It seems curious that Dickens should have presented two copies of the same book to Smith.)

B258(2)†

A second set. First edition with all "points" of first issue; binding and misprints as above.

Presentation copy from Jane Carlyle, inscribed on flyleaf: "Mrs. William Dods with best wishes Jane Carlyle 5 Cheyne Row 31st Decem^br. '61."

B258(3)

A third set of three volumes, first issue, with 32 pages advertising Chapman and Hall's publications, correctly dated. All points of first issue as in B258(1,2).

B259

GREAT EXPECTATIONS. AUTHOR'S AMERICAN EDITION. "For which he was paid one thousand pounds sterling, in gold, for the advanced proof-sheets." Philadelphia: T. B. Peterson & Brothers. [1861].

12°. First American edition in a unique green binding with gilt lettering and portrait of the author, yellow end papers; possibly publisher's special presentation binding.

Ex libris Mrs. LeRoy Crummer.

B260

GREAT EXPECTATIONS. COMPLETE IN ONE VOLUME. "Printed from the manuscript and early proof-sheets purchased from the author, for which Charles Dickens has been paid in cash the sum of one thousand pounds sterling." Philadelphia: T. B. Peterson and Brothers. [1861].

12°. Peterson's Uniform Duodecimo Edition in original brown cloth.

B261(1)
GREAT EXPECTATIONS. "Printed from advanced proof-sheets, purchased from the author, for which early proof-sheets Charles Dickens was paid in cash the sum of twelve hundred and fifty pounds sterling, in gold." Philadelphia: T. B. Peterson & Brothers. [1861].

8°. In salmon-pink wrapper, as issued, with 8 pages of advertisements following text. (Petersons' Cheap Edition for the Million)

B261(2)
GREAT EXPECTATIONS. "Printed from the manuscript and early proof-sheets purchased from the author, for which Charles Dickens has been paid in cash the sum of one thousand pounds sterling." Philadelphia: T. B. Peterson and Brothers. [1861].

8°. A variant issue of B261(1); only spine of original salmon-pink wrapper remains. Full length lithographic portrait of Dickens precedes title page, which also differs from B261(1). Title page includes list of "Petersons' Uniform Edition of Dickens' Works" with 22 titles. Four pages of advertisements, numbered 5-10, follows text [different from B261(1)].

B262
GREAT EXPECTATIONS. London: Chapman and Hall. [c. 1873].

4°. Bound together with *Nicholas Nickleby* in one volume. (Household Edition)

B263
GREAT EXPECTATIONS UNCOMMERCIAL TRAVELLER MISCELLANEOUS. Chicago, New York: Belford, Clarke & Company. [n.d.].

8°. In original brick-red cloth decorated in black and gilt with light brown flowered end papers.

B264
GREAT EXPECTATIONS. WITH A NEW PREFACE BY BERNARD SHAW. Edinburgh: Printed for the Limited Editions Club by R. & R. Clark Limited. 1937.

8°. In green cloth.

No. 9 of 1500 copies "with the ending which he [Dickens] originally wrote and which has not previously appeared in book form."

B265(1)
GREAT EXPECTATIONS. New York: For the Heritage Club. [1939].

8°. In grey cloth decorated in red.

Illustrations by Edward Ardizzone.

B265(2)
A binding variant in original brown cloth with darker brown decoration.

B266

GREAT EXPECTATIONS. ILLUSTRATED. Boston: Gardner A. Fuller. [n.d.].

8°. In original white wrapper, back detached.

EXTRA ILLUSTRATIONS TO *Great Expectations*

B267(1)

Extra Illustrations to *Great Expectations* by F. W. Pailthorpe. London: Robson & Kerslake. 1885.

Portfolio with 21 plates in black on Japanese paper. No. 13 of 50 sets (6⅞" by 10⅜").

B267(2)

A second set, colored, on plate paper (3¾" by 7½").

B268(1)

OUR MUTUAL FRIEND. London: Chapman and Hall. 1865.

8°. In 19/20 monthly numbers in original green wrappers, as issued.

First edition.

No. 1 wrapper, first issue without printer's imprint.

Deviations from Hatton and Cleaver:

> No. I. Back Advertisements, "Fry's Homeopathic Cocoa" on bright yellow paper.
>
> No. IV. Back Advertisements lack "The Queen Insurance Company," 1 leaf.
>
> No. IX. Back Advertisements lack "Scottish Union . . . Insurance Company," 4 pp. and "Astra Castra," 8 pp.
>
> No. XI. Extra copy of "Chapman and Hall's New Publications," 4 pp., as in Back Advertisements, precedes *Our Mutual Friend Advertiser*.
>
> No. XVIII. Lacks slip, *All the Year Round*.
>
> No. XIX/XX. Front Advertisements, p. 2 "Chapman and Hall's New Publications," 16 titles. Lacks slip, "The Economic Life Assurance Society," 4 pp.

B268(2)

A second copy of 19/20 monthly numbers, as issued. Wrapper for No. I, first issue.

Deviations from Hatton and Cleaver:

> No. I. Back Advertisements, "Fry's Homeopathic Cocoa" on orange paper.
>
> No. V. Lacks slip, *All the Year Round*.
>
> No. IX. Front Advertisements, p. 14 unnumbered. Back Advertisements lack "Astra Castra," 8 pp.
>
> No. XIV. Lacks slip, "The Economic Life Assurance Society," 4 pp.
>
> No. XVI. Back Advertisements lack "Mappin, Webb & Co."

No. XIX/XX. Back Wrapper (inside) "Court Trains, Silk Robes, . . ."
Lacks slip, "The Economic Life Assurance Society," 4 pp. Back Advertisements lack "The Anthelmintic Bon Bon."

B268(3,4,5)
Three additional sets of 19/20 monthly numbers, as issued.

B269(1)
OUR MUTUAL FRIEND. New York: Harper & Brothers. 1865.

8°. In original green cloth.

First American edition. Illustrations reengraved after Marcus Stone; printed in
double columns.

B269(2)
A binding variant in original purple cloth.

B270
OUR MUTUAL FRIEND. Philadelphia: T. B. Peterson & Brothers.
[1865].

8°. In original purple cloth binding with brown end papers.

Ex libris Mrs. LeRoy Crummer.

B271
OUR MUTUAL FRIEND. New York: Harper & Brothers. 1875.

8°. In original green cloth decorated in black and gilt, with brown end papers.
Printed in double columns.

Ex libris E. A. Parsons.

B272
OUR MUTUAL FRIEND. London: Chapman and Hall Limited. [c.
1892].

16°. Two volumes in original marbled paper boards with grey cloth spine.
Inscribed with date.

B273
OUR MUTUAL FRIEND. CONDENSED BY ROSSITER JOHNSON.
New York: Henry Holt and Company. 1876.

12°. In original green cloth, with printed end papers. (Condensed Classics)
Inscribed "A. Bowers Feb. 10. 1880."

PLAGIARISMS, DRAMATIZATIONS, PARODIES, AND TRANSLATIONS OF *Our
Mutual Friend.*

B274
OUR MUTUAL FRIEND. A COMEDY IN FOUR ACTS. DRAM-
ATIZED FROM CHARLES DICKENS BY HARRIETTE R. SHAT-
TUCK. Boston: Lee & Shepard. 1879.

12°. In original yellow wrapper. (The Globe Drama)

B275

MR. BOFFIN'S SECRETARY. A COMEDY IN FOUR ACTS.
ADAPTED BY I. M. PAGAN FROM *OUR MUTUAL FRIEND*. London: J. M. Dent & Co. 1902.

8°. In original pink wrapper.

B276(1)

THE MYSTERY OF EDWIN DROOD. London: Chapman and Hall.
1870.

8°. Six monthly parts in original blue paper wrappers.

First edition. A perfect set; collation agrees exactly with Hatton and Cleaver.

B276(2)

A second set of monthly parts, pages unopened. Part II has "Cork Hat" slip.

Deviations from the collation of Hatton and Cleaver:

> No. I. Back Advertisements lack (3) Cassell, Petter and Galpin Publications, 4 pp.

> No. VI. "Edwin Drood Advertiser" correct for No. IV. Back Advertisements substitute for (1) "To Whom it may Concern!" Wilcox & Gibbs, 4 pp. (as in No. II); followed by "Reasons for Insuring in the Scottish Widows' Fund," 4 pp. (as in No. IV).

B276(3)

A third set of monthly parts, as issued.

Deviations from the collation of Hatton and Cleaver:

> No. II. Back Advertisements have only a remnant of the sheet of cork advertising "Cork Hats."

> No. IV. Back Advertisements include irregularly "Chapman & Hall's Recent Publications," 8 pp.

> No. V. Back Advertisements lack "Chapman & Hall's Recent Publications," 8 pp.

B276(4-7)

Four additional sets of monthly parts, as issued.

B276(8)

THE MYSTERY OF EDWIN DROOD. London: Chapman and Hall.
1870.

8°. Parts bound in tan cloth with top edge gilt; side and bottom uncut. Wrapper of Part V at back.

B277(1)

THE MYSTERY OF EDWIN DROOD. London: Chapman and Hall.
1870.

8°. In original green cloth with yellow end papers.

Bound at back is 32-page "Catalogue of Books" by Chapman and Hall, dated "Aug. 31, 1870."

B277(2)
A variant issue in original green cloth with yellow end papers. Bound at back are 42 pages of advertisements, the second leaf headed "May, 1872." In other respects this issue resembles the first edition.

B278(1)
THE MYSTERY OF EDWIN DROOD, AND SOME UNCOLLECTED PIECES. Boston: Fields, Osgood & Co. 1870.

8°. In original green cloth with brown end papers. Printed in double columns.

First American edition. The "Uncollected Pieces" include "George Silverman's Explanation," "Holiday Romance," "Sketches of Young Couples," "New Uncommercial Samples," and Charles Dickens's will.

B278(2)
A binding variant in original wine-colored cloth with brown end papers.

B278(3)
A copy in original buff wrapper.

B279
THE MYSTERY OF EDWIN DROOD. New York: Harper & Brothers. 1870.

8°. Covered with brown wrapping paper; with autograph of Vincent Starrett.

B280
THE MYSTERY OF EDWIN DROOD. New York: D. Appleton & Company. 1870.

12°. In original printed buff wrapper, top loose.

B281
THE MYSTERY OF EDWIN DROOD. In "The Dickens Supplement to *Harper's Weekly.*" New York: April 23, May 21, June 25, July 23, Aug. 27, 1870.

4°. Newspaper supplement.

B282
THE MYSTERY OF EDWIN DROOD. WORKS OF CHARLES DICKENS. GLOBE EDITION. New York: Hurd and Houghton. Cambridge: Riverside Press. 1872.

12°. In original purple cloth.

B283
THE MYSTERY OF EDWIN DROOD. London: Chapman & Hall, Ltd. 1908.

12°. In original red cloth with gilt lettering and decoration. With cast of characters of the play by J. Comyns Carr at His Majesty's Theatre.

Ex libris Vincent Starrett, with his autograph.

B284

THE MYSTERY OF EDWIN DROOD. EDITED BY VINCENT STAR-
RETT. ILLUSTRATED BY EVERETT SHINN. New York: The Heritage
Press. 1941.

8°. In original brown cloth.

DROODIANA: SOLUTIONS, SEQUELS, PLAGIARISMS, AND COMMENTARIES ON
Edwin Drood.

B285(1)

THE MYSTERY OF MR. E. DROOD. AN ADAPTATION BY OR-
PHEUS C. KERR. London: John Camden Hotten. [c. 1871].

8°. In original stiff yellow wrapper. With 36 pages advertising Hotten's "Very
Important New Books. Special List for 1871."

B285(2)

A variant issue in original stiff white wrapper with colored illustration. With
12 pages advertising "New Books and New Editions . . . Ward, Lock, & Tyler."
[n.d.].

B285(3)

A third variant issue in marbled paper boards with leather spine. Advertising
omitted. Type somewhat contracted as compared with B285(1,2), with page
signatures added.

B286

THE CLOVEN FOOT: BEING AN ADAPTATION OF THE ENGLISH
NOVEL "THE MYSTERY OF EDWIN DROOD," TO AMERICAN
SCENES, CHARACTERS, CUSTOMS, AND NOMENCLATURE. BY
ORPHEUS C. KERR. New York: Carleton. London: S. Low, Son & Co.
MDCCCLXX.

8°. In original green cloth with lavender end papers.

B287

JOHN JASPER'S SECRET. A SEQUEL TO CHARLES DICKENS'
UNFINISHED NOVEL "THE MYSTERY OF EDWIN DROOD." WITH
EIGHTEEN ILLUSTRATIVE ENGRAVINGS. Philadelphia: T. B.
Peterson & Brothers. 1871.

8°. In original black cloth with gilt lettering and decoration.

B288(1)

JOHN JASPER'S SECRET: BEING A NARRATIVE OF CERTAIN
EVENTS FOLLOWING AND EXPLAINING "THE MYSTERY OF
EDWIN DROOD." WITH TWENTY ILLUSTRATIONS. London: 342
Strand. MDCCCLXXII.

8°. A set of eight monthly parts in original blue wrappers, as issued.

B288(2)

A second, incomplete, set of three monthly parts, as issued.

B289

JOHN JASPER'S SECRET: BEING A NARRATIVE OF CERTAIN EVENTS FOLLOWING AND EXPLAINING "THE MYSTERY OF EDWIN DROOD." WITH TWENTY ILLUSTRATIONS. London: 342 Strand. MDCCCLXXII.

8°. A bound volume made up of parts, the last part separate. In original purple cloth with yellow end papers.

Ex libris Vincent Starrett with his holograph notations.

B290

JOHN JASPER'S SECRET: BEING A NARRATIVE OF CERTAIN EVENTS FOLLOWING AND EXPLAINING "THE MYSTERY OF EDWIN DROOD." London: 342 Strand. MDCCCLXXII.

8°. Bound volume following the issue in parts. In original green cloth with yellow end papers.

Ex libris Vincent Starrett, with his autograph.

B291(1)

THE MYSTERY OF EDWIN DROOD. COMPLETE. BY CHARLES DICKENS. Brattleboro, Vt.: T. P. James. 1873.

8°. In original brick-red cloth.

First edition.

This curious work includes "Part Second . . . by the spirit-pen of Charles Dickens, through a medium [T. P. James]. Embracing, also, that part of the Work which was published prior to the termination of the Author's Earth-Life."

B291(2)

A copy of the edition of 1874 in original green wrappers.

B292(1)

A GREAT MYSTERY SOLVED: BEING A SEQUEL BY GILLAN VASE. London: Remington and Co. 1878.

8°. Three volumes in original blue-grey cloth.

B292(2)

A new edition edited by Shirley Jevons. London: Sampson Low, Marston & Co., Ltd. [c. 1901].

8°. In original blue cloth.

Ex libris Vincent Starrett, with his autograph. See B307.

B293

"RIFTS IN THE VEIL." A COLLECTION OF INSPIRATIONAL POEMS AND ESSAYS GIVEN THROUGH VARIOUS FORMS OF MEDIUMSHIP; ALSO OF POEMS AND ESSAYS BY SPIRITUALISTS. London: W. H. Harrison. 1878.

8°. In original green cloth with elaborate gilt and black decoration, dark green end papers.

Ex libris Vincent Starrett, with his autographed inscription.

B294

CHARLES DICKENS AND ROCHESTER. BY ROBERT LANGTON. London: Chapman & Hall, Limited. 1880.

8°. In original grey illustrated wrapper.

B295

LEISURE READINGS. BY EDWARD CLODD, ANDRES WILSON, THOMAS FOSTER, AND OTHERS. NEW EDITION. London: Longmans, Green, & Co. [1884].

8°. In original brown cloth. "The Mystery of Edwin Drood" by Thomas Foster [pseudonym of R. A. Proctor].

B296(1)

WATCHED BY THE DEAD: A LOVING STUDY OF DICKENS' HALF-TOLD TALE. BY RICHARD PROCTOR. London: W. H. Allen & Co. 1887.

8°. In original brown cloth with brown end papers. With catalogue, "Books, &c. issued by Messrs. W. H. Allen & Co." 48 pages dated November 1887.

B296(2)

A second copy in brown cloth with brown end papers. Catalogue dated December 1887.

B296(3)

A variant issue in original illustrated buff paper boards. Catalogue of 44 pages, dated December 1887, lacks first leaf.

B297(1)

JOHN JASPER'S SECRET. SEQUEL TO CHARLES DICKENS'S MYSTERY OF EDWIN DROOD. BY CHARLES DICKENS, JR. AND WILKIE COLLINS. New York: R. F. Fenno & Co. 1898.

8°. In original dark green cloth.

Ex libris Vincent Starrett, with his autograph.

B297(2)

JOHN JASPER'S SECRET. SEQUEL TO CHARLES DICKENS' MYSTERY OF EDWIN DROOD. BY CHARLES DICKENS, THE YOUNGER, AND WILKIE COLLINS. New York: R. F. Fenno & Company. 1901.

8°. Two volumes in original green cloth. With three pages of publisher's advertisements at the end of vol. II.

Ex libris Vincent Starrett, with his autograph.

B297(3)

JOHN JASPER'S SECRET   SEQUEL TO CHARLES DICKENS' MYSTERY OF EDWIN DROOD BY HENRY MORFORD [pseud.]. New York: R. F. Fenno & Company. 1905.

8°. In original green cloth.

B298

THE PUZZLE OF DICKENS'S LAST PLOT. BY ANDREW LANG.
London: Chapman & Hall, Ltd. 1905.

8°. In original red cloth.

Ex libris Waldo Leon Rich and Baron Dickinson Webster.

B299

CLUES TO DICKENS'S "MYSTERY OF EDWIN DROOD." BY J.
CUMING WALTERS. London: Chapman & Hall, Ltd. London, Manchester: John Haywood. 1905.

8°. In original green cloth.

B300(1)

KEYS TO THE DROOD MYSTERY. BY EDWIN CHARLES. ILLUS-
TRATED BY ERNEST COFFIN. London: Collier & Co. 1908.

8°. Bound in stiff white wrapper.

Presentation copy from the author.

B300(2)

A copy of the "Author's Edition de luxe" in wine-colored cloth with gilt
lettering, edges gilt.

Ex libris Vincent Starrett, with his autograph.

B301(1)

"The Mystery of Edwin Drood. A Drama in Four Acts." By J. Comyns Carr.
Mounted clippings and playbill of performance of H. Beerbohm Tree at His
Majesty's Theatre, January 1908. With autograph of Vincent Starrett.

B301(2)

A second copy from the library of Vincent Starrett, with his autograph.

B302

A NEW SOLUTION OF THE MYSTERY OF EDWIN DROOD. BY
MARY KAVANAGH. London: John Long, Ltd. [c. 1910].

8°. Leaflet of 32 pages in original blue wrapper.

B303

ABOUT EDWIN DROOD. By H. J. Cambridge: University Press. 1911.

8°. In original blue cloth.

B304

THE COMPLETE MYSTERY OF EDWIN DROOD BY CHARLES
DICKENS. THE HISTORY, CONTINUATIONS, AND SOLUTIONS
(1870–1912). BY J. CUMING WALTERS. London: Chapman & Hall,
Ltd. 1912.

8°. In original red cloth.

B305

THE COMPLETE MYSTERY OF EDWIN DROOD BY CHARLES DICKENS. THE HISTORY, CONTINUATIONS, AND SOLUTIONS (1870–1912). BY J. CUMING WALTERS. Boston: Dana Ester & Company. 1913.

8°. In original red cloth.

This issue is made up from the English plates with the name of the publisher altered on the base of the spine and on the title page together with altered place and date.

B306(1)

THE PROBLEM OF "EDWIN DROOD" A STUDY IN THE METHODS OF DICKENS. BY W. ROBERTSON NICOLL. London, New York, Toronto: Hodder and Stoughton. [1912 ?].

8°. In original brown cloth with gilt lettering.

Ex libris Vincent Starrett, with his autograph and notations on the bibliography.

B306(2)

A later edition. 1914. In olive green cloth with paper label.

B307

A GREAT MYSTERY SOLVED. BEING A CONTINUATION OF AND CONCLUSION TO "THE MYSTERY OF EDWIN DROOD." BY GILLAN VASE. EDITED BY SHIRLEY BYRON JEVONS. London: Sampson Low, Marston & Co., Ltd. [c. 1912].

8°. In original blue cloth.

Ex libris Vincent Starrett, with his autograph. See B292(1,2).

B308(1)

'THE OPIUM-WOMAN' AND 'DATCHERY' IN "THE MYSTERY OF EDWIN DROOD." BY C. A. M. FENNELL. Cambridge: Simpkin, Marshall and Co. 1913.

8°. Leaflet of 32 pages, inserted in cloth cover.

B308(2)

Typescript of the above with autographed inscription of Vincent Starrett: "Typescript of a rare pamphlet made for me before I acquired the pamphlet. V.S."

B309

TRIAL OF JOHN JASPER LAY PRECENTOR OF CLOISTERHAM CATHEDRAL IN THE COUNTY OF KENT, FOR THE MURDER OF EDWIN DROOD ENGINEER. HEARD BY MR. JUSTICE GILBERT KEITH CHESTERTON SITTING WITH A SPECIAL JURY, IN THE KING'S HALL, COVENT GARDEN, W.C. ON WEDNESDAY, THE 7th JANUARY, 1914. London: Chapman & Hall, Ltd. 1914.

8°. Verbatim report of the proceedings from the shorthand notes of J. W. T. Ley. In original blue wrapper.

B310
TRIAL OF JOHN JASPER FOR THE MURDER OF EDWIN DROOD IN AID OF SAMARITAN, CHILDREN'S HOMEOPATHIC, ST. AGNES AND MT. SINAI HOSPITALS. Philadelphia: Dickens Fellowship. 1914.

8°. In dark blue cloth with paper label. No. 248 of 500 numbered copies.

Ex libris Vincent Starrett.

B311
THE MYSTERY OF EDWIN DROOD. COMPLETED IN 1914 BY W. E. C. NEW TEXT DRAWINGS BY ZOFFANY OLDFIELD. NEW TEXT REVISED AND EDITED BY MARY L. C. GRANT. London: J. M. Ouseley & Sons. [1914].

8°. In original red cloth.

B312
THE MURDER OF EDWIN DROOD RECOUNTED BY JOHN JAS-PER BEING AN ATTEMPTED SOLUTION OF THE MYSTERY BASED ON DICKENS' MANUSCRIPT AND MEMORANDA. BY PERCY T. CARDEN WITH AN INTRODUCTION BY B. W. MATZ. London: Cecil Palmer. [1920].

8°. In original red cloth.

B313
THE MYSTERY OF JOHN JASPER. BY H. R. LEAVER, Alberta, Canada: For the author. 1925.

12°. In original buff paper boards with gilt lettering.

Ex libris Vincent Starrett. Inscribed "With the compliments of H. R. Leaver Feb. 1928." With letter of H. R. Leaver to Vincent Starrett.

B314
DICKENS' MYSTERY OF EDWIN DROOD COMPLETED BY A LOYAL DICKENSIAN. London: C. W. Daniel Company. 1927.

8°. In original tangerine cloth.

Ex libris Vincent Starrett, with his autograph.

B315
GENERALLY SPEAKING. A BOOK OF ESSAYS. BY G. K. CHESTER-TON. London: Methuen & Co. Ltd. 1928.

16°. In original blue cloth. From the library of Vincent Starrett, with his autograph. Includes "On Detective Novels" and "On 'Edwin Drood'."

B316
PEN-DRIFT. AMENITIES OF COLUMN CONDUCTING. BY THE PENDRIFTER, CHARLES EDWARD CRANE. Brattleboro, Vt.: Stephen Daye Press. 1931.

8°. In original buff cloth with blue lettering and illustration. Includes "The Mystery of Edwin Drood." With autograph of Vincent Starrett.

B317(1)
JOHN JASPER'S GATEHOUSE. BY EDWIN HARRIS. Rochester: Mackays Limited. 1931.

8°. In original white cardboard cover. Inscribed: "To Vincent Starrett, Esq. This book is inscribed with the compliments and autograph of the author. Edwin Harris 15th Feb. 1932 'Hereward' New Road Rochester."

B317(2)
A second copy in original blue cloth binding. With the autograph of Vincent Starrett.

B318(1)
EPILOGUE. BY BRUCE GRAEME. Philadelphia, London: J. B. Lippincott Company. 1934.

8°. In original tangerine cloth.

B318(2)
A second copy. London: Hutchinson & Co., Ltd. [c. 1938].

8°. In original black cloth with yellow lettering. From the library of Vincent Starrett, with his autograph.

B319
A NEW ANGLE ON THE DROOD MYSTERY. BY AUBREY BODY. Reprinted from WASHINGTON UNIVERSITY STUDIES, IX HUMANISTIC SERIES, NO. 1. [n.d.].

8°. Monograph in buff paper wrapper. *Ex libris* Vincent Starrett.

ARTICLES CONCERNING *Edwin Drood* FROM VARIOUS PERIODICALS:

B320
"The Mystery of Edwin Drood." By George B. Woods. In *Old and New*. November 1870.

B321
"Part Second of the Mystery of Edwin Drood. By the Spirit-pen of Charles Dickens, through a Medium. Brattleboro: T. P. James." Review in *The Southern Magazine*. Baltimore: February 1874.

B322
"How Edwin Drood Was Illustrated." By Alice Meynell. Excised from *Century Magazine*. February 1884.

B323
"The Mystery of Edwin Drood Suggestions for a Conclusion." In *Cornhill Magazine*. London: Smith, Elder & Co. March 1887. With autograph of Vincent Starrett.

B324

"The Crime of Jasper." By Andrew Lang. In *The Independent.* 14 September 1905.

B325

"The History of a Mystery A Review of the Solutions to 'Edwin Drood'." By George F. Gadd. Together with six other articles excised from *The Dickensian,* 1905 and 1906.

B326

"The Question of Edwin Drood." By Andrew Lang. Dated "London, March 22." In *The Nation,* 6 April 1911.

B327

"The Problem of Edwin Drood." By W. Robertson Nicoll. Book review in *The Nation,* 16 January 1913.

B328

"The Fate of Edwin Drood." By Burton E. Stevenson. In *The Bookman.* May 1913.

B329

"The Case of Edwin Drood." In *The Outlook.* 17 January 1914.

B330

"Tried for the Murder of 'Edwin Drood'." In *The Literary Digest.* 7 February 1914.

B331

"Another 'Edwin Drood' Trial." In *The Nation.* 9 April 1914.

B332

"The Acquittal of John Jasper." By Curtis Wager-Smith. In *The Book News Monthly.* June 1914.

B333

"The City of 'Edwin Drood'." By Burton Egbert Stevenson. In *The Bookman.* June 1914.

B334

" 'Edwin Drood' Again." By Edmund Lester Pearson. In *The Nation.* 1 October 1914.

B335

"The Mystery of *Edwin Drood* and Its Interpreters." In *The Living Age.* 7 July 1917.

B336

"Illustrated Guide to Dickensian Rochester." By Edwin Harris. Rochester: 1920. With autograph and notations of Edwin Harris. Leaflet of 16 pages.

B337

"A New Solution of Edwin Drood." In *The Living Age.* 12 February 1921.

B338

"Trial of John Jasper for the Murder of Edwin Drood." Produced for The Dickens Fellowship Players at Masonic Hall, Toronto, Canada. 18 November 1921. Illustrated program.

B339

"A Parody of 'Edwin Drood' (Recalled by the Assistant Editor)." By F. Gordon Roe. In *The Connoisseur.* March 1926.

B340

"The Edwin Drood Case. New Light on the Mystery." By Florizel Von Reuter. Excised from *Light.* 1 October 1927.

B341

"Alleged Posthumous Writing of Great Authors." By A. Conan Doyle. Excised from *The Bookman.* December 1927.

B342

"Was Edwin Drood Murdered?" By Sir Frederic Maugham. Excised from *The Daily Mail.* 30 October 1928.

B343

"John Jasper—Strangler." By Howard Duffield. In *The Bookman.* February 1930.

B344

"The Mystery of Edwin Drood. Do You Remember It?" By Grant Overton. In *The Mentor-World Traveler.* December 1930.

B345

"The Mystery of Edwin Drood Dramatized by Burton E. Stevenson." Excised from *The Mystery Magazine.* August 1934.

B346

"The Track of Edwin Drood." By Charles Willis Thompson. In *The Catholic World.* October 1934.

B347

"What's in a Name." By Stephen Leacock. In *Answers to Correspondents.* December 1938.

B348

"The Trial of John Jasper for the Murder of Edwin Drood." The Dickens
Fellowship. King's Hall, Covent Garden. Wednesday, 7th January 1914.

Judge: G. K. Chesterton; Counsels for the Prosecution and the Defense: Mr.
J. Cuming Walters, Mr. B. W. Matz, Mr. Cecil Chesterton, and Mr. W. Walter
Crotch. Foreman of the jury: G. Bernard Shaw.

B349

Twenty-eight letters to Vincent Starrett concerning *Edwin Drood*.

Notes of Vincent Starrett on *Edwin Drood*; typewritten letter from Starrett to Sotheran & Co. concerning Droodiana; typewritten bibliography,
"Addenda," and introduction, initialed "V.S." dated, "7 Feb. 1935."

Letter from Mary Roberts Rinehart to Vincent Starrett concerning *Edwin
Drood*. Envelope addressed to Vincent Starrett by A. Conan Doyle.

Historical guide to "The Rochester of Edwin Drood," together with photographs. Autographed "Edwin Harris."

B350

Original typescript of Vincent Starrett's introduction to the Heritage Press
Edition of *Edwin Drood*. Inscribed: "To John S. Barnet with grateful good
wishes Vincent Starrett." Together with letters from Starrett, Barnet, and
Laurence Gomme of Brentano's, New York, concerning notes on *Edwin Drood*.
Catalogue of G. A. Baker & Co., New York, listing Starrett's collection of
Droodiana.

B351

"The Cloisterham Murder Case A Discussion of the 'Edwin Drood' Problems."
By Edward S. Everett. Typescript signed by Edward S. Everett together with
signed typewritten letter of Everett to Vincent Starrett. [n.d.].

B352

"Jasper's Gatehouse, Rochester." Original drawings by Edwin Harris [signed]
for Vincent Starrett.

B353

"The Significance of the Ring." By Henry Leffmann. Philadelphia. Typescript.

B354

Two typescripts of "Key to the Mystery of 'Edwin Drood'. Light Thrown on
the Problem by a Cypher. Astounding—If a Coincidence." By Arthur Machen.
One inscribed: "Extract from *The Evening News*. Monday May 31st, 1920."
The second, undated.

B355

"Charles Collins's Unpublished Sketches for *Edwin Drood*" and "Dickens's 'Number Plans' for *The Mystery of Edwin Drood*." Reproduced in facsimile. With notes by P.T.C. London: The Dickens Fellowship. [n.d.].

Limited to 100 copies in portfolio. With autograph of Vincent Starrett.

2.CHRISTMAS BOOKS

B356(1-10)

A CHRISTMAS CAROL. IN PROSE. BEING A GHOST STORY OF CHRISTMAS. London: Chapman & Hall. MDCCCXLIII.

8°. A series of ten variants in original reddish-brown cloth.

First edition. Based on the study of Dr. William B. Todd [THE BOOK COLLECTOR X (Winter 1961)] and previously unrecorded early corrections, the sequence of copies at The University of Texas is as follows. We adopt the form suggested by Dr. Todd to indicate 1) color of end papers, 2) blue or green on title page, 3) date, 4) heading of chapter 1: a = Roman numeral, b = Gothic numeral, c = regularized "One" without textual corrections of the second edition, d = "One" with corrected text of the second edition. Additional textual points are indicated by page and line number: Preface. date line = no comma, 144 mm. length. P. 49. pagination = "9" extends into right margin. P. 101.10 = misspelling "barred" for "bared." P. 110.17 = serif of "w" extends into left margin. P. 127.22 = 4 mm. space between sentences, compared with 5½ mm. in other copies. See illustration of VanderPoel 1.

	Identified as	Cover design	Left of blind-stamping to gilt design	Additional textual points
1. GB43a	VanderPoel 1	sharp, intact	23 mm.	Preface. date line P. 49. pagination P. 101.10 P. 110.17 P. 127.22
2. GG44a	Texas 1 (Stark)	sharp, intact	24 mm.	P. 49. pagination
3. YB43a	Texas 3 (Stark)	sharp, intact	25 mm.	
4-7. GB43a	Texas Ulizio/Hanley	intact	25 mm.	P. 127.22
	Texas 2 (Stark)	sharp, intact	25 mm.	
	Texas B 1 (Bachman)	worn	25 mm.	
	Drake 1	sharp, intact	25 mm.	P. 127.22
8-9. GB43c	Texas 4 (Stark)	sharp, intact	25 mm.	
	VanderPoel 2	sharp, intact	25 mm.	
10. GB43b	Texas 5 (Stark)	worn	23 mm.	Mixed text with some corrections of second edition.

B357(1-3)

Second edition. Three variant copies of this edition: one with title page of first edition; one with "Second Edition" on title page; one copy with number of the edition erased. All copies have corrected text of the second and later editions; all are YB43d (i.e. with yellow end papers, blue and red title, 1843, "Stave One" with corrected text.) Covers of these copies are as follows:

	Design	Left of blind-stamping to left of gilt design	Title page
1. Texas 6 (Stark)	sharp, intact	25 mm.	with "Second Edition"
2. Bachman 2	worn. "D" lacks serif	24 mm.	with title page of first edition. blue-black ink; does not correspond to title page marked "Second Edition"
3. Drake 2	worn. "D" lacks serif; "E" in CHARLES and "N" in DICKENS also broken	26 mm.	number of edition erased; possibly later than second edition.

B358

Fourth edition. YB44d. Cover design, "D" lacks serif. Measurement from left of blind stamping to left of gilt design 24 mm.

Ex libris Watkin Watkins.

B359

Sixth edition. Copy inscribed "F. Le Grix-White Xmas 1843"; YB44d. Cover design, "D" lacks serif; left of blind-stamping to left of gilt design 27 mm. Undulating border of title page worn.

B360(1)

Eleventh edition. In original bright red cloth. Inscription excised from end papers. Cover design, "D" lacks serif; left of blind-stamping to left of gilt design 25 mm. MDCCCXLV.

B360(2)

Eleventh edition "printed and published for the author." London: Bradbury and Evans. 90 Fleet Street and Whitefriars. MDCCCXLVI. In original bright red cloth. Cover design worn, "D" lacks serif, "C" of DICKENS also broken; left of blind-stamping to left of gilt design 24 mm. Undulating border of title page very faint. Type completely reset.

B361

A CHRISTMAS CAROL IN PROSE. COPYRIGHT EDITION. Leipzig: Bernard Tauchnitz. 1843.

8°. In original bright red cloth. This edition came out within a few days of 19 December 1843, the publication date of the English edition.

B362(1)
A CHRISTMAS CAROL. Philadelphia: Carey & Hart. 1844.

16°. In original purple cloth with white end papers. With four colored lithographs and four woodcuts from the original plates by John Leech; blue and red title page; all staves numbered with Roman numerals.

First American edition.

B362(2)
A second copy. Preface with type adjusted in lines 4-7; otherwise as B362(1).

B363
A CHRISTMAS CAROL. London: Chapman and Hall, Limited. [n.d.].

12°. In original green wrapper. (Shilling Issue)

B364
A CHRISTMAS CAROL. Boston: Fields, Osgood, & Co. Successors to Ticknor and Fields. 1869.

8°. In original wine-colored cloth with gilt decoration; brown end papers.

B365(1)
A CHRISTMAS CAROL. Boston: James R. Osgood and Company. 1876.

16°. In original brick-red cloth stamped with black and gold. (Vest-Pocket Series)

B365(2)
A binding variant in original green cloth.

Ex libris James T. Fields. With envelope dated 2nd May 1869 addressed to Fields by Dickens attached to front cover, inscribed "In the handwriting of Dickens J. T. Fields."

B366
THE CHRISTMAS CAROL. A FACSIMILE REPRODUCTION OF THE AUTHOR'S ORIGINAL MS. WITH AN INTRODUCTION BY F. G. KITTON. London: Elliot Stock. 1890.

4°. In original grey paper boards with cloth spine.

B367
A CHRISTMAS CAROL. Troy, New York: Nims and Knight. 1890.

4°. In original green and white cloth decorated in black, gilt and green.

B368
A CHRISTMAS CAROL AND THE CRICKET ON THE HEARTH. New York: Baker & Taylor Company. [1905].

8°. In black cloth with colored illustrations on cover; text with red ruled borders.

B369

A CHRISTMAS CAROL. Philadelphia: Henry Altemus Company. [inscribed "Christmas 1910"].

16°. In green cloth with gilt lettering. (Altemus Classics Series)

B370

A CHRISTMAS CAROL. PICTURED BY A. I. KELLER. Philadelphia: David McKay. 1914.

8°. In original dark blue cloth decorated in gilt.

B371(1)*

A CHRISTMAS CAROL. London: William Heinemann. Philadelphia: J. B. Lippincott Co. [n.d.].

4°. On large hand-made paper, bound in white vellum, edges gilt. With 12 colored plates mounted on cartridge paper and 18 vignettes in black and white by Arthur Rackham.

Ex libris E. A. Parsons. No. 167 of 525 copies. With original pen and ink sketch signed by Arthur Rackham and dated "Xmas 1915" on half title page.

B371(2,3)

Two additional copies, Nos. 29 and 409 of 525 copies, signed by Arthur Rackham.

B372

A CHRISTMAS CAROL. Boston: Atlantic Monthly Press. [n.d.].

8°. Bound as original first edition except in bright red. Facsimile of the first edition (with textual errors). Introduction by A. Edward Newton.

B373

A CHRISTMAS CAROL IN PROSE BEING A GHOST STORY OF CHRISTMAS. WITH FOUR ILLUSTRATIONS IN COLOUR AND FOUR WOODCUTS BY JOHN LEECH. Boston: Charles E. Lauriat Co. [n.d.].

8°. In rust cloth with gilt decoration simulating the original edition; bright green end papers and gilt edges. Facsimile printed in England of the first edition.

B374

"A Christmas Carol in Prose." In BOSTON TRAVELER CHRISTMAS BOOK. Boston: 22 December 1928.

4°. Newspaper supplement printed in green ink on green background and brown ink on buff background.

B375
A CHRISTMAS CAROL. New York: Privately printed. 1930.

12°. Two small volumes bound in red levant morocco, richly tooled and gilt. Printed by Edwin Rudge at Mt. Vernon, New York; typography and binding by Frederic Warde.

B376
A CHRISTMAS CAROL. New York: Cheshire House. 1932.

8°. In cream paper boards printed in red.

No. 894 of 1200 copies printed by Richard Ellis; illustrations in sepia and red by Louis Koster.

B377
A CHRISTMAS CAROL IN PROSE BEING A GHOST STORY OF CHRISTMAS. WITH ILLUSTRATIONS BY GORDON ROSS AND AN INTRODUCTION BY STEPHEN LEACOCK. Boston: The Merrymount Press. 1934.

8°. In original green decorated paper boards with green cloth spine and paper label. For members of the Limited Editions Club.

B378
A CHRISTMAS CAROL. London, New York: George Routledge and Sons. [n.d.].

16°. In marbled paper boards with grey cloth spine and corners. Reproductions, reduced, of original title page and illustrations. (Copyright Edition)

B379
A CHRISTMAS CAROL IN PROSE BEING A GHOST STORY OF CHRISTMAS. ILLUSTRATED BY PHILIP REED. Chicago: The Monastery Hill Press. 1940.

16°. In original illustrated paper boards with red cloth spine and paper label.

B380
A CHRISTMAS CAROL. New York: Robert K. Haas, Inc. [n.d.].

32°. In flexible brown leather wrapper. (Little Leather Library)

B381
A CHRISTMAS CAROL. London & Glasgow: Collins Clear-Type Press. Chicago, Philadelphia, Toronto: The John C. Winston Company. [n.d.].

32°. In white cardboard cover with colored illustrations. (2⅞″ by 4″).

EXTRA ILLUSTRATIONS TO *A Christmas Carol*

B382

Two colored plates by John Leech: "Marley's Ghost" and "Scrooge's third Visitor," mounted.

PLAGIARISMS AND DRAMATIZATIONS OF *A Christmas Carol*

B383(1)

A CHRISTMAS CAROL; OR, THE MISER'S WARNING! (ADAPTED FROM CHARLES DICKENS'S CELEBRATED WORK.) BY C. Z. BARNETT. New York: Samuel French. [n.d.].

12°. In orange paper wrapper. (The Minor Drama No. CCCCI)

B383(2)

A copy in pink wrapper. [French's Acting Edition (Late Lacy's)]

B384

MR. SCROOGE. A DRAMATIC FANTASY AFTER CHARLES DICKENS' "A CHRISTMAS CAROL." BY ASHLEY MILLER. New York: Dodd, Mead & Company. 1928.

8°. In original red cloth.

B385(1)

THE CHIMES: A GOBLIN STORY OF SOME BELLS THAT RANG AN OLD YEAR OUT AND A NEW YEAR IN. London: Chapman and Hall. MDCCCXLV.

8°. In original red cloth.

First edition, first issue, with name of publishers within border of design on vignette title page.

B385(2–9)

Eight additional copies with vignette title of the first issue. Of these, one has the reset title page and list of illustrations of the second issue (list of illustrations with heavier, more contracted type, line 3 with 4 dots instead of 3 between title and name of engraver). Variations occur in typography: one copy with lines generally contracted, a second copy with lines expanded horizontally.

B386(1)

THE CHIMES: A GOBLIN STORY OF SOME BELLS THAT RANG AN OLD YEAR OUT AND A NEW YEAR IN. London: Chapman and Hall. MDCCCXLV.

8°. In original red cloth.

First edition, second issue. Vignette title with name of publishers in open type. Type on title page expanded vertically and horizontally. List of illustrations reset.

B386(2–3)
Two additional copies of the second issue of the first edition.

B387°
THE CHIMES. London: Chapman and Hall. MDCCCXLV.
8°. In flexible red cloth with gilt design on front and back covers, edges gilt.
A slim volume about ¼″ in thickness, lacking many pages of text, presumably a salesman's sample.

B388(1)°
THE CHIMES. Philadelphia: Lea and Blanchard. 1845.
12°. In original blue cloth, with twelve plates.
First American edition, resembling the first edition.
This issue varies from the description of William Glyde Wilkins only in color of binding; illustrations altered from the original as described; 96 pages of text. Mr. Wilkins, in *Early American Editions of Dickens,* stated that he has never "seen or heard of any other copy" than his own.

B388(2)
A duplicate copy of the first American edition in original blue cloth, as issued.

B389(1)
THE CHIMES. New York: Harper & Brothers. 1845.
8°. In original white wrapper, as issued. Pamphlet of 31 pages printed in double columns without illustrations.

B389(2)
A second copy bound with wrapper in marbled paper boards and buckram spine, edges trimmed.

B390
THE CHIMES. New York: E. Winchester, New World Press. [1844].
8°. In original buff paper wrapper. Pamphlet of 32 pages printed in double columns without illustrations.

B391°
THE CHIMES. Elmira, New York: F. Hall & Co. [1845].
8°. In original yellow wrapper. Pamphlet of 32 pages printed in double columns without illustrations. Advertisement on back dated "Elmira, Feb. 1845." An apparently unrecorded American piracy; in perfect condition. See illustration.

B392
THE CHIMES. New York: The Century Co. 1905.
8°. In original old calf, blind stamped, with brown marbled end papers; edges gilt. Title page in red and green.

B393

THE CHIMES. London: For The Limited Editions Club. 1931.

4°. In buff cloth with cover design in black and gold; illustrations by Arthur Rackham.

No. 522 of 1500 copies.

B394

THE CHIMES. New York: The Platt & Peck Co. [n.d.].

12°. In green imitation leather with silver end papers.

PLAGIARISMS, PARODIES, DRAMATIZATIONS, AND TRANSLATIONS OF *The Chimes*

B395

THE CHIMES; OR, SOME BELLS THAT RANG AN OLD YEAR OUT AND A NEW YEAR IN. A GOBLIN DRAMA, IN FOUR QUARTERS. DRAMATISED BY MARK LEMON AND G. A. À' BECK-ETT, FROM THE STORY BY CHARLES DICKENS. First Performed at the Adelphi Theatre, on Tuesday, 19 December 1844 [London: John Dicks. n.d.].

8°. In original pink paper wrapper. (Dicks' Standard Plays)

B396

THE CHIMES, A GOBLIN STORY, OR SOME BELLS THAT RANG AN OLD YEAR OUT AND A NEW YEAR IN: IN THREE PEALS, DRAMATISED BY EDWARD STIRLING. CORRECTLY PRINTED FROM THE PROMPT BOOK, AS PERFORMED AT THE THEATRE ROYAL, LYCEUM. London: W. Barth. 1844.

12°. Leaflet rebound in full tan morocco.

B397

THE WEDDING BELLS. AN ECHO OF "THE CHIMES," WITH COLOURED ILLUSTRATIONS BY THE AUTHOR. London: Thomas Allman. MDCCCXLVI.

8°. In original red binding imitating the Christmas books; edges gilt, blue and red title page.

B398

OLD JOLLIFFE: NOT A GOBLIN STORY. BY THE SPIRIT OF A LITTLE BELL, AWAKENED BY "THE CHIMES." THIRD EDITION. London: W. N. Wright. MDCCCXLVI.

8°. In original purple cloth.

An "answer" to *The Chimes* by Mrs. H. S. Mackarness.

B399

A second copy. "FIFTH EDITION. . . . MDCCCXLIX." In original grey cloth.

B400

THE SEQUEL TO OLD JOLLIFFE. [London: 1846?].

8°. In original purple cloth.

B401

A HARANGJÁTÉK: TÖRTÉNET A ROSSZ TÜNDÉREKROL ÉS NÉ-
HÁNY HARANGRÓL, MELY KIHARANGOZOTT EGY Ó-ESZTEN-
DOT ÉS BEHARANGOZOTT EGY ÚJ ÉVET IRTA DICKENS KÁ-
ROLY Budapest: Balla Mihály Az Ifjuság konyvkiadó. [1920].

12°. In original half leather with grey paper boards.

No. 6 of a limited edition. Hungarian translation.

B402(1–12)

THE CRICKET ON THE HEARTH. A FAIRY TALE OF HOME.
London: Printed and Published for the Author by Bradbury and Evans.
MDCCCXLVI.

8°. Twelve copies of the first edition in variant states, in original red cloth, as
issued. Variations occurring in varying combinations suggest the simultaneous
use of several steels for the illustrations and of stereotypes for the text. Except for
one correction on page 82, line 11, where ' is corrected to " at the beginning
of the sentence, alterations consist in tightening, expanding, or straightening
the type.

	Vignette Title: Top of crescent to base of date: 1) 150 mm. 2) 150½ mm.	Title Page: Top of "THE" to base of date	Dedication: "The Author" and date line: 1) contracted 2) expanded	Illustrations: Typeface. Number of dots after last 2 titles: 1) sharp, contracted. 4 and 4. 2) heavy, expanded. 3 and 5.
1.	1	128 mm.	1	1
2.	1	126 mm.	2	2
3.	2	126 mm.	2	2
4.	2	128 mm.	1	1
5.	1	126 mm.	2	2
6.	1	125 mm.	2	2
7.	1	125 mm.	2	2
8.	1	126 mm.	2	2
9.	1	128 mm.	1	1
10	2	125 mm.	2	2
11.	2	126 mm. precedes Vignette Title	2	2
12.	2	128 mm.	1	1

Text: P.1: *Depth of box enclosing text:* 1) 22 mm. 2) 20 mm.	P.33: 1) as D 1 2) contracted horizontally 3) expanded horizontally	P.52.19 1) as D 1 2) L.19 shifted right 3) tightened horizontally	P.82.11 1) as D 1 2) L.11 tightened 3) ' corrected to "	P.88 1) as D 1 2) straightened
1	1	1	1	1
1	1	2	2	1
1	1	1	2	1
2	1	2	2	1
2	2	3	1	2
2	1	2	2	1
2	1	2	2	2
2	1	3	2	1
2	3	2	2	2
2	1	3	1	1
	3	2	2	1
2	3	3	3 extended horizontally	2 tightened horizontally

P.129 1) as D 1 2) extended horizontally 3) L.23 shifted	P.144.4,7 1) as D 1 2) left margin straightened	P.150.7 1) as D 1 2) first 6 words shifted left 3) tightened horizontally	P.161 1) as D 1 2) extended horizontally	Adv. for *Oliver Twist* 1) 10 lines no heading 2) 11 lines plus heading
1	1	1	1	1
1	1	3	1	2
1	1	1	1	2
1	2	2	2	2
2	2	1	1	2
3	1	1	1	2
1	2	3	1	2
3	1	1	1	2
1	1	3	1	2
1	1	1	1	2
1	1			
1	1	3	1	2

B403(1)

THE CRICKET ON THE HEARTH. New-York: Harper & Brothers. 1846.

8°. In original brown wrapper. Pamphlet of 32 pages, printed in double columns, with 16 pages of advertisements: "Valuable Books of Travel," 8 pp., "Valuable Standard Productions," 8 pp.

First American edition, published simultaneously with that of Wiley & Putnam; no priority of issue established.

B403(2)
A second copy. Advertisements differ, "Catalogue of Books Published by Harper & Brothers . . . ," 16 pages.

B404
THE CRICKET ON THE HEARTH. Boston: Jordan and Wiley. [n.d.].
8°. In original brown wrapper. Pamphlet of 42 pages, printed in double columns, with 6 pages of advertisements.

B405
THE CRICKET ON THE HEARTH. New York: Wiley & Putnam. 1846.
8°. In original red cloth binding. Bound in one volume with *The Book of Christmas; Descriptions of the Customs, Ceremonies, Traditions, Superstitions, Fun, Feeling, and Festivities of the Christmas Season*. By Thomas K. Hervey. (Library of Choice Reading)

B406
THE CRICKET ON THE HEARTH. EDITION SANCTIONED BY THE AUTHOR. Leipzig: Bernhard Tauchnitz Junior. 1846.
12°. In original black paper boards with cloth spine. On light weight paper.

B407
GUILLAUME'S NELUMBOS DICKENS THE CRICKET ON THE HEARTH. London, Manchester, New York: George Routledge & Sons, Ltd. 1894.
8°. In stiff white paper wrapper, printed in red, blue, and black.

B408
THE CRICKET ON THE HEARTH. New York, London: G. P. Putnam's Sons. [1900].
8°. In original green cloth printed in black, red, and gold.

B409
THE CRICKET ON THE HEARTH. Waltham St. Lawrence, Berks.: For The Limited Editions Club. 1933.
F°. In original yellow cloth printed in green. No. 1,167 of 1500 copies printed.

EXTRA ILLUSTRATIONS TO *The Cricket on the Hearth*

B410
Sixteen illustrations for *The Cricket on the Hearth* by F. S. Coburn [1900]. Extracted from bound volume.

PLAGIARISMS AND DRAMATIZATIONS OF *The Cricket on the Hearth*

B411
THE ENTIRELY NEW AND ORIGINAL DRAMA, IN THREE PARTS, ENTITLED THE CRICKET ON THE HEARTH A FAIRY TALE OF HOME. DRAMATIZED BY ALBERT SMITH, ESQ. FROM EARLY PROOFS OF THE WORK, BY THE EXPRESS PERMISSION OF THE AUTHOR. As performed at the Theatre Royal, Lyceum. London: W. S. Johnson, "Nassau Steam Press." [MDCCCXLV].

8°. Pamphlet in white paper wrapper.
First edition.

B412
THE CRICKET ON THE HEARTH A DRAMA IN THREE ACTS. DRAMATIZED BY ALBERT SMITH, ESQ. BY THE EXPRESS PERMISSION OF THE AUTHOR. Boston: Walter H. Baker & Co. [1859].

8°. Pamphlet in original brown paper wrapper.

B413
Program of performance of Albert Smith's drama by The Dickens Fellowship of Toronto at Margaret Eaton Theatre, 10-13 February 1926. Facsimile of original wrapper. No. 353 of 1500 copies.

B414
THE CRICKET ON THE HEARTH: A FAIRY TALE OF HOME IN THREE CHIRPS. Leeds: F. R. Spark and Co. [n.d.].

8°. In original green wrapper. For private circulation.

B415
THE CRICKET ON THE HEARTH; OR, A FAIRY TALE OF HOME. A DRAMA, IN THREE ACTS. DRAMATIZED BY ALBERT SMITH, ESQ. BY THE EXPRESS PERMISSION OF THE AUTHOR. New York: Samuel French. [n.d.].

12°. In original orange wrapper. (French's Standard Drama No. CCCXLII)

B416
THE CRICKET ON THE HEARTH, A FAIRY TALE OF HOME. BY EDWARD STIRLING, ESQ. AS PERFORMED AT THE THEATRE ROYAL, ADELPHI. CORRECTLY PRINTED FROM THE PROMPTER'S COPY. London: Webster and Co. [n.d.].

12°. Pamphlet of 36 pages in original white wrapper, as issued.

B417(1–16)
THE BATTLE OF LIFE. A LOVE STORY. London: Bradbury & Evans. MDCCCXLVI.

8°. In original red cloth.
First edition. A series of sixteen copies, as issued. The sequence of states, established by William B. Todd in "Dickens's Battle of Life: Round Six," *The*

Book Collector XV (Spring 1966), 48-54, is represented by copies at The University of Texas as follows.

State	Description of Title Page	No. of Copies
B	Subtitle in light type	1
C2	Subtitle on simple scroll; 3-line imprint; "d" of "Bradbury" broken	5
E1	Subtitle in scroll with cupid; petals, upper right, intact	6
E2	As E1, but with petals broken	4

Of these one copy, vignette title in state E1, is the binding variant described by Dr. Todd, page 54, as "an early remainder binding," blind stamped front and back with double rule borders.

B418
THE BATTLE OF LIFE. Philadelphia: Lea and Blanchard. 1847.

8°. Pamphlet of 32 pages in original yellow paper wrapper, printed in double columns.

Priority of American editions not established.

B419
THE BATTLE OF LIFE. New York: Harper & Brothers. 1847.

8°. Pamphlet of 32 pages in original brown wrapper, printed in double columns.

B420
THE BATTLE OF LIFE. Boston: Williams & Co. 1847.

8°. Pamphlet of 56 pages with ruled borders, in original yellow wrapper, front detached.

Ex libris William Glyde Wilkins.

B421
THE BATTLE OF LIFE. New York: Williams and Co. [1847].

8°. In original yellow wrapper; text with ruled border.

B422
THE BATTLE OF LIFE. London: A. & F. Pears, Ltd. [n.d.].

8°. In rust cloth, printed in black and gold.

DRAMATIZATION OF *The Battle of Life*

B423
THE BATTLE OF LIFE. DRAMATIZED BY ALBERT SMITH, ESQ. FROM EARLY PROOFS OF THE WORK BY THE EXPRESS PERMISSION OF THE AUTHOR. As performed at the Theatre Royal, Lyceum, Monday, 21 December 1846. London: W. S. Johnson, "Nassau Steam Press." [1846].

12°. Leaflet lacking wrapper.

B424

Playbill advertising THE BATTLE OF LIFE for Friday, 29 January 1847.
[n.p.].

B425(1–7)

THE HAUNTED MAN AND THE GHOST'S BARGAIN. A FANCY
FOR CHRISTMAS-TIME. London: Bradbury & Evans. 1848.

8°. In original red cloth, with yellow end papers.

First edition, first issue. Seven copies of the first issue; in three the numeral
"166" is intact; in four it is broken.

B426(1)

THE HAUNTED MAN AND THE GHOST'S BARGAIN. New York:
Harper & Brothers. [1849].

8°. Pamphlet of 34 pages with 1 leaf of advertising, in original brown wrapper.

First American edition.

Inside front wrapper, "Webster's Octavo Dictionary, Revised." Adv. leaf, recto,
"Choice Library of Modern Romance"; verso, "Harper's New Catalogue."

B426(2)

A variant issue in original brown wrapper.

Inside front wrapper, "Important New Works." Adv. leaf, recto, "Harper's New
Catalogue"; verso, "Popular Sterling Productions."

B427(1)

PITMAN'S SHORTHAND LIBRARY, NO. 3 THE HAUNTED MAN.
ENGRAVED IN THE EASY REPORTING STYLE OF PITMAN'S
SHORTHAND. WITH ILLUSTRATIONS BY S. J. LOXTON. London,
Bath, New York: Sir Isaac Pitman & Sons, Ltd. [n.d.].

8°. In drab green paper boards with cloth spine.

B427(2)

A second copy in rust cloth with yellow end papers.

B428

AZ ELÁTKOZOTT EMBER ÉS AZ ALKU, MELYET A SZELLEMMEL
KOTOTT. Budapest: Balla Mihaly Az Ifjusag konyvkiado. [1920].

12°. In half brown morocco with grey paper boards.

No. 20 of a limited edition. Hungarian translation.

B429

CHRISTMAS STORIES; CONSISTING OF A CAROL, THE CRICKET,
THE CHIMES, BATTLE OF LIFE. New York, London: John Wiley.
1849.

8°. In original green cloth.

First collected edition, preceding the first English edition by three years.

B430(1)
CHRISTMAS BOOKS. London: Chapman and Hall. [1852].

4°. In three-fourths green morocco with green marbled paper boards and end papers.

First cheap issue of Dickens's Works (Household Edition). The last volume of the first series comprised the Christmas Books, the first collected edition printed in England.

B430(2)
A second copy in original green cloth with cream end papers.

B431
CHRISTMAS STORIES. PETERSONS' CHEAP EDITION FOR THE MILLION. Philadelphia: T. B. Peterson & Brothers. [n.d.].

8°. In original salmon-pink wrapper.

B432
WHAT CHRISTMAS IS AS WE GROW OLDER. Boston: Smith & Porter Press. 1924.

8°. No. 203 of 220 copies privately printed. In marbled paper boards.

B433
FIVE CHRISTMAS NOVELS. A CHRISTMAS CAROL—THE CHIMES —THE CRICKET ON THE HEARTH—THE BATTLE OF LIFE—THE HAUNTED MAN. ILLUSTRATED BY REGINALD BIRCH. New York: The Heritage Press. 1939.

8°. In original brown cloth.

PLAGIARISMS, PARODIES, AND ADAPTATIONS OF *Christmas Books*

B434
TINY TIM DOT AND THE FAIRY CRICKET FROM THE CHRIST-MAS STORIES OF CHARLES DICKENS. ILLUSTRATED BY DAR-LEY. New York: Clark, Austin, Maynard & Co. 1862.

8°. In original purple cloth with yellow end papers. (Dickens' Little Folks)

B435
DICKENS' CHRISTMAS STORIES FOR CHILDREN. EDITED BY MOLLY K. BELLEW. New York, Boston: H. M. Caldwell Co. 1902.

8°. In red cloth with colored paper illustration.

B436
THOUGHTS FOR CHRISTMAS FROM THE CHRISTMAS BOOKS BY CHARLES DICKENS. COMPILED BY HARRIET A. TOWNSEND AND ILLUSTRATED BY T. H. ROBINSON. London: The Cowcross Press. 1910.

12°. In stiff white wrapper, printed in black and red.

B437

CHRISTMAS IN DICKENS. ILLUSTRATED BY EVERETT SHINN. Garden City, New York: Garden City Publishing Company. 1941.

8°. In illustrated paper boards with red cloth spine.

B438

CHRISTMAS STORIES. CONDENSED FOR USE IN SCHOOLS. New York, New Orleans: University Publishing Company. [n.d.].

8°. In buff cloth. (Standard Literature Series)

3 : CHRISTMAS STORIES

B439

A ROUND OF STORIES BY THE CHRISTMAS FIRE. New York: Stringer & Townsend. 1853.

8°. In original brown paper wrapper. Dickens contributed "The Poor Relation's Story" and "The Child's Story."

B440

THE SEVEN POOR TRAVELLERS. BEING THE EXTRA CHRISTMAS NUMBER OF *HOUSEHOLD WORDS*. Christmas 1854.

8°. Without wrapper.

"The First Traveller" and "The Road" are by Dickens.

B441

ANOTHER ROUND OF STORIES BY THE CHRISTMAS FIRE. Boston: Fetridge & Co. 1854.

8°. In original pink wrapper.

B442

A HOUSE TO LET. BEING THE EXTRA CHRISTMAS NUMBER OF *HOUSEHOLD WORDS*. Christmas 1858.

8°. Without wrapper.

"Going Into Society" is by Dickens.

B443

A HOUSE TO LET. A CHRISTMAS AND NEW YEAR'S STORY. Philadelphia: T. B. Peterson and Brothers. [1859].

8°. In original white wrapper.

B444

THE HAUNTED HOUSE. THE EXTRA CHRISTMAS NUMBER OF *ALL THE YEAR ROUND*. Christmas 1859.

8°. Without wrapper.

"The Mortals in the House," "The Ghost in Master B's Room," and "The Ghost in the Corner Room" are by Dickens. He also wrote opening paragraphs for other chapters.

B445

HOUSEHOLD WORDS and ALL THE YEAR ROUND. London: Bradbury & Evans and Chapman & Hall. Christmas Numbers 1850–1867.

8°. A complete set in original wrappers, as issued, except for 1850 number, which retains only a trace of green wrapper.

B446

ALL THE YEAR ROUND. Chapman & Hall. Christmas Numbers 1861–1867.

8°. A set of Extra Christmas Numbers, 1861-1867, as issued.

Tom Tiddler's Ground	1861
Somebody's Luggage	1862
Mrs. Lirriper's Lodgings	1863
Mrs. Lirriper's Legacy	1864
Doctor Marigold's Prescriptions	1865
Mugby Junction	1866
No Thoroughfare	1867

B447

TOM TIDDLER'S GROUND. THE EXTRA CHRISTMAS NUMBER OF *ALL THE YEAR ROUND*. Christmas 1861.

8°. Without wrapper.

Dickens wrote Chapters I, VI, and VII.

B448

SOMEBODY'S LUGGAGE. PETERSONS' CHEAP EDITION FOR THE MILLION. Philadelphia: T. B. Peterson & Brothers. [n.d.].

8°. In salmon-pink wrapper.

Dickens wrote: "His Leaving It Till Called For," "His Boots," "His Brown-Paper Parcel," "His Wonderful End," and part of Chapter III.

B449

MRS. LIRRIPER'S LODGINGS. THE EXTRA CHRISTMAS NUMBER OF *ALL THE YEAR ROUND*. Christmas 1863.

8°. In original blue wrapper.

Dickens wrote Chapters I and VII.

B450

MRS. LIRRIPER'S LODGINGS. New York: Harper & Brothers. 1864.

8°. In original white wrapper.

B451

MRS. LIRRIPER'S LODGINGS; AND MRS. LIRRIPER'S LEGACY. PETERSONS' CHEAP EDITION FOR THE MILLION. Philadelphia: T. B. Peterson & Brothers. [n.d.].

8°. In pink wrapper.

B452

MRS. LIRRIPER'S LEGACY. THE EXTRA CHRISTMAS NUMBER OF *ALL THE YEAR ROUND*. Christmas 1864.

8°. In original blue wrapper.

Dickens wrote Chapters I and VII.

B453

MRS. LIRRIPER'S LEGACY. New York: Harper & Brothers. 1865.

8°. In original white wrapper.

B454

DOCTOR MARIGOLD'S PRESCRIPTIONS. THE EXTRA CHRIST-MAS NUMBER OF *ALL THE YEAR ROUND*. Christmas 1865.

8°. In original blue wrapper.

Dickens wrote Chapters I, VI, and VIII.

B455

DR. MARIGOLD'S PRESCRIPTIONS. New York: Harper & Brothers. 1866.

8°. Pamphlet of 46 pages in original white wrapper.

Ex libris Barnaby Ross, "Ellery Queen."

B456

DR. MARIGOLD'S PRESCRIPTIONS. New York: Lewis & Conger. [n.d.].

12°. In white wrapper printed in green and black. Advertisement for a house-furnishings and hardware firm.

B457

MUGBY JUNCTION. EXTRA CHRISTMAS NUMBER OF *ALL THE YEAR ROUND*. Christmas 1866.

8°. In original blue wrapper.

Dickens wrote "Barbox Brothers," "Barbox Brothers and Co.," "Main Line (The Boy at Rugby)," and "No. 1 Branch Line (The Signal Man)."

B458

NO THOROUGHFARE. BY CHARLES DICKENS AND WILKIE COLLINS. EXTRA CHRISTMAS NUMBER OF *ALL THE YEAR ROUND.* Christmas 1867.

8°. In original blue wrapper.

Dickens wrote "The Overture," parts of Acts I and IV, and all of Act III.

B459

NO THOROUGHFARE. BY CHARLES DICKENS AND WILKIE COLLINS. EXTRA CHRISTMAS NUMBER OF *EVERY SATURDAY.* Boston: Ticknor and Fields. Christmas 1867.

8°. In original white wrapper.

B460

THE DICKENS-COLLINS CHRISTMAS STORIES COMPRISING NO THOROUGHFARE AND THE TWO IDLE APPRENTICES. Boston: William F. Gill & Company. 1876.

8°. In original green cloth binding, stamped in gold.

B461

THE HOLLY-TREE INN. Philadelphia: T. B. Peterson. [1855].

8°. In original white wrapper. Advertisements dated "November 1855."

B462

THE HOLLY TREE INN AND A CHRISTMAS TREE AS WRITTEN IN THE CHRISTMAS STORIES. New York: Baker & Taylor Company. [1907].

8°. In original green cloth with colored illustration.

Presentation copy from the artist, George Alfred Williams.

Dickens wrote "The Guest," "The Boots," and "The Bill."

B463

THE HOLLY-TREE INN. New York: Hodder & Stoughton. [n.d.].

8°. In grey paper boards printed in gold, red, and green; with colored illustration.

From *Household Words,* December 1855.

B464

BOOTS OF THE HOLLY-TREE INN. WITH ILLUSTRATIONS BY MARIE A. LAWSON. New York, London: Harper & Brothers. 1928.

4°. In original red cloth decorated in black and gilt with gilt lettering and illustrative end papers.

B465

A CURIOUS DANCE ROUND A CURIOUS TREE. [n.p., 1860].

12°. Leaflet reprinted from *Household Words,* bound together with "1860 Ball at St. Luke's Hospital" and "Contrast between 1852 and 1860."

B466

SELECTED STORIES FOR CHRISTMAS READING   DR. MARI-
GOLD   TWO GHOST STORIES. Chicago: Robert O. Law Company.
1906.

8°. In original purple suede stamped with gilt design and lettering.

B467

THE SEVEN POOR TRAVELLERS. WITH DECORATIONS BY
DORIS M. PALMER. London: Cecil Palmer. 1920.

12°. In stiff pink wrapper with colored illustration.

B468

SOMEBODY'S LUGGAGE. Philadelphia: Privately printed. 1957.

12°. In original buff cloth with brown leather spine and gilt decoration. (9" by
6" printed lengthwise)

No. 975 of 1,000 copies printed as Christmas greeting for Samuel A. Dalton.

PLAGIARISMS, PARODIES, DRAMATIZATIONS, AND ADAPTATIONS BASED ON
Christmas Stories

B469

TINY TIM DOT AND THE FAIRY CRICKET FROM THE CHRIST-
MAS STORIES OF CHARLES DICKENS. New York: Redfield. [n.d.].

12°. In original red embossed cloth with yellow end papers. Inscription dated
"Xmas 1856." (Dickens' Little Folk)

4:SECONDARY WORKS

B470(1)†

SUNDAY UNDER THREE HEADS. AS IT IS; AS SABBATH BILLS
WOULD MAKE IT; AS IT MIGHT BE MADE. BY TIMOTHY
SPARKS. London: Chapman and Hall. 1836.

12°. In original brown paper wrapper, with half title, uncut.

B470(2)°

A variant issue, bound in dark green levant morocco, richly gilt.

This appears to be an authentic printing (though sold to J. H. Wrenn by T. J.
Wise in 1908), on paper of two different varieties, both dissimilar in texture
to [B253(1)]. Illustration follows p. 18 in other issue and is there conjugate
with frontispiece; in this copy it is a disjunct leaf following p. 10. With half-
title and heading on p. 35.

B470(3)°

A third variant. Wrapper of heavy white paper, edges trimmed. Collation varies
from each of the above copies: Blank flyleaf; half title, verso blank; frontispiece
[corresponds to illustration following p. 30 in B253(1) and p. 10 in B253(2)];
vignette title, verso blank; p. 35 with half title and heading; second illustration
follows p. 42.

B471(1)

SUNDAY UNDER THREE HEADS. London: J. W. Jarvis & Son. 1884.

12°. In original grey paper wrapper.

Facsimile edition, without heading above "III" on p. [35], as described in Eckel.

B471(2)°

A variant issue of the facsimile with heading on p. [35].

The collection also includes a made-up copy from this issue with original wrapper attached.

B472(1)

SKETCHES OF YOUNG GENTLEMEN. DEDICATED TO THE YOUNG LADIES. London: Chapman and Hall. MDCCCXXXVIII.

12°. In original blue paper boards with yellow end papers.

First edition. In a set of three volumes with *Sketches of Young Ladies* and Dickens's *Sketches of Young Couples*. In very fine condition.

B472(2)

A second copy, in original blue paper boards with ivory end papers.

B473

SKETCHES OF YOUNG LADIES AND YOUNG GENTLEMEN. BY QUIZ. WITH SIX ILLUSTRATIONS BY PHIZ AND ORIGINAL SKETCHES BY TIZ, RIZ, AND BIZ. New York: Wiley and Putnam, and G. Dearborn & Co. MDCCCXXXVIII.

12°. In original half brown leather with marbled paper boards.

B474

SKETCHES OF YOUNG COUPLES; WITH AN URGENT REMON-STRANCE TO THE GENTLEMEN OF ENGLAND (BEING BACHE-LORS OR WIDOWERS), ON THE PRESENT ALARMING CRISIS. London: Chapman and Hall. MDCCCXL.

12°. In original blue paper boards with yellow end papers.

First edition.

B475(1)

DRAWN FROM LIFE. SKETCHES OF YOUNG LADIES, YOUNG GENTLEMEN, AND YOUNG COUPLES. New York: E. J. Hale & Son. 1875.

8°. In original green cloth, printed in gold.

First American edition.

B475(2)

A second copy in original rust-colored cloth with brown end papers.

B476(1)

AMERICAN NOTES FOR GENERAL CIRCULATION. London: Chapman and Hall. MDCCCXLII.

8°. Two volumes in original purple cloth with yellow end papers. As new.

First edition, first issue, with incorrect pagination. [Vol. I begins with p. xvi; Vol. II "Contents" numbered; p. 289 instead of 287 for "Concluding Remarks."]

B476(2)†

A second, presentation, copy of the first issue. Pagination as above.

Inscribed on half-title page: "David Colden Esquire   From his friend   Charles Dickens   Nineteenth October 1842."

B476(3)°

A third variant set. Vol. I begins with p. xvi; Vol. II, Contents unnumbered; p. [287] unnumbered.

B477(1)

AMERICAN NOTES. In *THE NEW WORLD*. New York: Park Benjamin, Editor. J. Winchester, Publisher. 1842.

4°. Forty-six pages printed in double columns; no wrapper.

First American edition [This distinction is also claimed for the extra number of the periodical, *Brother Jonathan*, published by Wilson & Co.].

B477(2)

A variant issue of 48 pages. Headings vary, B477(1): Vol. II . . . nos. 8, 9. New York. November, 1842. B477(2): Vol. II. New-York, November, 1842. Number 8, 9. Page 47/48 cognate with 33/34; p. 47, "An Appeal to the Reading Public"; p. 48, "New Works in Press."

B478(1)

AMERICAN NOTES. In *BROTHER JONATHAN*. New York: Wilson & Company. 7 November 1842.

4°. Forty-eight pages printed in double columns; no wrapper. Bound in red marbled paper boards with leather spine, covers detached.

B478(2)

A variant issue bound in black cloth. Forty-six pages plus an extra page tipped in showing facsimile American $50 note.

B479(1)

AMERICAN NOTES. New York: Harper & Brothers. 1842.

8°. In original brown wrapper.

In a set with companion edition of *Change for the American Notes*.

B479(2)

A second copy in original brown wrapper, as issued. Wrapper of different issue with design and type extended vertically.

B480(1)
AMERICAN NOTES. COPYRIGHT EDITION. Leipzig: Bernhard Tauchnitz, Jun. 1842.

8°. In original half leather with paper boards.

First Tauchnitz edition.

B480(2)
A variant issue in original green cloth. "Copyright Edition" omitted from title page.

B481
AMERICAN NOTES. London: Chapman and Hall. 186 Strand. MDCCCL.

8°. Three numbers, 1 May–1 July 1850, in original green wrappers. (Cheap Edition)

B482(1)
AMERICAN NOTES. London: Chapman and Hall. 193 Piccadilly. MDCCCL.

8°. In original green cloth. Text in double columns. (Cheap Edition)

B482(2)
A binding variant in half polished calf and marbled paper boards.

B483
AMERICAN NOTES. PETERSONS' CHEAP EDITION FOR THE MILLION. Philadelphia: T. B. Peterson & Brothers. [n.d.].

8°. In salmon-pink paper wrapper.

B484
AMERICAN NOTES AND PICTURES FROM ITALY. WITH EIGHT-EEN ILLUSTRATIONS BY A. B. FROST AND GORDON THOM-SON. London: Chapman and Hall. 193 Piccadilly. [n.d.].

4°. In original green cloth with gilt and black decoration, gilt lettering, and yellow end papers. (Household Edition)

PLAGIARISMS, PARODIES, AND REPLIES TO *American Notes*

B485(1)
CHANGE FOR THE AMERICAN NOTES: IN LETTERS FROM LONDON TO NEW-YORK. BY AN AMERICAN LADY. New York: Harper & Brothers. 1843.

8°. In original brown wrapper. Front wrapper, inside, "Valuable Dictionaries." Back wrapper, inside, "Important Standard Works"; outside, "Valuable Works."

B485(2)

A variant issue in original brown wrapper. Front wrapper, inside, "Important Works"; back wrapper, inside, "To be issued . . . A New Pictorial Bible"; outside, "Valuable Works." Four pages of advertisements, dated "February, 1843," precede title page.

B485(3)

A third copy as B485(2) bound with wrappers in brown cloth.

B486

QUOZZIANA: OR LETTERS FROM GREAT GOSLINGTON, MASS. GIVING AN ACCOUNT OF THE QUOZ DINNER, AND OTHER MATTERS. BY SAMPSON SHORT-AND-FAT. Boston: William White & H. P. Lewis. 1842.

12°. In original yellow wrapper.

B487(1,2)

ENGLISH NOTES A RARE AND UNKNOWN WORK BIENG A REPLY TO CHARLES DICKENS'S "AMERICAN NOTES." New York: Lewis M. Thompson. 1920.

8°. In original ivory paper boards with paper labels. Two copies with misprinted "bieng."

With a reprint of the "reply" by "Quarles Quickens" published in 1842. The attribution to E. A. Poe has been strongly questioned.

B487(3)

A third copy in original ivory paper boards with brown lettering. On spine: "English Notes | Quickens | Edgar Allan Poe | Boston | 1842."

With reprint of the "reply" by "Quarles Quickens." Misspelling of "being" in title corrected.

B488

ENGLISH NOTES FOR AMERICAN CIRCULATION. BY SIR RICHARD TANGYE, F.R.G.S. Birmingham: Hudson & Son. MDCCCXCV.

8°. In stiff white wrapper. Privately printed.

B489(1)

PICTURES FROM ITALY. London: Published for the Author by Bradbury & Evans. MDCCCXLVI.

8°. In original blue cloth.

First edition.

Ex libris B. George Ulizio.

B489(2)

A second copy with signature and seal of Henry Cole, Public Record Office, London.

B489(3)
A third, presentation copy inscribed, "Miss Griffin with the sincere regard of Charles Dickens Devonshire Terrace Twenty Ninth May 1846."

B490
THE DAILY NEWS. No. 1. London: 21 January 1846.
First number of the daily paper begun under Dickens's editorship, containing the first of the "Travelling Letters" later collected and published as *Pictures from Italy*.

B491
TRAVELLING LETTERS, WRITTEN ON THE ROAD. PART I. New York: Wiley & Putnam. 1846.
8°. Leaflet in original brown wrapper, as issued.

B492
TRAVELLING LETTERS. WRITTEN ON THE ROAD. New York: Wiley & Putnam. 1846.
8°. In original half polished calf and blue marbled paper boards.

B493
TRAVELLING LETTERS, WRITTEN ON THE ROAD. PART II. New York: Wiley & Putnam. 1846.
8°. In original brown wrapper, as issued.

B494
"Travelling Letters Written on the Road." Chaps. 1–3. In THE ECLECTIC MAGAZINE. May–October 1846 (April number lacking).
8°. Bound volume with covers removed. Separate number for October 1846.

B495
PICTURES FROM ITALY. New York: Wiley & Putnam. 1846.
8°. In original brown wrapper.

B496
PICTURES FROM ITALY. New York: William H. Colyer. 1846.
8°. In original buff wrapper, printed in double columns.

B497
PICTURES FROM ITALY. Paris: A. and W. Galignani and Co. 1846.
12°. In original contemporary half red morocco.

PARODY OF *Pictures from Italy*

B498

FACTS & FIGURES FROM ITALY. BY DON JEREMY SAVONA-
ROLA, BENEDICTINE MONK. ADDRESSED DURING THE LAST
TWO WINTERS TO CHARLES DICKENS, ESQ. BEING AN AP-
PENDIX TO HIS "PICTURES." London: Richard Bentley. 1847.

8°. In original orange cloth, with four pages of advertisements for "Mr. Bentley's
New Publications."

B499(1)†

A CHILD'S HISTORY OF ENGLAND. London: Bradbury & Evans.
1852.

8°. Three volumes in original red cloth.

First edition.

Pre-publication presentation copy to Marcus Stone, inscribed on title page:
"Marcus Stone. From his friend Charles Dickens Christmas 1853."

Dickens's attached holograph letter (A89).

B499(2)

A copy in variant state. Vol. I, dedication page, "w" dropped from "whom."

B500

A CHILD'S HISTORY OF ENGLAND. Boston: Jenks, Hickling, and
Swan. MDCCCLIV.

8°. Two volumes in original dark blue cloth.

B501

A CHILD'S HISTORY OF ENGLAND. NEW EDITION, IN ONE
VOLUME. London: Chapman and Hall. 1863.

8°. In original embossed red cloth.

Presentation copy to Mortimer Malleson, inscribed on title page: "Mortimer
Malleson From Charles Dickens Christmas, 1863."

B502

A CHILD'S HISTORY OF ENGLAND. NEW EDITION. Boston: Estes
and Lauriat. [n.d.].

8°. In original brown cloth.

B503(1,2)

HARD TIMES. FOR THESE TIMES. London: Bradbury & Evans. 1854.

8°. Two copies in original green cloth, as issued.

First edition.

B504

HARD TIMES. New York: Harper & Brothers. 1854.

8°. In original brown wrapper.

B505
HARD TIMES. New York: Dewitt & Davenport, T. L. McElrath & Co. 1854.

8°. In original grey wrapper.

B506
HARD TIMES. PETERSONS' CHEAP EDITION FOR THE MILLION. Philadelphia: T. B. Peterson & Brothers. [n.d.].

8°. In salmon-pink wrapper.

B507
HARD TIMES HUNTED DOWN HOLIDAY ROMANCE & GEORGE SILVERMAN'S EXPLANATION. London: Chapman & Hall, Ltd. and Henry Frowde. New York: Oxford University Press, American Branch. [n.d.].

12°. In original blue cloth with characters from Dickens blind stamped on cover.

TRANSLATION OF *Hard Times*

B508
HARTE ZEITEN. VON BOZ (DICKENS). Translated by J. Senbt. Illustrations by Ludwig Loffler. Leipzig: J. J. Weber. 1854.

8°. Three parts in one volume, in original grey cloth with orange paper label.

B509
THE TWO APPRENTICES, WITH A HISTORY OF THEIR LAZY TOUR. Philadelphia: T. B. Peterson. [1858].

8°. In original white wrapper, with "Peterson's Catalogue of Good Books," 22 pages, at end.

B510
THE LAZY TOUR OF TWO IDLE APPRENTICES. NO THOROUGH-FARE. THE PERILS OF CERTAIN ENGLISH PRISONERS. BY CHARLES DICKENS AND WILKIE COLLINS. London: Chapman and Hall, Limited. 1890.

8°. In original blue-green cloth with black end papers. In the "Ellery Queen" collection.

B511
THE UNCOMMERCIAL TRAVELLER. London: Chapman and Hall. MDCCCLXI.

8°. In original lilac cloth.

First edition. With 32-page Catalogue of Books published by Chapman and Hall, dated December 1860.

B512

THE UNCOMMERCIAL TRAVELLER, AND ADDITIONAL CHRIST-
MAS STORIES. WITH ORIGINAL ILLUSTRATIONS BY S. EYTINGE,
JR. Boston: Ticknor and Fields. 1867.

16°. In original green cloth with gilt stamping and brown end papers.

B513

THE UNCOMMERCIAL TRAVELLER. WITH ILLUSTRATIONS.
London: Chapman and Hall. 1868.

8°. In original red cloth with gilt stamping.

B514

THE UNCOMMERCIAL TRAVELLER. PETERSONS' CHEAP EDI-
TION FOR THE MILLION. Philadelphia: T. B. Peterson & Brothers.
[n.d.].

8°. In salmon-pink wrapper.

B515(1,2)

MRS. GAMP WITH THE STROLLING PLAYERS AN UNFINISHED
SKETCH BY CHARLES DICKENS. New York: Privately Printed.
MDCCCXCIX.

8°. In original white paper boards, lettered in gold.

First separate edition.

Two of 85 copies printed for Lowell M. Palmer from the original MS., with
portrait of Dickens and illustration by Pailthorpe.

This unfinished work was intended to supplement funds raised for the benefit of
Leigh Hunt by amateur theatricals in 1847. It was first published in Forster's
Life of Dickens.

B516†

A NEW PILJIANS PROJISS WRITTEN BY MRS. GAMP. EDITED
BY CHARLES DICKENS. London: F. T. Sabin. [n.d.].

4°. In three-fourths olive green morocco with marbled paper boards and wine-
colored end papers.

First edition. Facsimile of Dickens's MS. (*Mrs. Gamp With the Strolling
Players*), with illustrations by F. W. Pailthorpe, F. Barnard, and John Leech.

Ex libris George Barr McCutcheon.

B517°

THE LIFE OF OUR LORD WRITTEN BY CHARLES DICKENS FOR
HIS CHILDREN   1849   AND KEPT AS A PRECIOUS FAMILY
SECRET FOR EIGHTY-FIVE YEARS. This copy must be held strictly
confidential and must not be published in whole or in part or quoted in
any way prior to fixed dates of release.

Mimeographed press release for 5 March 1934: "From United Feature Syndi-
cate, Monte Bourjaily, General Manager, 220 East 42nd Street, New York. First
Publication Anywhere in World."

With typewritten letter from "The Inner Sanctum of Simon and Schuster," initialed MHS, sending this copy to Mrs. George Proctor.

B518
THE LIFE OF OUR LORD. Monday, 5 March 1934.

Clippings from the New York *World Telegram,* mounted on plates 12¾" by 16¾". Bound in blue cloth. With two prayers composed by Dickens for his young children.

B519
"The Life of Our Lord." Clippings from *The Cincinnati Post.*

B520
THE LIFE OF OUR LORD. London: Associated Newspapers Ltd. MCMXXXIV.

4°. In original red cloth, printed on heavy paper with double ruled border.

The order of issue of B520-B523 has not been determined.

B521
THE LIFE OF OUR LORD. London: Arthur Barker Limited. 1934.

4°. Bound in vellum, top edge gilt; printed in black and blue on hand-made paper.

First edition. No. 45 of an edition of 250 copies.

Inserted in this copy is holograph letter from Kate Perugini (A146): "Dear Sir. 'The Life of Christ' by my father, written for his children cannot be sold. Yours truly Kate Perugini 8th Oct 1902." [The MS. was later bequeathed to the British Museum by Sir Henry Fielding Dickens, who gave permission for its publication.]

B522(1)
THE LIFE OF OUR LORD. WRITTEN FOR HIS CHILDREN DURING THE YEARS 1846 to 1849 BY CHARLES DICKENS AND NOW FIRST PUBLISHED. New York: Simon and Schuster. 1934.

8°. In green cloth with cream end papers decorated with gold stars.

B522(2)
A binder's dummy of fine brown leather with blue end papers decorated with gold stars. Title and first five pages of different setting from B521(1), remainder blank.

B523
THE LIFE OF OUR LORD. New York: Simon and Schuster. 1934.

8°. In white paper boards, top edge gilt; title page in black and red, with red rulings throughout.

No. 2211 of an edition of 2387 copies.

B524

THE LIFE OF OUR LORD. New York: Grosset & Dunlap, Inc. [1936].

12°. In illustrated paper boards and illustrated end papers.

Children's edition; illustrated by Rachel Taft-Dixon.

5:POEMS AND PLAYS

B525(1)†

THE VILLAGE COQUETTES: A COMIC OPERA. IN TWO ACTS.
THE MUSIC BY JOHN HULLAH. London: Richard Bentley. 1836.

8°. Rebound in red levant morocco, richly gilt.

First edition.

Attached are a letter from John Hullah, the signature of J. P. Harley [the actor
who played the lead], and a letter from Dickens to [G. H.] Lewes (A50):
"Devonshire Terrace Twelfth April 1848. Many thanks for your book, . . . I
can't call a second farce for Saturday; having just got the review, and fearing
that I decry impracticabilities therein. C.D."

As a means of inviting criticism of *The Village Coquettes,* Dickens sent a copy
of the songs to Albany Fonblanque, editor of *The Examiner.* Fonblanque passed
the letter on to John Forster, who reviewed the performance at the St. James'
Theatre. On 11 December 1836, Dickens wrote to Hullah:

> "Have you seen the Examiner? It is *rather* depreciatory of the opera, but
> like all their inveterate critiques against Braham [manager of the theatre],
> so well done that I cannot help laughing at it, for the life and soul of me."

Forster had, at this time, written several notices of *Sketches by "Boz"* and
Pickwick Papers, though he and Dickens met only at Christmas of this year.
Of *The Village Coquettes* he had written:

> "When the curtain fell, Braham brought out Miss Rainforth, she pulled on
> Miss Smith, Bennet and Strickland followed, Barnett and all the rest
> paraded themselves,—and then the audience screamed for Boz! Now we
> have a great respect and liking for Boz; the *Pickwick Papers* have made
> him, as our readers are well aware, an especial favourite with us; and we
> have no idea of his being exhibited gratis. Bad as the opera is, however,
> we feel assured that if Mr. Braham will make arrangements to parade the
> real living Boz every night after that opera, he will insure for it a certain
> attraction. Boz appeared, and bowed and smiled and disappeared, and left
> the audience in perfect consternation that he neither resembled the portraits
> of Pickwick, Snodgrass, Winkle, nor Tupman. Some critics in the gallery
> were said to have expected Samuel Weller. The disappointment was deeply
> and generally felt." ["Theatrical Examiner," 11 Dec. 1836].

B525(2)

A second, unbound copy, stitched, uncut. From the collection of Jerome Kern.
Laid in, ALS from John Topham, dated 1886, discussing his recollection of the
original performance.

B525(3)

A third copy bound in dark green levant morocco by Riviere, richly gilt.

B526

THE VILLAGE COQUETTES: A COMIC OPERA. IN TWO ACTS.
London: Facsimile reprint by Samuel Bentley. [1871].

B527(1)†

THE STRANGE GENTLEMAN; A COMIC BURLETTA, IN TWO
ACTS. FIRST PERFORMED AT THE ST. JAMES'S THEATRE, ON
THURSDAY, SEPTEMBER 29, 1836. London: Chapman and Hall.
MDCCCXXXVII.

12°. Rebound in tan polished morocco, richly gilt; top edge gilt; original
lavender paper wrapper included.

First edition, large paper copy (7⅜″ by 4¾″), lacking frontispiece.

Typographical variations conform to the Edgar copy:

Title page and front wrapper:	"A" in "AT" smaller than "T".
Verso, leaf of "Costumes":	broken "Y" in "TWENTY."
P. 43:	misplaced hyphen at end of line 1.
P. 46:	broken "A" in "EVANS" in imprint.

B527(2)

A copy of the regular first edition with the frontispiece by Phiz, rebound, together with the 1871 reprint with the colored frontispiece by Pailthorpe, in red
morocco, richly gilt. Original lavender wrapper bound at back.

All errors as above, and, in addition, the last three words, "of mine. Some," on
page 41, damaged.

Ex libris John Croft Deverell.

B527(3)

A copy of the 1871 reprint, with illustration by Pailthorpe. Large paper (7½″
by 5″) issue with hand-colored frontispiece.

B528

THE STRANGE GENTLEMAN. A COMIC BURLETTA IN TWO
ACTS. NOW FIRST ILLUSTRATED WITH REPRODUCTIONS
FROM ORIGINAL DRAWINGS BY JOHN LEECH, JOHN ORLANDO
PARRY, ETC. ALSO A REPRINT OF THE SCARCE ORIGINAL
FRONTISPIECE BY "PHIZ." [n.p.] 1928.

4°. In blue-grey paper boards with white spine. No. 4 of 250 copies privately
printed on English hand-made paper, with colored illustrations.

PLAGIARISMS AND TRANSLATIONS OF *The Strange Gentleman*

B529

CHARLES DICKENS THÉATRE INÉDIT EN FRANCAIS L'É-
TRANGE GENTLEMAN   LE MEMORIAL DE M. ROSSIGNOL
Á PROPOS DU JEU DRAMATIQUE DE FECHTER. Trans. Jean
Auzanet. Paris: M. P. Tremois. [1930].

8°. In orange wrapper.

B530(1)

IS SHE HIS WIFE? OR, SOMETHING SINGULAR. A COMIC BUR-
LETTA IN ONE ACT. Boston: James R. Osgood and Company, Late
Ticknor & Fields, and Fields, Osgood & Co. 1877.

32°. In original rust cloth.

First American edition.

B530(2)

A second copy in original green cloth.

B531(1)

MR. NIGHTINGALE'S DIARY: A FARCE IN ONE ACT. Boston:
James R. Osgood and Company, Late Ticknor & Fields, and Fields,
Osgood, & Co. 1877.

32°. In original rust cloth.

First American edition. Revised by Dickens from the original by Mark Lemon.

B531(2)

A second copy in original green cloth.

B532

THE LAMPLIGHTER A FARCE. (1838) NOW FIRST PRINTED
FROM A MANUSCRIPT IN THE FORSTER COLLECTION AT THE
SOUTH KENSINGTON MUSEUM. London: 1879.

8°. In original blue-grey paper wrapper.

No. 55 of 250 copies printed.

B533

THE LAMPLIGHTER. A FARCE IN ONE ACT AND AS A SHORT
STORY. PREFACE BY WILLIAM LYON PHELPS. New York: D.
Appleton and Company. MCMXXVI.

8°. In blue and gold paper boards with cloth spine and paper label. Illustrative
end papers.

B534

NO THOROUGHFARE. A DRAMA IN FIVE ACTS AND A PRO-
LOGUE. BY CHARLES DICKENS AND WILKIE COLLINS. New
York: Robert M. DeWitt. [n.d.].

12°. Pamphlet of 39 pages, lacking wrapper.

First American edition.

B535

NO THOROUGHFARE. A DRAMA, IN FIVE ACTS AND A PRO-
LOGUE. New York: Robert M. DeWitt. [n.d.].

12°. Pamphlet of 40 pages with 4 pages of advertisements for DeWitt's Acting
Plays. In original yellow wrapper, as issued.

PLAGIARISMS AND ADAPTATIONS OF *No Thoroughfare*

B536

IDENTITY; OR, NO THOROUGHFARE. BY LOUIS LEQUEL. New
York, London: Samuel French & Son. [n.d.].

12°. In orange paper wrapper. (French's Standard Drama No. CCCXLVIII)

B537

NO THROUGHFARE [sic]. BY C————s D————s, BELLAMY
BROWNJOHN, AND DOMBY. Boston: Loring. 1868.

8°. In original white wrapper. Second edition "Revised, corrected, and enlarged
upon by Brownjohn."

B538(1)

THE PLAYS AND POEMS. WITH A FEW MISCELLANIES IN
PROSE. NOW FIRST COLLECTED BY RICHARD HERNE SHEP-
HERD. London: W. H. Allen & Co. 1882.

8°. Two volumes in original three-fourths blue morocco with marbled paper
boards and end papers.

First, suppressed edition, including "No Thoroughfare."

Because of the copyright on "No Thoroughfare," this edition was suppressed;
a second issue omitted the work in question.

B538(2)

A second set of two volumes in drab green cloth with paper labels and red end
papers. No. 17 of 150 sets on large paper. Includes "No Thoroughfare."

B539(1)

THE PLAYS AND POEMS. London: W. H. Allen & Co. 1885.

8°. Two volumes in three-fourths maroon morocco with green marbled paper
boards and end papers.

No. 27 of 250 sets on large paper. *Ex libris* William Elliott Baillie.

B539(2)

A second set of two volumes. Regular edition in bright blue cloth with yellow
end papers.

B540(1)

THE COMPLETE POEMS. New York: White, Stokes, & Allen.
MDCCCLXXXV.

12°. In original floral paper boards with grey cloth spine embossed in gold.
Title page printed in red.

B540(2)
A second copy in stiff white paper cover with wrapper.

B540(3)
A third copy in original drab green cloth with gilt lettering and design. Title page in red.

B541
THE POEMS AND VERSES. New York, London: Harper & Brothers. 1903.

8°. In original olive green cloth, printed in red and gold. Title page in red and black.

B542
THE POEMS AND VERSES. COLLECTED AND EDITED, WITH BIBLIOGRAPHICAL NOTES, BY F. G. KITTON. London: Chapman and Hall, Limited. 1903.

8°. In original red cloth.

B543
THREE POEMS. Monroe, North Carolina: Privately Printed. [1935].

12°. In brown cardboard cover with paper label. Printed for Clarke W. Walton.

6 : PERIODICAL PUBLICATIONS AND REPRINTED PIECES

B544
THE SELECT CIRCULATING LIBRARY. PART II. Philadelphia: Adam Waldie. 1834.

4°. In original half old calf with brown marbled paper boards.

Pp. 136–138, "Mrs. Joseph Porter, 'Over The Way.'"

B545(1)
THE LIBRARY OF FICTION. Vols. I, II. London: Chapman and Hall. 1836.

8°. A set of two volumes bound from the parts in blue cloth with yellow end papers.

Vol. I, pp. 1-17, "The Tugg's at Ramsgate," with Illustrations by Seymour; pp. 113-118, "A Little Talk about Spring and the Sweeps."

B545(2)
A second set of two volumes rebound in full polished calf. No frontispiece; title page dated 1837.

B545(3)

A third copy of Vol. I in original dark blue cloth with yellow end papers. Frontispiece differs from B545(1).

B546

THE TUGG'S AT RAMSGATE. TOGETHER WITH OTHER TALES, BY DISTINGUISHED WRITERS. Philadelphia: Carey, Lea & Blanchard. 1837.

12°. In original grey paper boards with cloth spine.

Half title: The Library of Fiction, consisting of Tales, Essays, and Sketches of Character.

B547

THE TUGGS'S AT RAMSGATE, AND OTHER SKETCHES ILLUS-TRATIVE OF EVERY-DAY LIFE AND EVERY-DAY PEOPLE. TO WHICH IS ADDED "THE PANTOMIME OF LIFE." Philadelphia: Carey, Lea & Blanchard. 1837.

12°. Rebound in half morocco with marbled paper boards and end papers. Reprint in one volume of the second series, containing material of the first English edition preceded by "The Tuggs's at Ramsgate" reprinted from "The Select Library of Fiction." With advertisement: "The rapid sale of the volume containing the 'Tuggs's at Ramsgate,' by Boz, . . ."

B548(1)

BENTLEY'S MISCELLANY. I–XXXV. London: Richard Bentley. 1837–1854.

8°. A complete set in original half old calf and marbled paper boards.

B548(2)

A second group of vols. I-V in various bindings. Contains the original printing of *Oliver Twist*.

B549

MUDFOG AND OTHER PAPERS CONTRIBUTED TO *BENTLEY'S MISCELLANY*. London: 1837.

8°. Bound together in blue paper boards: "Extraordinary Gazette," addresses and prefaces to vols. I and II, "Public Life of Mr. Tulrumble," with specially printed title page.

B550(1)

EXTRAORDINARY GAZETTE. SPEECH OF HIS MIGHTINESS ON OPENING THE SECOND NUMBER OF *BENTLEY'S MISCELLANY*, EDITED BY "BOZ." London: Richard Bentley. 1837.

8°. Leaflet of 4 pages (6″ by 9¼″), extracted from a magazine.

Ex libris Harry Bache Smith.

B550(2)

Variant issue. Leaflet of 8 pages (4⅛″ by 6⅝″), in smaller type. Text of the "Gazette" followed by advertisement, "The New Comic Periodical Work, Edited by 'Boz,'" with list of contributors to *Bentley's Miscellany* and "Contents" of the first three numbers; followed by "A Few of the Opinions of the Press." Leaves stitched; extracted from magazine.

B551

PUBLIC LIFE OF MR. TULRUMBLE, ONCE MAYOR OF MUD-FOG. WITH OTHER TALES AND SKETCHES, FROM *BENTLEY'S MISCELLANY*, AND *THE LIBRARY OF FICTION*. Philadelphia: Carey, Lea and Blanchard. 1837.

12°. In original buff paper boards with cloth spine.

First American edition.

B552

CHARLES DICKENS ON FECHTER'S ACTING; FOLLOWED BY THE CRITICAL NOTICES (EXTRACTED FROM THE LONDON JOURNALS) ON HIS HAMLET, OTHELLO, RUY BLAS, LADY OF LYONS, &C. Leeds: J. H. Clark, Steam Printer. [1867].

12°. Leaflet of 24 pages in original green wrapper.

B553

"On Mr. Fechter's Acting." In THE ATLANTIC MONTHLY. Boston: Fields, Osgood & Co. August 1869.

8°. In original peach colored wrapper.

B554

THE MUDFOG PAPERS. London: Richard Bentley and Son. 1880.

8°. In original red cloth with black end papers.

B555(1)

THE MUDFOG PAPERS. NOW FIRST COLLECTED. New York: Henry Holt and Company. 1880.

16°. In original white cloth. (Leisure Hour Series)

Taken from *Bentley's Miscellany*, Vols. I, II, and IV, 1837–1838. Advertising leaf, front: "Troublesome Daughters," "Christy Carew," etc.

B555(2)

A second copy with variant advertising leaf. Front leaf, "Christy Carew," "Democracy," etc.

B556

THE KEEPSAKE FOR MDCCCXLIV. EDITED BY THE COUNTESS OF BLESSINGTON. London: Longman, Browne, Green, and Longmans. 1844.

8°. In original pink silk binding.

P. 73, "A Word in Season" by Dickens.

B557(1)
HOUSEHOLD WORDS. A WEEKLY JOURNAL. London: 16 Wellington Street, North. 1850 [1851–1859].

8°. Volumes I-XIX plus six supplements; bindings vary, most volumes in original dark brown or dark green cloth.

Original printing of *Hard Times.*

B557(2)
A second set of 19 volumes in three-fourths contemporary dark green morocco with marbled paper boards.

B557(3)
A third set of 13 volumes, in original green cloth bindings. Volumes 5–13, American edition. Two extra copies of Vol. I, one English and one American edition.

B557(4)
An incomplete set of unbound copies for 1856, lacking February, March, and May. In original buff paper wrappers, fine condition.

B557(5)†
An incomplete set of 8 volumes, in original green cloth bindings. With Charles Dickens's bookplate and slip, "From the Library of Charles Dickens, Gadshill Place, June, 1870."

B558
TO BE READ AT DUSK. London: 1852.

8°. A Wise forgery, printed ca. 1891. See illustration.

B559
TO BE READ AT DUSK AND OTHER STORIES, SKETCHES AND ESSAYS. NOW FIRST COLLECTED. London: George Redway. 1898.

8°. In original green cloth.

B560
MY LOST HOME AND OTHER TALES. New York: F. A. Brady. [1859].

8°. Copies of American issue of *Household Words* from 5 Dec. 1857, to 22 Jan. 1859, assembled in buff paper wrapper.

B561
HOME AND SOCIAL PHILOSOPHY: OR, CHAPTERS ON EVERY-DAY TOPICS. FROM *HOUSEHOLD WORDS.* New York: George P. Putnam. 1852.

12°. In original brown cloth. (Putnam's Library for the People)

B562

HOME NARRATIVES; STORIES FROM "HOUSEHOLD WORDS."
New York: G. P. Putnam. [1852].

12°. In original pink cardboard cover. (Putnam's Semi-monthly Library for Travellers and the Fireside, No. VI)

B563

THE WORLD HERE AND THERE: OR, NOTES OF TRAVELLERS.
FROM "HOUSEHOLD WORDS." New York: G. P. Putnam. 1852.

8°. In original purple cloth and yellow end papers. (Putnam's Library for the People)

B564

THE WORLD HERE AND THERE. OR, NOTES OF TRAVELLERS.
FROM "HOUSEHOLD WORDS." New York: Bunce & Brother. MDCCCLIV.

8°. In original purple cloth with gilt lettering and yellow end papers.

B565

TALES AND TRAVELS. FROM "HOUSEHOLD WORDS." New York: Bunce & Brother. 1854.

8°. In original purple cloth. Combines "Home Narratives" and "The World Here and There: or, Notes of Travellers."

B566(1)

PEARL-FISHING. CHOICE STORIES, FROM DICKENS' *HOUSE-HOLD WORDS*. Auburn: Alden, Beardsley & Co. Rochester: Wanzer, Beardsley & Co. 1854.

8°. In original blue embossed cloth with yellow end papers. On spine in gilt lettering: "Pearl | Fishing | Chas. Dickens | First Series | Auburn | & Rochester." Verso of p. 351, adv.: "Immense Sale! | Lewie; | or, | The Bended Twig! | by Cousin Cicely."

B566(2)

Variant issue bound in purple cloth with cream end papers. Title, author, and "First Series" in gilt letters on front cover; "Auburn & Rochester" omitted from spine. Verso of p. 351, adv.: "Fun-Jottings; | or, | Laughs I have taken a Pen to! | By N. P. Willis."

B566(3)

A third copy in original purple cloth with yellow end papers. Gilt lettering on spine and verso of p. 351 as in B566(1).

B567

PEARL-FISHING. CHOICE STORIES, FROM DICKENS' *HOUSE-HOLD WORDS*. SECOND SERIES. Auburn: Alden, Beardsley & Co. Rochester: Wanzer, Beardsley & Co. 1854.

8°. In original embossed purple cloth.

B568

HARPER'S NEW MONTHLY MAGAZINE. NO. XLV. New York: Harper & Brothers. February 1854.

8°. In original white wrapper.

Pp. 365-369, "The Schoolboy's Story," by Dickens.

B569

HARPER'S NEW MONTHLY MAGAZINE. VOLS. IV–VIII, X, XII, XIV, XXII, XXVI, XXIX–XXXII, XXXVI–XXXVIII. New York: Harper & Brothers.

8°. In various bindings.

B570°

"THE LATE MR. JUSTICE TALFOURD," BY CHARLES DICKENS. [Pre-print of article for *Household Words*, 25 March 1854.]

8°. Printed with black border on heavy paper, edges gilt.

Inscribed at top in Dickens's holograph: "Household Words, Saturday 25th. March 1854. Not yet published." On recto of second leaf in Dickens's holograph: "Mr. Charles Dickens presents his compliments to Mr. Justice Wigitmen [*sic*], and offers no apology for troubling him with the accompanying few words of remembrance of one, whose loss Mr. Justice Wightman has so feelingly deplored. Tavistock House, Tavistock Square   Seventeenth March 1854."

This was purchased from the estate of Sir James E. Tennent, a close friend of Dickens and Talfourd. See illustration.

B571

SUNSHINE ON DAILY PATHS; OR THE REVELATION OF BEAUTY AND WONDER IN COMMON THINGS. FROM *HOUSEHOLD WORDS*. Philadelphia: H. C. Peck & Theo. Bliss. 1854.

8°. In original red cloth.

B572

HARPER'S NEW MONTHLY MAGAZINE. NO. LVII. New York: Harper & Brothers. February 1855.

8°. In original white wrapper.

Pp. 371-377, "The Redeemed Profligate"; pp. 385-391, "A Lawyer's Story"; pp. 393-397, "The Widow's Story" by Dickens.

B573

DICKENS' SHORT STORIES, CONTAINING THIRTY-ONE STORIES NEVER BEFORE PUBLISHED IN THIS COUNTRY. Philadelphia: T. B. Peterson and Brothers. [1859].

12°. In original dark brown cloth with yellow end papers. With 38-page "List of Publications" at end. (Uniform Duodecimo Edition)

Includes "A Child's Dream of a Star" and "The Noble Savage" by Dickens.

Ex libris George Barr McCutcheon.

B574(1)

ALL THE YEAR ROUND. A WEEKLY JOURNAL. WITH WHICH
IS INCORPORATED HOUSEHOLD WORDS. London: 11 Wellington
Street North. 1859 [1860–1865].

8°. Volumes I-XIII bound in three-fourths polished calf with marbled paper
boards and end papers.

Original printing of *A Tale of Two Cities, Great Expectations,* and *The Uncommercial Traveller.*

B574(2)

A second complete set. Vols. I-XX. London: 1859-1868. Also New Series I-
XXIX. London: Chapman and Hall. 1869–1882.

8°. In original half dark green calf and fabric. Charles Dickens II succeeded his
father as editor with Vol. IV of the New Series.

B574(3)

Unbound parts for September and October 1864, in original blue wrappers;
October issue lacks front wrapper.

B575

"Hunted Down." In THE NEW YORK LEDGER. New York: R. Bonner. 1859.

F°. Issues for 20, 27 August and 3 September 1859, with the original printing
of "Hunted Down." The editor remarks that "this is the first and only story
that Mr. Dickens has ever written for an American publication."

B576

"Hunted Down." In THE PICCADILLY ANNUAL. London: John Camden Hotten. 1870.

8°. In stiff white wrapper illustrated in color.

B577

HUNTED DOWN A STORY, THE UNCOMMERCIAL TRAVELLER
A SERIES OF OCCASIONAL PAPERS. COPYRIGHT EDITION.
Leipzig: Bernhard Tauchnitz. 1860.

8°. In three-fourths red morocco with embossed cloth.

First edition in book form. "Hunted Down" was reprinted in *All the Year
Round* 4, 11 April 1860.

B578

THE LAMPLIGHTER'S STORY; HUNTED DOWN; THE DETEC-
TIVE POLICE; AND OTHER NOUVELLETTES. Philadelphia: T. B.
Peterson and Brothers. [1861].

12°. In original black cloth. (Uniform Duodecimo Edition)

First American edition.

B579(1)

HUNTED DOWN A STORY. WITH SOME ACCOUNT OF THOMAS GRIFFITHS WAINEWRIGHT, THE POISONER. London: John Camden Hotten. [1870].

16°. In original green wrapper.

First English edition.

B579(2)

A second copy bound in half green levant morocco, edges trimmed and gilt. Wrapper and advertisements included.

B580

THE PICCADILLY ANNUAL OF ENTERTAINING LITERATURE RETROSPECTIVE AND CONTEMPORARY. London: John Camden Hotten. [1870].

8°. Rebound in green morocco.

Pp. 5-14, "Hunted Down."

B581

HUNTED DOWN; AND OTHER REPRINTED PIECES. PETERSONS' CHEAP EDITION FOR THE MILLION. Philadelphia: T. B. Peterson & Brothers. [n.d.].

8°. In salmon-pink paper wrapper.

B582

AN ENLIGHTENED CLERGYMAN. London: 1862.

8°. In black levant morocco.

Included in this volume are:

(1) Holograph letter from Dickens to Edward Dove concerning the "enlightened clergyman." 18 February 1862 (A121).

(2) *All the Year Round,* Saturday, 8 March 1862, first issue, with Dickens's article.

(3) "The Bloomsbury Christening" extracted from *Sketches by Boz.*

(4) "Picking up Waifs at Sea," by Wilkie Collins, extracted from *All the Year Round,* 12 December 1861.

(5) Newspaper clipping from the London *Standard,* 1862, referring to the "Enlightened Clergyman."

B583(1)

THACKERAY THE HUMOURIST AND THE MAN OF LETTERS. BY THEODORE TAYLOR, ESQ. TO WHICH IS ADDED IN MEMORIAM—BY CHARLES DICKENS, AND A SKETCH, BY ANTHONY TROLLOPE. New York: D. Appleton and Company. 1864.

8°. In original green cloth.

Pp. 224–231 "In Memoriam," reprinted from *Cornhill Magazine,* February 1864.

B583(2)
A second copy in original purple cloth.

B584(1)
"In Memoriam." In CORNHILL MAGAZINE, February 1864.
8°. In original orange wrapper, as issued.

B584(2)
A second copy extracted from the magazine.

B585
"George Silverman's Explanation." In THE ATLANTIC MONTHLY.
Boston: Ticknor and Fields. January–March 1867.
8°. In original pink wrappers.
Dickens wrote this story at the request of James T. Fields. The only issue in book form, according to Eckel, was a piracy by a Brighton printer in 1878.

B586
"Holiday Romance." In OUR YOUNG FOLKS AN ILLUSTRATED MAGAZINE FOR BOYS AND GIRLS. Boston: Ticknor and Fields. 1868.
8°. A set of four numbers, January through May, in original orange wrappers, as issued.

B587°
ROMANCE FROM THE PEN OF MISS ALICE RAINBIRD AGED SEVEN THE MAGIC FISHBONE. New York, London: Frederick Warne & Co. Ltd. [n.d.].
4°. In white paper boards printed in color, with green cloth spine. Illustrated by F. D. Bedford.
An extract from "Holiday Romance."

B588(1)
A CHILD'S DREAM OF A STAR. Boston: Fields, Osgood, & Co. 1871.
8°. In original green cloth with gilt design, gilt edges, and brown end papers.
First edition in book form, reprinted from *Household Words*, 6 April 1850.

B588(2)
A second copy in original rust cloth with gilt design and white end papers, edges gilt.

B589
A CHILD'S DREAM OF A STAR. London: Privately printed. 1899.
8°. In original white cardboard cover printed in blue and gilt.

B590

TWICE-TOLD TALES. IN THREE PARTS. New York: The World
Publishing House. 1877.

8°. In original red cloth stamped with black and gilt. Pt. 1: "Life and Travels
in Italy"; Pt. 2: "The French in Algiers"; Pt. 3: "Prisoners of Abd-El-Kader."

B591(1)

OLD LAMPS FOR NEW ONES AND OTHER SKETCHES AND ES-
SAYS HITHERTO UNCOLLECTED. New York: New Amsterdam Book
Company. [1897].

8°. In original red cloth stamped with blue and gold.

First American edition. Reprinted from *Household Words*, 15 June 1850.

B591(2)

A second copy bound in white stamped with red.

B592(1)

A POTTERY STORY. Boston: Jones, McDuffee & Stratton. 1878.

8°. Pamphlet in original grey paper wrapper.

Reprinted from *Household Words*, 24 April 1852. As Eckel observes, this
pamphlet was "clearly used for advertising propaganda"; however, though he
repudiates Dickens's connection with it, it is a reprint of the leading article from
this issue of Dickens's magazine and was included in *Reprinted Pieces* [Vol.
VIII, Library Edition, 1858].

B592(2)

A second copy in original white wrapper.

B593(1)

A PLATED ARTICLE. Stoke-upon-Trent: W. T. Copeland & Sons (late
Spode & Copeland). [n.d.].

8°. In olive green paper boards decorated with squares of black and gold, with
paper label.

A reprint, for advertising purposes, of the article, "A Pottery Story."

B593(2)

A binding variant in original grey paper boards.

B594

MISCELLANEOUS PAPERS FROM 'THE MORNING CHRONICLE,'
'THE DAILY NEWS,' 'THE EXAMINER,' 'HOUSEHOLD WORDS,'
'ALL THE YEAR ROUND,' ETC. AND PLAYS AND POEMS. London:
Chapman & Hall, Ltd. New York: Charles Scribner's Sons. [n.d.].

8°. Two volumes in original red cloth. (Gadshill Edition, Additional Volumes
XXXV, XXXVI)

B595

THE CHRISTMAS TREE. [London]: Hodder & Stoughton. [n.d.].

8°. Leaflet in stiff dark red wrapper with colored illustration.

B596

"Hiram Power's Greek Slave." In THE LIVING AGE. Boston: The Arakelyan Press. 15 December 1906.

8°. In original buff wrapper. Reprinted from *Household Words*.

B597

THE DICKENSIAN. I–XII. London: 1905–1916.

8°. Twelve volumes in original half dark red morocco with marbled paper boards and end papers, top edge gilt.

B598

THE DICKENSIAN. XXVIII–XLV. London: 1932–1949.

8°. Eighteen volumes in original red cloth with gilt lettering.

7 : CONTRIBUTIONS

B599(1)

MEMOIRS OF JOSEPH GRIMALDI. EDITED BY "BOZ." London: Richard Bentley. 1838.

8°. Two volumes in original pink cloth.

First edition, first issue. No border on "The Last Song"; incorrect pagination (128 instead of 182) on list of "Embellishments"; Mr. Bentley's "List of New Works," 36 pages, at end of Vol. II.

B599(2)

A set of the first edition, second issue. Two volumes in original pink cloth. No border on "The Last Song"; pagination corrected on list of "Embellishments."

B599(3)

A second set of the first edition, second issue, rebound in full tan morocco, including the original binding, black for Vol. I, green for Vol. II, with elaborate gilt design on spine. No border on "The Last Song"; list of "Embellishments" omitted.

Ex libris E. DeGolyer.

B599(4)

A third variant set of the first edition, second issue. Two volumes in original black cloth with elaborate gilt design on spine and yellow end papers. Pagination corrected on list of "Embellishments"; "The Last Song" with border.

B600*

MEMOIRS OF JOSEPH GRIMALDI. London: Richard Bentley. 1838.

8° extended to F°. Two volumes of red morocco, richly gilt.

First edition, first issue. Pages of text mounted together, extra-illustrated with 350 portraits and character prints, playbills, a sketch of Grimaldi's residence, theatrical advertisements, newspaper clippings, and tickets. Also bound in are holograph letter of Charles Dickens to William Upcott (A7) and letters of Howard Payne, P. Egerton, Alfred Bunn, Thomas Dibdin, and others.

This was the work of William Upcott, well-known antiquarian, to whom Dickens's letter is addressed. Additional Illustrations in Upcott's hand signed and dated "Islington 102 Upper Street 1844."

Ex libris Gustavia A. Senff.

B601

MEMOIRS OF JOSEPH GRIMALDI. Philadelphia: Carey, Lea & Blanchard. 1838.

12°. Two volumes in original pink cloth with paper labels. No illustrations.

First American edition.

B602(1)

MEMOIRS OF JOSEPH GRIMALDI. New York: William H. Colyer. 1838.

12°. In original blue paper boards with pink cloth spine and paper label. With lithographed portrait of Grimaldi by N. Currier bound in.

Second American edition.

B602(2)

A second copy lacking portrait. Etched portrait of Grimaldi laid in.

B603*

MEMOIRS OF JOSEPH GRIMALDI. A NEW EDITION. London: Richard Bentley. 1846.

8° extended to F°. Two volumes bound in lilac morocco by Rivière. Text mounted on plate paper together with 236 extra illustrations, holograph letters, playbills, MS. music, and clippings from newspapers.

Ex libris Augustin Daly, Clarence Bement, and Joseph Widener.

B603a

MEMOIRS OF JOSEPH GRIMALDI. London: John Dicks. [1883-1884].

8°. In original stiff white wrapper, printed in color. (Bow Bells Annual)

B604(1,2,3)

THE PIC NIC PAPERS. BY VARIOUS HANDS. EDITED BY CHARLES DICKENS, ESQ. London: Henry Colburn. MDCCCXLI.

8°. Three sets of three volumes in original green cloth with cream end papers. First edition, second issue. Corrected reading of "young publisher" on p. iii of introduction.

B605
THE PIC-NIC PAPERS. SERIES IV. ESTHER: A SPANISH TALE.
London: Ward and Lock. [n.d.].

8°. In original stiff yellow wrapper. (Railway Volumes)

Including "The Crooked Disciple" and "Esther" by Dickens.

B606
EVENINGS OF A WORKING MAN, BEING THE OCCUPATION OF
HIS SCANTY LEISURE: BY JOHN OVERS. WITH A PREFACE
RELATIVE TO THE AUTHOR, BY CHARLES DICKENS. London:
C. Newby. 1844.

8°. In original pink cloth, spine repaired, with yellow end papers. Title page
in blue and red.

Inserted is Dickens's holograph letter to Overs on prospective publishers (A32).

B607(1)
EVENINGS OF A WORKING MAN. New York: J. Winchester, New
World Press. [n.d.].

8°. In original brown wrapper, as issued.

B607(2)
A second copy bound in three-fourths blue morocco. (Also in this volume
Arrah Neil by G. P. R. James.)

B608
THE HUMORIST. EDITED BY THEODORE HOOK. Philadelphia:
E. L. Carey & A. Hart. 1837.

12°. In original buff paper boards and blue cloth spine. Includes "Mr. Minns
and His Cousin" by "Boz."

B609
THE CONFESSIONS OF AN ATTORNEY. BY GUSTAVUS SHARP,
ESQ. TO WHICH ARE ADDED SEVERAL PAPERS ON ENGLISH
LAW AND LAWYERS BY CHARLES DICKENS. New York: Cornish,
Lamport & Co. 1852.

From *Household Words.*

B610
LEGENDS AND LYRICS. BY ADELAIDE ANNE PROCTER. WITH
AN INTRODUCTION BY CHARLES DICKENS. NEW EDITION.
WITH ADDITIONS. Boston: Ticknor and Fields. 1866.

8°. In original full brown morocco with red marbled end papers and gilt edges.

8 : SPEECHES BY AND ABOUT DICKENS

B611†

AN ADDRESS DELIVERED IN THE CHAPEL IN LITTLE PORT-
LAND STREET, JULY THE NINTH, MDCCCXLIV, BY THE REV.
EDWARD TAGART. London: Printed by Walton and Mitchell. [1844].

8°. Pamphlet in original yellowish paper wrapper.

First and apparently only edition. Few copies known.

With the inscription written by Dickens for the presentation of a silver tea
service to the Rev. Edward Tagart by members of his congregation. Before the
inscription is a note in the handwriting of Miss Lucy Tagart, "Composed by
Charles Dickens. He was unable to present it before leaving for Italy. 1844."

B612

THE CHARLES DICKENS DINNER. AN AUTHENTIC RECORD OF
THE PUBLIC BANQUET GIVEN TO MR. CHARLES DICKENS, AT
THE FREEMASONS' HALL, LONDON, ON SATURDAY, NOVEM-
BER 2, 1867, PRIOR TO HIS DEPARTURE FOR THE UNITED
STATES. WITH A REPORT OF THE SPEECHES FROM SPECIAL
SHORTHAND NOTES. London: Chapman and Hall. Boston: Ticknor
and Fields. 1867.

8°. Leaflet of 32 pages, as issued. With unsigned ticket to the dinner.

B613

ADDRESS DELIVERED AT THE BIRMINGHAM AND MIDLAND
INSTITUTE, ON THE 27th SEPTEMBER 1869. BY CHARLES DICK-
ENS, ESQUIRE, PRESIDENT. Birmingham: Printed by Josiah Allen,
Jun. [n.d.].

8°. Pamphlet rebound in full drab green morocco, richly gilt, original green
wrapper included.

B614

THE NEWSVENDORS' BENEVOLENT AND PROVIDENT INSTITU-
TION. SPEECHES IN BEHALF OF THE INSTITUTION BY THE
LATE MR. CHARLES DICKENS, PRESIDENT. London: Printed by
Buck and Wooton. [1870].

8°. Leaflet in original pink wrapper.

B615

SPEECHES, LITERARY AND SOCIAL, BY CHARLES DICKENS.
NOW FIRST COLLECTED. WITH CHAPTERS ON "CHARLES
DICKENS AS A LETTER WRITER, POET, AND PUBLIC READER."
London: John Camden Hotten. [1869].

8°. In bright green cloth with gilt lettering and light brown end papers.

B616(1)
SERMON PREACHED BY ARTHUR PENRHYN STANLEY, D.D.
DEAN OF WESTMINSTER IN WESTMINSTER ABBEY JUNE 19,
1870 . . . BEING THE SUNDAY FOLLOWING THE FUNERAL OF
CHARLES DICKENS. London: Macmillan and Co. 1870.

8°. Pamphlet in original purple wrapper, as issued.

B616(2)
A second copy lacking wrapper, extracted from binding.

B617
SERMONS ON SPECIAL OCCASIONS PREACHED IN WEST-
MINSTER ABBEY. BY ARTHUR PENRHYN STANLEY. London: John
Murray. 1882.

8°. In original purple cloth with dark grey end papers. Includes the funeral
sermon on Dickens.

B618
WHITHER BOUND? A SERMON OCCASIONED BY THE CANONI-
ZATION OF CHARLES DICKENS. BY JUSTIN D. FULTON, TRE-
MONT TEMPLE. Boston: John W. Olmstead & Co. [1870].

12°. Leaflet in original lavender wrapper.

B619*
THE SWORD, THE PEN, AND THE PULPIT; WITH A TRIBUTE TO
THE CHRISTIAN GENIUS AND MEMORY OF CHARLES DICKENS.
A DISCOURSE DELIVERED IN BOSTON MUSIC HALL, ON
SUNDAY, JUNE 19, 1870, BY WILLIAM ROUNSEVILLE ALGER.
Boston: Roberts Brothers. 1870.

8°. Pamphlet in original pink paper wrapper.

First edition.

B620
SPEECHES, LETTERS, AND SAYINGS OF CHARLES DICKENS.
New York: Harper & Brothers. 1870.

8°. In original white wrapper.

Includes Dean Stanley's sermon and a sketch of Dickens by George Augustus
Sala.

B621
THE SPEECHES OF CHARLES DICKENS, 1841–1870. EDITED
AND PREFACED BY RICHARD HERNE SHEPHERD WITH A NEW
BIBLIOGRAPHY REVISED AND ENLARGED. London: Chatto and
Windus. 1884.

8°. In original olive drab cloth with paper label.

No. 39 of a large-paper edition of 50 copies.

B622

A copy of the regular edition in olive drab cloth decorated with black.

B623

SPEECH OF CHARLES DICKENS DELIVERED AT GORE HOUSE, KENSINGTON, MAY 10, 1851. Printed from the Original Autograph Manuscript Exclusively for Members of the Bibliophile Society. Boston: MDCDIX.

8°. Pamphlet in original blue wrapper.

Ex libris William Glyde Wilkins.

B624

REPORT OF THE PUBLIC DINNER GIVEN TO CHARLES DICKENS AT THE WATERLOO ROOMS EDINBURGH ON FRIDAY, JUNE 25, 1841. Cedar Rapids, Iowa: Privately Printed. 1915.

8°. In original blue wrapper.

9 : LETTERS

B625

MRS. PECK'S PUDDING, BY TOM HOOD. A HUMOROUS PAPER, BY CHARLES DICKENS. AND A DRAMATIC SKETCH, BY SIR E. LYTTON BULWER. Philadelphia: Carey and Hart. 1845.

12°. Rebound in three-fourths red crushed levant morocco with marbled paper boards, edges gilt. Illustrations by Darley.

Pp. 28–34 "Threatening Letter to Thomas Hood, From An Ancient Gentleman. By Favour of Charles Dickens," dated Tuesday, 23 April 1844.

First American edition. Reprinted from *Hood's Magazine and Comic Miscellany*, May 1844.

Forster, in his biography of Dickens, in a chapter captioned "1838-1839," mentions an article on Thomas Hood contributed to *The Examiner*, sending Mr. Ley and Mr. Matz on a fruitless search for a review of Hood's *Up the Rhine*. I would like to suggest that the review in question is that on *Hood's Comic Annual* in *The Examiner* for 3 February 1839. In a sprightly, pun-filled paragraph, the reviewer wrote:

> Other annuals come as regularly as Lord Mayor's day or that solemn holiday whereon geese are plucked and sheriffs plumed; there be land annuals and water annuals; and there be annuals wherein land and water are both so impartially depicted, that each has something of the properties of the others. . . . But Mr. Hood defies all seers and conjurors, weatherwise or otherwise. He is a perfect marvel in this respect—always out of season and always in it. You give him up for lost; hold that he has made up his mind to return no more; and suddenly like a late spring, he comes upon us one fine day, all smiles and sunshine, as we remember him of yore; and we give him house-room and hearty welcome.

The book he reviewed, Dickens wrote to Forster was "rather poor," but he had not said so "because Hood is too, and ill besides."

B626(1)

IN AND OUT OF DOORS WITH CHARLES DICKENS. BY JAMES T. FIELDS. Boston: James R. Osgood and Company, Late Ticknor & Fields, and Fields, Osgood, & Co. 1876.

32°. In original green cloth printed in black and gold.

Included are many letters to Professor Felton, James T. Fields, and others. Reprinted from Fields's *Yesterdays with Authors*. Back advertising leaf, "The Vest Pocket Series."

B626(2)

A second copy, as B626(1) except back advertising leaf, "Yesterdays with Authors."

B627

ST. NICHOLAS. New York: Scribner & Co. May 1877.

8°. In original white wrapper printed in black and red.

Pp. 438-441, "Our Letter" by M. F. Armstrong. Facsimile of letter by Dickens, dated "Monday tenth February 1862."

B628(1)

THE LETTERS OF CHARLES DICKENS EDITED BY HIS SISTER-IN-LAW AND HIS ELDEST DAUGHTER. New York: Charles Scribner's Sons. 1879.

8°. Two volumes in original dark blue cloth.

B628(2)

8°. Two volumes in original wine-red cloth with gilt and black decoration. Second edition.

B629

A WONDERFUL GHOST STORY. WITH UNPUBLISHED LETTERS FROM CHARLES DICKENS RESPECTING IT. BY THOMAS HEAPLEY. London: Griffith & Farran. [1882].

12°. In white cardboard cover with illustrations in color.

B630

"Letters of Charles Dickens to Wilkie Collins." In HARPER'S NEW MONTHLY MAGAZINE. New York: 1891.

8°. Pp. 527-536, 675-687, 894-906 extracted from the magazine; with original wrappers, backs reinforced.

B631

LETTERS OF CHARLES DICKENS TO WILKIE COLLINS, 1851–1870. SELECTED BY MISS GEORGINA HOGARTH. EDITED BY LAURENCE HUTTON. London: James R. Osgood, McIlvaine & Co. 1892.

12°. In original blue cloth with gilt lettering.

B632

LETTERS OF CHARLES DICKENS TO WILKIE COLLINS. EDITED BY LAURENCE HUTTON. New York: Harper & Brothers. 1892.

12°. In blue cloth printed in dark blue and gold.

B633(1)

A STRAY LEAF FROM THE CORRESPONDENCE OF WASHINGTON IRVING AND CHARLES DICKENS. New York: DeVinne Press. 1894.

8°. In original blue cloth decorated in gold.

First edition. One of 15 copies with proofs of three states of the engraving, "Britannia." Printed on Japanese vellum.

B633(2)

A second copy, No. 34 of 77 copies printed on Japanese vellum.

B634

"Lady DeLancey's Remarkable Narrative of the Week Succeeding the Battle of Waterloo. With Unpublished Letters from Sir Walter Scott and Charles Dickens. Written in Admiration of the Narrative." In THE APRIL CENTURY MAGAZINE. London: Macmillan and Co., Ltd. 1906.

8°. In original wrapper, as issued.

B635

"The Death of Dickens's Little Dora. A Memorable Letter and Prayer." By John Suddaby. In THE LIVING AGE. Boston: The Living Age Company. 10 April 1909.

8°. In original bluff wrapper, as issued.

B636

CHARLES DICKENS AND MARIA BEADNELL PRIVATE CORRESPONDENCE. Boston: For Members of The Bibliophile Society. 1908.

8°. In three-fourths vellum with grey paper boards.

Edition limited to 493 copies.

B637(1,2)

THE SECOND BOOK OF THE DOFOBS. Chicago: Society of the Dofobs. MDCCCCIX.

4°. Two copies in brown paper boards with leather spine.

Pp. 21-26, "Charles Dickens and Douglas Jerrold," being Dickens's letter to Sir W. H. Russell, dated Wednesday 7th June 1857, concerning the death of Douglas Jerrold.

B638(1,2)
THE DICKENS-KOLLE LETTERS. Boston: For Members of the Bibliophile Society. 1910.

8°. Two copies in three-fourths vellum with brown paper boards.

Edition limited to 483 copies.

B639
THE EARLIEST LETTERS OF CHARLES DICKENS (WRITTEN TO
HIS FRIEND HENRY KOLLE). Cambridge, Mass.: The University
Press. MCMX.

8°. In three-fourths vellum with brown paper boards.

One of 100 complimentary copies printed for Harry Bache Smith.

B640
CHARLES DICKENS AS EDITOR. BEING LETTERS WRITTEN BY
HIM TO WILLIAM HENRY WILLS HIS SUB-EDITOR. SELECTED
AND EDITED BY R. C. LEHMANN. WITH PORTRAITS. London:
Smith, Elder & Co. 1912.

8°. In original red cloth.

First edition.

B641(1)
CHARLES DICKENS AS EDITOR BEING LETTERS WRITTEN BY
HIM TO WILLIAM HENRY WILLS HIS SUB-EDITOR. New York:
Sturgis & Walton Company. 1912.

8°. In original grey cloth printed in gold, top edge gilt. At base of spine:
"Sturgis & Walton/Company."

First American issue of sheets printed in London.

B641(2)
Remainder issue in light grey cloth; printed in black, edges trimmed. At base
of spine: "The Macmillan Company."

B642
"Some New Dickens' Letters." Edited by S. M. Ellis. In THE LIVING
AGE. Boston: The Living Age Company. 29 January 1916.

8°. In original buff wrapper, as issued.

B643
"From the Land of Letters." By Thomas F. Plowman. In THE LIVING
AGE. Boston: The Living Age Company. 4 March 1916.

8°. In original buff wrapper. Includes several letters from Dickens.

B644
"A Letter from Dickens to C. C. Felton." In THE NORTH AMERICAN
REVIEW. June 1917.

8°. In original blue and white wrapper, as issued.

B645

"Dickens in America, 1842 (Unpublished Letter)." In THE MAGAZINE OF HISTORY WITH NOTES AND QUERIES. Tarrytown, New York: William Abbott. November-December 1917.

8°. In original grey wrapper.

B646

CHARLES DICKENS' ORIGINAL AUTOGRAPH COPY OF HIS LETTER TO HENRY COLBURN UPON THE CONTROVERSY OCCASIONED BY THE CONTRIBUTION OF WALTER SAVAGE LANDOR TO PIC NIC PAPERS TOGETHER WITH A NOTE TO FORSTER ON THE SUBJECT APRIL 1st 1841. London: Printed at the Chiswick Press for Cumberland Clark. 1918.

8°. In rose paper boards with white cloth spine.

Presentation copy. Inscribed on flyleaf: "Presentation copy to Prof. Hugh Candy with the cordial regards & best wishes of Cumberland Clark 1918."

B647

CHARLES DICKENS AND HIS JEWISH CHARACTERS. London: Printed at the Chiswick Press. 1918.

8°. In original red cloth.

Included is the "Autograph Correspondence Between the Novelist and Mrs. Eliza Davis (wife of James P. Davis) Relative to the Jewish People, and as to the Characters of 'Fagin' in 'Oliver Twist,' and 'Riah' in 'Our Mutual Friend'; Also Concerning the Presentation By Mrs. Davis to Charles Dickens of a copy of The Hebrew Bible. . . . 1863-1870."

First edition. Privately printed.

Ex libris George Barr McCutcheon.

B648

AN AMERICAN NOTE NEVER INTENDED FOR GENERAL CIRCULATION ALTHOUGH ISSUED AT THE SEAT OF GOVERNMENT IN MARCH 1842 BY CHARLES DICKENS. [Cambridge, Mass.: 1924].

8°. In green paper wrapper.

First edition.

A letter (now in the Harvard Library) written by Dickens from Washington to Charles Sumner. (Printed "At the Sign of the George" by George Parker Winship on the 82nd anniversary of Dickens's first trip to America.)

B649

"Dickens in Genoa." By F. Yeats-Brown. In THE SPECTATOR. London: 22 September 1928.

4°. As issued. Includes letters from Dickens to Angus Fletcher and Timothy Yeats-Brown.

B650(1,2)
THE UNPUBLISHED LETTERS OF CHARLES DICKENS TO MARK LEMON. London: Halton & Turscott Smith, Ltd. 1927.

4°. Two copies in three-fourths vellum with purple cloth.

Nos. 162 and 248 of 500 copies.

Inserted in No. 248 is a holograph letter from Mark Lemon to Mr. Macmillan, dated "Vine Cottage, Crawley, Wednesday."

B651(1,2)
DICKENS V. BARABBAS FORSTER INTERVENING A STUDY BASED UPON SOME HITHERTO UNPUBLISHED LETTERS WITH FACSIMILES. London: Charles J. Sawyer. MCMXXX.

8°. Two copies in original green paper boards with cloth spine.

Nos. 57 and 67 of 100 copies on Abbey Mill Antique paper. (A total of 200 copies were printed on three types of paper.)

B652(1)
LETTERS OF CHARLES DICKENS TO THE BARONESS BURDETT-COUTTS. EDITED BY CHARLES C. OSBORNE. WITH A BIO-GRAPHICAL INTRODUCTION. London: John Murray. [1931].

8°. In original green cloth. First edition.

B652(2)
A second copy in original green cloth with black rule border.

B653
"Letters of Charles Dickens to Baroness Burdett-Coutts." Edited by Charles C. Osborne. In THE CORNHILL MAGAZINE. London: John Murray. June 1931.

8°. In original orange wrapper, as issued.

B654
LETTERS OF CHARLES DICKENS TO THE BARONESS BURDETT-COUTTS EDITED BY CHARLES C. OSBORNE WITH A BIO-GRAPHICAL INTRODUCTION. New York: E. P. Dutton & Co., Inc. [1932].

8°. In black cloth printed in gold.

B655
AN AMERICAN FRIEND OF DICKENS. New York: Thomas F. Madigan, Inc. MCMXXXIII.

8°. In original blue-green paper boards with design by "Phiz" for the original numbers of *David Copperfield*. Letters to Dr. Elisha Bartlett.

No. 72 of 150 copies designed and printed by William E. Rudge's Sons.

B656

NOT SO BAD AS WE SEEM; OR, MANY SIDES TO A CHARACTER. A COMEDY IN FIVE ACTS. BY SIR EDWARD BULWER LYTTON, BART. AS FIRST PERFORMED AT DEVONSHIRE HOUSE, IN THE PRESENCE OF HER MAJESTY AND HIS ROYAL HIGHNESS THE PRINCE ALBERT. New York: Harper & Brothers. 1851.

12°. In original purple cloth. With a copy of the program of the performance at Devonshire House, 16 May 1851.

B657(1)

AN ACCOUNT OF THE FIRST PERFORMANCE OF LYTTON'S COMEDY "NOT SO BAD AS WE SEEM." London: Printed by Richard Clay and Sons, Ltd. for Private Circulation. 1919.

8°. Pamphlet in original yellow wrapper. Thirty copies printed for Thomas J. Wise of a letter from Dickens to R. H. Horne, who was in Australia.

B657(2)

A second copy in MS. collection together with original letter (A81).

B658

NOTES AND COMMENTS ON CERTAIN WRITINGS IN PROSE AND VERSE BY RICHARD HENRY HORNE. London: Printed by Richard Clay and Sons, Ltd. for Private Circulation. 1920.

8°. In stiff green wrapper. Inscribed on half-title "For the Wrenn Library, Austin, Texas. Thos. J. Wise."

Thirty copies printed. Letters from Dickens to Horne concerning articles for *Household Words*.

B659

DICKENS TO HIS OLDEST FRIEND. SOME UNPUBLISHED LETTERS TO THOMAS BEARD IN THE COLLECTION OF COUNT DE SUZZANNET WITH A FOREWORD BY SIR HENRY FIELDING DICKENS, K. C. [n.p.] 1931.

12°. In original stiff brown wrapper. Inscribed to Harry B. Smith Esq.

Fifty copies privately printed for Walter Dexter.

B660

"Charles Dickens and His Oldest Friend. Forty Years of Unpublished Letters." Edited by Bernard Darwin. In THE BOOKMAN. Camden, New Jersey: October 1931—February 1932.

8°. As issued. Issue for November 1931 lacking.

B661

DICKENS TO HIS FIRST PUBLISHER, JOHN MACRONE. SOME HITHERTO UNPUBLISHED LETTERS. [n.p.] 1931.

12°. In stiff brown wrapper.

Fifty copies privately printed for Walter Dexter.

B662

CHARLES DICKENS'S LETTERS TO CHARLES LEVER. EDITED BY FLORA V. LIVINGSTON. WITH AN INTRODUCTION BY HYDER E. ROLLINS. Cambridge, Mass. 1933.

12°. In original red cloth. Letters from the Widener Collection, Harvard College Library.

B663

MR. AND MRS. CHARLES DICKENS. HIS LETTERS TO HER. WITH A FOREWORD BY THEIR DAUGHTER KATE PERUGINI AND NOTES, APPENDICES, ETC. BY WALTER DEXTER. London: Constable & Co., Ltd. 1935.

8°. In original lavender cloth with lemon-yellow end papers.

B664

"Letter from Dickens to Ben Farjeon." In BLACKWOOD'S MAGAZINE. Edinburgh: William Blackwood & Sons, Ltd. September 1935.

8°. In original white wrapper.

10: WORKS ATTRIBUTED TO DICKENS

B665(1)

SERGEANT BELL, AND HIS RAREE-SHOW. London: Printed for Thomas Tegg. 1839.

16°. In original brown cloth with gilt design on cover, and yellow end papers.

First edition of the work by George Mogridge.

B665(2)

A second copy, rebound in crimson levant morocco, richly gilt, lacking "Table of Contents."

B666(1)

THE LOVING BALLAD OF LORD BATEMAN. London: Charles Tilt. Constantinople: Mustapha Syried. MDCCCXXXIX.

16°. In original flexible green cloth with gilt design.

First edition, first issue: "wine" for "vine" in Stanza V; center pagination. Leaf of music precedes preface; four leaves of advertisements at end, beginning "George Cruikshank's Works."

Attached to flyleaf is concluding portion of document designed by George Cruikshank and Charles Dickens and an envelope addressed in Thackeray's hand.

B666(2)

A second copy of the first issue, bound in original flexible cover in full red morocco, richly gilt. Leaf of music follows preface; four leaves of advertisements vary from B666(1), beginning "Drawing Books for Beginners."

B666(3)

A third copy, rebound in crimson levant morocco, richly gilt; original cover included.

Not first issue. Error in Stanza V corrected; center pagination; advertisements lacking. With a double set of illustrations, one in color.

B667

THE LOVING BALLAD OF LORD BATEMAN. London: David Bogue. Constantinople: Mustapha Syried. MDCCCLI.

16°. In original flexible green cloth with gilt design.

B668

THE LOVING BALLAD OF LORD BATEMAN. New York: G. W. Carleton & Co. London: Bell & Daldy. MDCCCLXXI.

8°. Pamphlet of sixteen pages on plate paper, text outlined with blue border.

B669

SISTER ROSE. IN SEVEN CHAPTERS. Philadelphia: T. B. Peterson. [n.d.].

8°. In original white wrapper, as issued.

B670

"The Cousin-Seeker of Berlin. By Charles Dickens." In ROMANCE. April 1892.

8°. In original grey wrapper.

11 : COLLECTED EDITIONS

B671

WORKS OF CHARLES DICKENS. London: Chapman and Hall. 1861–1863.

8°. Twenty-three of thirty volumes in original red embossed cloth.

First "Illustrated" Library Edition. This set belonged to Sir James Emerson Tennent. The first volume of *Pickwick Papers* [B14(2)] bears Dickens's inscription; several other volumes bear the inscription, "Emerson Tennent."

B672

WORKS OF CHARLES DICKENS. Cambridge: Printed at the Riverside Press. 1867–1869.

8°. Fifty-seven volumes of a large paper edition of 100 copies; in original red cloth with paper label and yellow end papers.

B673
THE WORKS OF CHARLES DICKENS. New York: P. F. Collier. [c. 1880].

4°. Six volumes in original green cloth. (Collier's Unabridged Edition)

B674
THE WORKS OF CHARLES DICKENS. New York: The International Press. MCM.

8°. Black roan gilt-stamped "Charles Dickens." A salesman's specimen, apparently of an unpublished edition, containing colored frontispiece of the author, four specimen titles (each indicating on verso that this is to be designated the "International Edition" and limited to 100 copies), sixteen illustrations (four of them colored), and pages 129-176 of *David Copperfield*.

B675(1)
THE WORKS OF CHARLES DICKENS. London: Chapman and Hall Limited. 1907—1908.

8°. A complete set of forty volumes in original half blue morocco and marbled paper boards and end papers; top edges gilt.

Vol. I autographed "A. Tennyson Dickens." Holograph letter and two signed checks attached. (National Edition)

B675(2)
An incomplete second set in original green cloth printed in gold.

Vol. XXVII: A Tale of Two Cities

Vol. XXIX: Great Expectations

Vol. XXXVII: Letters and Speeches, I

Vol. XXXVIII: Letters and Speeches, II

Vols. XXXIX-XL: The Life of Charles Dickens by John Forster

Edition limited to 750 sets.

B676
WORKS. Boston: Dana Estes & Company. [c. 1910].

8°. Forty-seven volumes in red morocco.

No. "F" of 26 lettered copies (Edition Magnifique)

B677(1)
THE NONESUCH DICKENS. Bloomsbury: The Nonesuch Press. 1937—1938.

8°. Twenty-three volumes in linen buckram of various colors with black leather labels printed in gold.

Edition limited to 877 sets.

B677(2)
A second copy of *Dickensiana. Retrospectus and Prospectus.* Thomas Hatton's copy of the first issue with his notations. See A214.

12:SELECTED EXCERPTS

B678
THE READINGS OF MR. CHARLES DICKENS, AS CONDENSED BY HIMSELF. WITH ORIGINAL ILLUSTRATIONS. Boston: Ticknor and Fields. 1848.

8°. In original green cloth with gilt lettering and brown end papers.

B679
SIMPLE SETTINGS, IN VERSE, FOR SIX PORTRAITS AND PICTURES. FROM MR. DICKENS'S GALLERY. Boston: Ticknor and Fields. MDCCCLV.

8°. In original embossed brown cloth with yellow end papers. With eight pages of advertising, dated "Boston, 135 Washington Street. December, 1854."

B680
IMMORTELLES FROM CHARLES DICKENS. BY ICH. London: John Moxon. 1856.

8°. In original dark blue cloth with gilt lettering.

B681
THE POOR TRAVELLER: BOOTS AT THE HOLLY-TREE INN: AND MRS. GAMP. London: Bradbury & Evans. 1858.

8°. In original green wrapper, as issued. (Reading Edition)

B682
THE STORY OF LITTLE DOMBEY. London: Bradbury & Evans. 1858.

8°. In original green wrapper, as issued. (Cheap and Uniform Editions of Mr. Dickens's Christmas Books.)

B682a
THE CRICKET ON THE HEARTH. London: Bradbury & Evans. 1858.

8°. In original green wrapper, as issued. (Cheap and Uniform Editions of Mr. Dickens's Christmas Books.)

B683(1-5)
THE READINGS OF MR. CHARLES DICKENS, AS CONDENSED BY HIMSELF. Boston, New York: Ticknor and Fields. 1868.

12°. Five books in original blue wrappers, as issued. (Illustrated Copyright Edition)

A Christmas Carol and The Trial from *Pickwick; Nicholas Nickleby* (at Mr. Squeers's School) and *Boots at the Holly-Tree Inn; Doctor Marigold* and *Mrs. Gamp; Doctor Marigold* and The Trial from *Pickwick; David Copperfield* and Mr. Bob Sawyer's Party (from *Pickwick*).

B684

CHILD-PICTURES FROM DICKENS. WITH ILLUSTRATIONS BY S. EYTINGE, JR. Boston: Ticknor and Fields. 1868.

8°. In original green binding and gilt lettering and decoration.

B685

DIALOGUES FROM DICKENS FOR SCHOOL AND HOME AMUSE-MENT. Boston: Lee and Shepard. 1870.

8°. In original green cloth and brown end papers.

B686

DIALOGUES FROM DICKENS. SECOND SERIES. DIALOGUES AND DRAMAS. ARRANGED BY W. ELIOT FETTE, A.M. Boston: Lee and Shepard. New York: Lee, Shepard and Dillingham. 1871.

12°. In original green cloth and brown end papers.

B687

SCHOOLS AND SCHOOLMASTERS. FROM THE WRITINGS OF CHARLES DICKENS. EDITED BY T. J. CHAPMAN, M.A. New York, Chicago: A. S. Barnes & Company. [1871].

8°. In original green embossed cloth.

B688

BEAUTIES OF DICKENS. A SELECTION OF BEAUTIFUL THOUGHTS FROM THE WORKS OF CHARLES DICKENS. BY ALFRED I. HOLMES. Brooklyn, New York: By the Author. 1872.

8°. In original green cloth with yellow end papers.

B689

A CYCLOPEDIA OF THE BEST THOUGHTS OF CHARLES DICK-ENS. COMPILED AND ALPHABETICALLY ARRANGED BY F. G. DE FONTAINE. New York: E. J. Hale & Son. 1873.

8°. In original half polished calf and red marbled paper boards and end papers, edges marbled. Inscribed "E. H. Wales from D.W.C.W. 1872."

B690

TEARS AND LAUGHTER. THE CHARLES DICKENS PARLOR AL-BUM OF ILLUSTRATIONS. New York: G. W. Carleton & Co. MDCCCLXXIX.

8°. In original brown cloth printed in black and gold.

B691

A PICKWICKIAN PILGRIMAGE. BY JOHN R. G. HASSARD. Boston: James R. Osgood and Company. 1881.

8°. In original blue cloth printed in black and gold.

B692

DOLLY VARDEN THE LITTLE COQUETTE FROM THE BARNABY RUDGE LITTLE NELL FROM THE OLD CURIOSITY-SHOP TINY TIM DOT AND THE FAIRY CRICKET FROM THE CHRISTMAS STORIES. New York: John B. Alden. 1883.

8°. In original drab cloth with pinkish end papers. (Dickens' Little Folks)

B693

THE FIRESIDE DICKENS. A CYCLOPEDIA OF THE BEST THOUGHTS OF CHARLES DICKENS. COMPRISING A CAREFUL SELECTION OF HIS BEST WRITINGS. BY F. G. DE FONTAINE. [New York]: G. W. Carleton & Co. 1883. [Sold only by subscription]

8°. In original olive drab cloth decorated in gilt and black, edges gilt.

B694

TEN BOYS FROM DICKENS. BY KATE DICKINSON SWEETSER. ILLUSTRATED BY GEORGE ALFRED WILLIAMS. New York, London. [1901].

8°. In tan cloth with paper illustration.

B695

MASTERPIECES OF DICKENS. New York: G. W. Dillingham, Successor to G. W. Carleton & Co. MDCCCXCII.

8°. In original red cloth printed in black and gold.

B696

CHOICE BITS FROM CHARLES DICKENS' FAVOURITE WORKS. London: The Hop Bitters Company. [c. 1896].

8°. Leaflet in paper wrapper, advertising Dr. Soule's Hop Bitters.

B697

THE COMEDY OF CHARLES DICKENS A BOOK OF CHAPTERS AND EXTRACTS TAKEN FROM THE WRITER'S NOVELS. BY HIS DAUGHTER KATE (MRS. PERUGINI). FIRST SERIES. London: Chapman & Hall, Ltd. 1906.

8°. In original green cloth.

B698

CHARACTER PORTRAITS FROM DICKENS. SELECTED AND ARRANGED BY CHARLES WELSH. Boston: Small, Maynard and Company. 1907.

8°. In original green cloth with gilt lettering and decorations.

B699

TEN GIRLS FROM DICKENS. BY KATE DICKINSON SWEETSER. ILLUSTRATED BY GEORGE ALFRED WILLIAMS. New York, London: Harper & Brothers. [1905].

8°. In green cloth with paper illustration.

B700

TEN GIRLS FROM DICKENS. New York: Duffield & Company. MCMVIII.

8°. In green cloth with illustrations.

Illustrated by George Alfred Williams.

B701

THE WISDOM OF DICKENS. New York: Mitchell Kennerley. [1908].

8°. In contemporary green morocco.

B702

CHARACTER PORTRAITS FROM DICKENS. SELECTED AND AR-RANGED BY CHARLES WELSH. London: Chatto & Windus. 1908.

8°. In original red cloth with gilt lettering.

B703

A DICKENS DRAMATIC READER SCENES FROM PICKWICK SCENES FROM NICHOLAS NICKLEBY THE CRICKET ON THE HEARTH A CHRISTMAS CAROL. BY FANNY COMSTOCK. Boston, New York, etc.: Ginn and Company. 1913.

8°. In brown cloth.

B704

THE CHILDREN OF DICKENS. BY SAMUEL McCORD CROTHERS. ILLUSTRATED BY JESSIE WILCOX SMITH. New York: Charles Scribner's Sons. MCMXXV.

8°. In black cloth with colored illustration on paper.

B705

SCENES FROM DICKENS TRIALS, SKETCHES, AND PLAYS. AR-RANGED BY THE DICKENS FELLOWSHIP PLAYERS OF TORON-TO. COMPILED BY JAMES EDMUND JONES, B.A. Toronto: McClelland & Steward. 1923.

8°. In original dark red cloth.

B706

SIKES AND NANCY. A READING. REPRINTED FROM THE COPY OF THE PRIVATELY PRINTED EDITION, FORMERLY IN THE COLLECTION OF SIR HENRY IRVING. WITH AN INTRODUCTION AND A GENERAL BIBLIOGRAPHY OF THE READING EDITIONS BY JOHN HARRISON STONEHOUSE. London: Henry Sotheran & Co. 1921.

8°. In original grey paper boards with paper label. No. 7 of 275 copies.

B707

DAVID COPPERFIELD. A READING, IN FIVE CHAPTERS. RE-
PRINTED FROM THE PRIVATELY PRINTED EDITION OF 1866.
WITH A NOTE ON THE ROMANTIC HISTORY OF CHARLES
DICKENS AND MARIA BEADNELL. BY JOHN HARRISON STONE-
HOUSE. London: Henry Sotheran & Co. 1921.

8°. In original blue-grey boards with paper label.

No. 158 of 275 copies reprinted from the privately printed edition of 1866.

B708

SOME ROGUES AND VAGABONDS OF DICKENS. London: Cecil
Palmer. [1927].

8°. In light blue cloth.

First edition.

B709

SOME ROGUES AND VAGABONDS OF DICKENS. Philadelphia:
J. B. Lippincott Company. [n.d.].

8°. In dark blue cloth.

B710

TALES FROM DICKENS. RETOLD BY CALISTA McCABE COUR-
TENAY. ILLUSTRATED BY A. M. TURNER AND HARRIET
KAUCHER. New York: Samuel Gabriel Sons & Company. 1917.

8°. In blue illustrated paper boards with cloth spine.

B711

SOME DICKENS WOMEN. BY EDWIN CHARLES. New York:
Frederick A. Stokes Company. [n.d.].

8°. In purple cloth.

B712

VIGNETTES OF COUNTRY LIFE. Chicago: Reilly & Britton Co.
[n.d.].

8°. In original red leather; 4¾″ by 3½″. (The Elzevir Library)

Selected and arranged by Norman J. Davidson.

B713

THE GIRLS OF DICKENS. New York: McLoughlin Brothers. [n.d.].

8°. In green cloth.

B714

THE GIRLS OF DICKENS RETOLD. ILLUSTRATED. Springfield,
Mass.: McLoughlin Bros., Inc. [n.d.].

8°. In brown paper boards.

B715

THE BOYS OF DICKENS. New York: McLoughlin Brothers. [n.d.].

8°. In green cloth.

B716

BOYS & GIRLS FROM DICKENS. TWENTY OF THE MOST FAMOUS CHILDREN FROM THE WORKS OF CHARLES DICKENS. EDITED BY BROUGHTON SCOTT. ILLUSTRATIONS AND DEC-ORATIONS BY JOSEPH CLEMENT COLL. New York: The Macaulay Company. 1910.

8°. In original green cloth with paper illustration.

B717

CHARACTER SKETCHES FROM DICKENS FOR LADIES. New York, London: Samuel French. [n.d.].

8°. In lavender wrapper.

B718

CHIPS FROM DICKENS. SELECTED BY THOMAS MASON. New York: T. Y. Crowell and Co. [n.d.].

16°. In original blue cloth with gilt decoration and lettering; 2½″ by 3¾″.

B719

MR. PICKWICK'S PILGRIMAGES. Philadelphia: J. B. Lippincott Company. 1927.

8°. In blue cloth.

B720

CAPTAIN BOLDHEART AND OTHER STORIES IN A HOLIDAY ROMANCE. NEWLY ILLUSTRATED BY BEATRICE PEARSE. New York: The Macmillan Company. 1927.

8°. In blue cloth, with illustrative end papers.

B721

THE GREATEST PAGES OF CHARLES DICKENS. Garden City, New York: Doubleday Doran and Company, Inc. 1934.

8°. In green cloth.

B722

PEOPLE FROM DICKENS A PRESENTATION OF LEADING CHARACTERS FROM THE BOOKS OF CHARLES DICKENS AR-RANGED BY RACHEL FIELD. WITH ILLUSTRATIONS BY THOMAS FOGARTY. New York, London: Charles Scribner's Sons. MDMXXXV.

8°. In black cloth with paper illustration in color and illustrated end papers.

B723

A HANDY DICKENS. SELECTIONS FROM THE WORKS OF CHARLES DICKENS MADE AND INTRODUCED BY ARTHUR MACHEN. WITH A FRONTISPIECE BY EDWARD ARDIZZONE. London: Constable & Co., Ltd. 1941.

8°. In original dark blue cloth.

B724

THE DICKENS DIGEST FOUR GREAT DICKENS MASTERPIECES CONDENSED FOR THE MODERN READER DAVID COPPER-FIELD • PICKWICK PAPERS • OLIVER TWIST • MARTIN CHUZ-ZLEWIT. CONDENSED BY MARY LOUISE ASWELL. ILLUS-TRATED BY DONALD McKAY. New York, London: Whittlesby House, McGraw-Hill Book Company, Inc. 1943.

8°. In original brown cloth with yellow spine and printed yellow end papers.

B725

PICTURES FROM DICKENS WITH READINGS. WITH ILLUSTRA-TIONS BY H. M. PAGET, FRED BARNARD, HAROLD COPPING, JOHN H. BACON, VICTOR VENNER, AND G. H. THOMPSON. London: Ernest Nister. New York: E. P. Dutton & Co. [n.d.].

8°. In original blue cloth with lettering and illustration in gilt and brown.

B726

HOLLY BERRIES FROM DICKENS. Boston: DeWolfe, Fiske & Co. [n.d.].

4°. In original white cloth with gilt lettering and red and green decoration.

B727

SCENES FROM DICKENS FOR DRAWING-ROOM AND PLATFORM ACTING. ADAPTED BY GUY PERTWEE. EDITED BY ERNEST PERTWEE. WITH 48 COSTUME-PLATES BY EDWARD HANDLEY-READ. London: George Routledge & Sons, Limited. New York: E. P. Dutton & Co. [n.d.].

8°. In original dark green cloth.

B728

DRAMATIC EPISODES FROM DICKENS. HENRY CHARLES SUTER. London: Arthur Stockwell, Ltd. [n.d.].

8°. In original blue cloth. Autographed, "Henry Chas. Suter."

B729

CHARLES DICKENS' CHILDREN STORIES RE-TOLD BY HIS GRANDDAUGHTER AND OTHERS. Philadelphia: Henry Altemus Co. [n.d.].

8°. In blue cloth and paper illustration.

B730

CHILDREN'S STORIES FROM DICKENS. RE-TOLD BY HIS GRANDDAUGHTER MARY ANGELA DICKENS AND OTHERS. ILLUSTRATED BY HAROLD COPPING. Philadelphia: David McKay Company. [n.d.].

8°. In rust-colored cloth with paper illustration.

B731

STORIES FROM DICKENS RETOLD FOR CHILDREN. ILLUS- TRATED. New York: Manhattan Press. [n.d.].

8°. In original orange cloth with colored illustration.

B732

THE CHILDREN'S DICKENS. STORIES SELECTED FROM VARI- OUS TALES. New York, London: Hodder & Stoughton. [n.d.].

8°. In red cloth with paper illustration in color.

B733

CHILD CHARACTERS FROM DICKENS RE-TOLD BY L. L. WEE- DON WITH 6 COLOUR PLATES AND 70 HALF-TONE ILLUSTRA- TIONS BY ARTHUR A. DIXON. London: Ernest Dister. New York: E. P. Dutton & Co. [n.d.].

8°. In green cloth illustrated in color.

B734

COMIC DIALOGUES FROM DICKENS. Boston: Walter H. Baker & Co. [n.d.].

8°. In original grey paper wrapper.

B735

DICKENS ALL THE YEAR ROUND. A DICKENS ANTHOLOGY. ARRANGED BY H. N. WETHERED & CHARLES TURLEY. WITH AN INTRODUCTION BY BERNARD DARWIN. Philadelphia: J. B. Lippincott Company. [n.d.].

8°. In original orange cloth.

Devonshire Terrace

Thursday The tenth October
1845

My dear Lady Blessington

More thanks than I can
say you, or than you would care
to receive, for your inestimably
useful kindness!

Will you tell me where the
Baboo is to be found? I will leave
a card at this Hotel, straightway.

Shall I speak to Dr Southwood
Smith, who is manager of the
Sanatorium committee arrangements

XIII, XIV and XV : Letter to the Countess of Blessington (A36)

about a good box for you on the 15th.
otherwise I fear they will all be
gone. For, how many, do you wish it?

I am very sorry I had gone out
for a walk when you called yesterday.
It would have delighted me to have
installed you into my Sanctum.

Mrs Dickens, I am glad to say,
is going on quite brilliantly. I wish
I could say as much for myself, but
in the distraction of these great
newspaper arrangements, I find

the little book trots along – sometimes
walks indeed – and sometimes stops
altogether.

Dear Lady Blessington

believe Yours most cordially

Charles Dickens

The Countess of Blessington

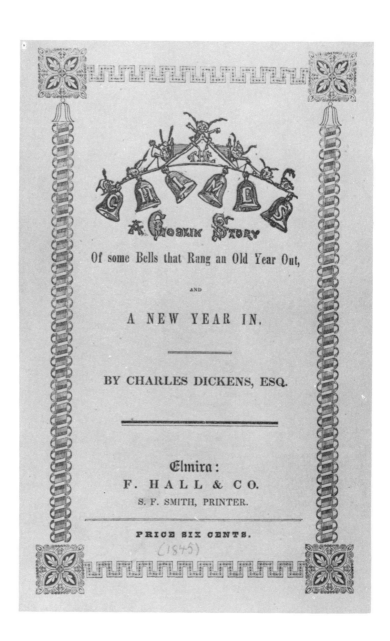

THE CHIMES

A Goblin Story

Of some Bells that Rang an Old Year Out,

AND

A NEW YEAR IN.

BY CHARLES DICKENS, ESQ.

Elmira:
F. HALL & CO.
S. F. SMITH, PRINTER.

PRICE SIX CENTS.

(1845)

XVI : THE CHIMES. An unrecorded American piracy (B391)

A LETTER FROM HOP·O'·MY·THUMB

TO CHARLES DICKENS, Esq.

UPON "FRAUDS ON THE FAIRIES," "WHOLE HOGS," ETC.

RIGHT TRUSTY, WELL-BELOVED, MUCH-READ AND ADMIRED SIR,

Y attention has lately been called to an article in "Household Words," entitled, "Frauds on the Faries," in which I recognise your master hand as the author,—and in which article, as it appears to me, you have gone a *leetle* out of your way to find fault with our mutual friend George Cruikshank, for the way in which he has edited "Hop-o'-my Thumb and the Seven-League Boots." You may, perhaps, be surprised at receiving a letter from so small an individual as myself; but, independently of the deep debt of gratitude which I feel that I owe to that gentleman, for the way in which he has edited my history, as well as an anxiety to maintain the honour and credit of the noble family to which I belong, impels me to take up my pen (made from the quill of a humming-bird), to endeavour to justify the course adopted by my editor,—and also to take the liberty of setting you right upon one or two points, in which you are entirely mistaken; to show, in fact, that, when you wrote your criticism, you knew little or nothing of that history you so strongly condem our friend for altering.

These may seem bold words, from such a mite as I am to such a literary giant as you are; but I have had to deal with giants in my time, and I am not afraid of them and I shall, therefore, take leave to tell you that, although you may have held in your memory some of the remarkable facts in my interesting history, yet that you were ignorant of the general character of the whole; and the only way in which I can account for a man of your remarkable acuteness making such a great mistake is, that you have suffered that extraordinary seven-league boot imagination of yours to run away with you into your *own* Fairy Land,—and thus have given your *own* colour to this history; and, consequently, a credit and a character to the old editions, which do not belong to them. Your article of "Frauds on the Faries" commences thus :—

"We may assume that we are not singular in entertaining a very great tenderness for the fairy literature of our childhood. What enchanted us then, and is captivating a million of young fancies now, has, at the same blessed time of life, enchanted vast hosts of men and women who have done their long day's work, and laid their grey heads down to rest. It would be hard to estimate the amount of gentleness

XVII : Cruikshank's reply to Charles Dickens (A147)

Household Words, Saturday 25th March 1854. Not yet published.

THE LATE MR. JUSTICE TALFOURD.

THE readers of these pages will have known, many days before the present number can come into their hands, that on Monday the thirteenth of March, this upright judge and good man died suddenly at Stafford in the discharge of his duties. Mercifully spared protracted pain and mental decay, he passed away in a moment, with words of Christian eloquence, of brotherly tenderness and kindness towards all men, yet unfinished on his lips.

As he died, he had always lived. So amiable a man, so gentle, so sweet-tempered, of such a noble simplicity, so perfectly unspoiled by his labors and their rewards, is very rare indeed upon this earth. These lines are traced by the faltering hand of a friend ; but none can so fully know how true they are, as those who knew him under all circumstances, and found him ever the same.

In his public aspects ; in his poems, in his speeches, on the bench, at the bar, in Parliament ; he was widely appreciated, honoured, and beloved. Inseparable as his great and varied abilities were from himself in life, it is yet to himself and not to them, that affection in its first grief naturally turns. They remain, but he is lost.

The chief delight of his life was to give delight to others. His nature was so exquisitely kind, that to be kind was its highest happiness. Those who had the privilege of seeing him in his own home when his public successes were greatest,—so modest, so contented with little things, so interested in humble persons and humble efforts, so surrounded by children and young people, so adored in remembrance of a domestic generosity and greatness of heart too sacred to be unveiled here, can never forget the pleasure of that sight.

If ever there were a house, in England justly celebrated for the reverse of the picture, where every art was honoured for its own sake, and where every visitor was received for his own claims and merits, that house was his. It was in this respect a great example, as sorely needed as it will be sorely missed. Rendering all legitimate deference to rank and riches, there never was a man more composedly, unaffectedly, quietly, immovable by such considerations than the subject of this sorrowing remembrance. On the other hand, nothing would have astonished him so much as the suggestion that he was anybody's patron or protector. His dignity was ever of that highest and purest sort which has no occasion to proclaim itself, and which is not in the least afraid of losing itself.

In the first joy of his appointment to the judicial bench, he made a summer-visit to the sea-shore, " to share his exultation in the gratification of his long-cherished ambition with the friend"—now among the many friends who mourn his death and lovingly recall his virtues. Lingering in the bright moonlight at the close of a happy day, he spoke of his new functions, of his sense of the great responsibility he undertook, and of his placid belief that the habits of his professional life rendered him equal to their efficient discharge ; but, above all, he spoke, with an earnestness never more to be separated in his friend's mind from the murmur of the sea upon a moonlight night, of his reliance on the strength of his desire to do right before God and man. He spoke with his own singleness of heart, and his solitary hearer knew how deep and true his purpose was. They passed, before parting for the night, into a playful dispute at what age he should retire, and what he would do at three-score years and ten. And ah ! within five short years, it is all ended like a dream !

But, by the strength of his desire to do right, he was animated to the last moment of his existence. Who, knowing England at this time, would wish to utter with his last breath a more righteous warning than that its curse is ignorance, or a miscalled education which is as bad or worse, and a want of the exchange of innumerable graces and sympathies among the various orders of society, each hardened unto each and holding itself aloof ? Well will it be for us and for our children, if those dying words be never henceforth forgotten on the Judgment Seat.

An example in his social intercourse to those who are born to station, an example equally to those who win it for themselves ; teaching the one class to abate its stupid pride : the other, to stand upon its eminence, not forgetting the road by which it got there, and fawning upon no one ; the conscientious judge, the charming writer and accomplished speaker, the gentle-hearted, guileless, affectionate man, has entered on a brighter world. Very, very many have lost a friend ; nothing in Creation has lost an enemy.

The hand that lays this poor flower on his grave, was a mere boy's when he first clasped it—newly come from the work in which he himself began life—little used to the plough it has followed since—obscure enough, with much to correct and learn. Each of its successive tasks through many intervening years has been cheered by his warmest interest, and the friendship then begun has ripened to maturity in the passage of time ; but there was no more self-assertion or condescension in his winning goodness at first, than at last. The success of other men made as little change in him as his own.

XIX : H. K. Browne. Extra illustration for MARTIN CHUZZLEWIT
(B182)

TO BE READ

AT

DUSK.

BY

CHARLES DICKENS.

———◆———

LONDON:

1852.

Tavistock House

Nineteenth December 1853.

My Dear Marcus

You made an excellent
sketch from a book of mine, which I
received (and have preserved) with
great pleasure. Will you accept from
me, in remembrance of it, this little
book. I believe it will teach, though it
may be sometimes not as genteel
as History has a habit of being.

Faithfully Yours
Charles Dickens

XXI : Letter to Marcus Stone (A89)

Saturday Twenty Eighth May 1870

Dear Mr Day

№ III   See page 75 Edwin Drood, last paragraph.

It stands:

In the days when christchurch took offence at the existence of a railroad afar off, as menacing that sensitive constitution, the property of us Britons. The odd fortune of which sacred institution it is the

It should stand:

In the days when christchurch took offence at the existence of a railroad afar off, as menacing that sensitive constitution, the property of us Britons, the odd fortune of which sacred institution it is

Faithfully yours
Charles Dickens

XXII and XXIII: Letter and Memorandum on EDWIN DROOD (A132, 133)

Memorandum

Twenty Eighth May 1870

I have left Hyde Park Place; therefore please
Send proofs in future, either to Gad's Hill,
or Wellington Street. I am at the latter place
every Thursday

CD.

XXIV : Everett Shinn. Illustration in water color for EDWIN DROOD (A191)

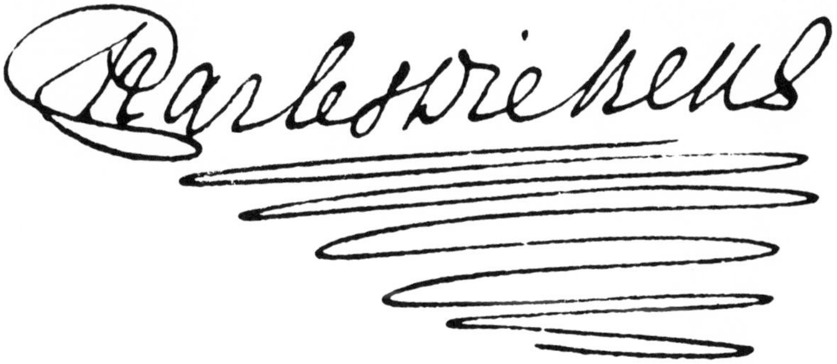
Charles Dickens

C1

Twenty-two illustrations in miniature by "Phiz" mounted on plate paper and bound in full levant morocco. [1859].

C2

Twenty-two vignette titles for the Library Edition of Dickens's *Works* by "Phiz." [1859].

C3

SKETCHES BY SEYMOUR. London: G. S. Tregear. [n.d.].

8°. Five volumes bound in one, in full polished red calf. Complete set. First edition.

C4

Five proofs of vignette titles by "Phiz" mounted on plate paper.

4°. Without titles or imprint.

C5

Illustrations by John Leech and Frederick Barnard.

Various sizes. Removed from bound volumes.

C6

Illustrations by F. O. C. Darley and Sir John Gilbert. [1872].

12°. Fifty-four illustrations on plate paper.

C7

Illustrations by Frederick Barnard.

4°. One hundred thirty-four India proofs in green cloth portfolio.

C8(1)

THE CHARACTERS OF CHARLES DICKENS POURTRAYED IN A SERIES OF ORIGINAL WATER COLOUR SKETCHES BY "KYD." London, Paris, New York: Raphael Tuck & Sons. [c. 1887].

4°. In brown illustrated paper boards with cloth spine.

C8(2)

A second copy in original blue cloth with gilt illustration and lettering; with figured end papers.

Also a set of postcards by "Kyd" (J. C. Clarke) and scenes "In Dickens Land" published by Raphael Tuck & Sons.

C9

CHARLES DICKENS: A GOSSIP ABOUT HIS LIFE, WORKS, AND CHARACTERS. WITH EIGHTEEN FULL-PAGE CHARACTER SKETCHES (REPRODUCED IN PHOTOGRAVURE) BY FREDERICK BARNARD, AND OTHER ILLUSTRATIONS BY WELL-KNOWN ARTISTS. BY THOMAS ARCHER. London, Paris, New York, Melbourne: Cassell & Company, Limited. [1885].

F°. Specially prepared in six sections, in stiff paper folders. For subscribers only.

C10

CHARACTER SKETCHES FROM DICKENS. BY FREDERICK BARNARD. London, Paris, Melbourne: Cassell and Company, Limited. [n.d.].

Sixteen illustrations on coated paper, 7″ by 10″.

C11

Eight Illustrations by F. O. C. Darley. 1888.

8°. Removed from bound volume.

C12

CHARACTER SKETCHES FROM DICKENS BY FELIX O. C. DARLEY. REPRODUCED IN THIRTEEN PHOTOGRAVURES. Boston: Estes and Lauriat. 1892.

8°. On plate paper in portfolio of olive drab cloth with gilt lettering.

C13(1)

CHARLES DICKENS BY PEN AND PENCIL. BY FREDERIC G. KITTON. WITH ONE HUNDRED ILLUSTRATIONS ON COPPER STEEL AND WOOD. London: Frank T. Sabin and John F. Dexter. 1889.

F°. In 13/12 parts with 5/2 supplements in grey wrappers; supplements in orange wrappers, as issued.

C13(2)

Two volumes in three-fourths black contemporary morocco with marbled paper boards, edges gilt. Extra title page with India-proof illustration in each volume.

C14

Fourteen Illustrations by "Phiz" from the Imperial Edition of Dickens's *Works*. Boston: Estes & Lauriat. 1895.

8°. Signed "H.B." or "H.K.B." (Hablot K. Browne)

C15

DICKENS PICTURES BY FRED BARNARD, H. M. PAGET, & VICTOR VENNER. WITH READINGS. [Printed in Bavaria]. E. Nister. [1896].

8°. In stiff wrapper with colored illustrations.

C16

People of Dickens. Drawn by C. D. Gibson. New York: R. H. Russell. MDCCCXCVII.

F°. Six plates in buff cloth portfolio.

C17

Twenty-nine original illustrations on plate paper. By Arthur Jule Goodman, F. H. Townsend, Hutton, Mitchell, Maurice Greiffenhagen, and others. [c. 1898].

C18

DICKENS ILLUSTRATIONS   FACSIMILES OF ORIGINAL DRAWINGS, SKETCHES, AND STUDIES FOR ILLUSTRATIONS IN THE WORKS OF CHARLES DICKENS. BY CRUIKSHANK, BROWNE, LEECH, STONE, AND FILDES. NOTES BY FREDERIC G. KITTON. London: George Redway. 1900.

Twenty-eight plates with title page, prefatory note, and list of plates in green cloth portfolio.

C19

Character Sketches from Dickens. By Frederick Barnard. Reproduced by Rembrandt Photogravure. London, Paris, New York, Melbourne: Cassell & Company, Limited. [1879–1885].

Cassell's Art Postcards, ten cards, sets B and C, from original lithographs.

C20

Twenty-four colored prints of Dickens's characters. On cards ½" by 4⅛".

C21

A SERIES OF CHARACTER SKETCHES FROM CHARLES DICKENS. BEING FAC-SIMILES OF ORIGINAL DRAWINGS BY FRED BARNARD. New York, London, Paris: Cassell, Petter, Galpin & Co. [n.d.].

F°. Six illustrations, 11" by 14" in size, with accompanying text. In portfolio of green paper boards with portrait of Dickens, as issued.

C22

DICKENS PICTURES. London: Ernest Nister. New York: E. P. Dutton & Co. [n.d.].

12°. In stiff wrapper with colored illustrations.

C23

CHARLES DICKENS RARE PRINT COLLECTION. Philadelphia: R. G. Kennedy & Co. For Private Circulation. [1900].

4°. In portfolio of grey paper boards with cloth spine and paper label. (Connoisseur Edition No. 266)

C24

Dickens Character Sketches. Twelve Photogravures Executed by the Gebbie & Husson Co. From Designs by F. Barnard and Others. Philadelphia: The Gebbie Publishing Co., Ltd. 1900.

4°. Five plates only, India proofs, in tan cloth portfolio printed in brown and gold.

C25

SCENES AND CHARACTERS FROM THE WORKS OF CHARLES DICKENS BEING EIGHT HUNDRED AND SIXTY-SIX DRAWINGS BY FRED BARNARD, HABLOT K. BROWNE (PHIZ), J. MAHONEY, CHARLES GREEN, A. B. FROST, GORDON THOMSON, J. McL. RALSTON, H. FRENCH, E. G. DALZIEL, F. A. FRASER, AND ENGRAVED FOR THE HOUSEHOLD EDITION. London: Chapman and Hall, Limited. MCMVIII.

4°. In original red cloth.

C26

Characters from Dickens. A Portfolio of 20 Van Dyke Gravures from the Drawings by F. G. Lewin, with an Introduction by B. W. Matz. London: Chapman and Hall, Ltd. 1912.

4°. Sepia prints mounted on stiff grey paper.

C27

Famous Dickens Pictures by Wallace L. Crowdy. London: W. M. Power. [1912].

4°. In purple wrapper.

C28

In Dickens's London Twenty-two Photogravure Proofs Reproducing the Charcoal Drawings by F. Hopkinson Smith. New York: Charles Scribner's Sons. MCMXIV.

F°. In portfolio of brown paper boards.

No. 2 of 150 sets printed. Reproduced also in book form [D231 (1, 2)].

C29

NELSON'S NEW DICKENS CONTAINING ALL THE ORIGINAL ILLUSTRATIONS. Edinburgh: Thomas Nelson & Sons, Ltd. 1920–1921.

4°. In original grey paper boards, by Zaehnsdorf.

Set of 18 jackets with colored illustrations by C. Lovat Fraser.

C30

Dickens Portfolio DeLuxe Collection. [n.p.]. J. A. Hill & Company. [n.d.].

4°. Reproductions from various artists issued in nine parts. In portfolio of dark green paper boards with paper label.

C31

Character Sketches from Dickens from Original Drawings by Frederick Barnard. Hartford, Conn.: Hartford Fire Insurance Co. [n.d.].

F°. Twelve plates in portfolio of grey paper boards.

C32

A SERIES OF CHARACTER SKETCHES FROM CHARLES DICKENS. BY FREDERICK BARNARD. Philadelphia: A. Edward Newton & Company. [n.d.].

4°. In original white cloth with floral decoration and gilt lettering.

C33

"A Set of Seven Dickens' Etchings." By Gerald M. Burn. London: The British Art Company, Ltd. [n.d.].

F°. Mounted with matting, 10″ by 12½″.

C34

The Buchanan Portfolio of Characters from Dickens. Glasgow, London: James Buchanan & Co., Ltd. [n.d.].

F°. Thirteen illustrations in color and a portrait of Dickens. In black cloth portfolio.

C35

Two hundred thirty-six illustrations and portraits by contemporary artists in Van Dyke Gravure.

C36

Extra Illustrations to Dickens's *Works*–a Miscellaneous Collection by Various Hands: Cruikshank, Phiz, Marcus Stone, D. Maclise, John Leech, Luke Fildes, Charles Green, and Others.

8°. Two hundred thirty-three portraits and illustrations.

C37
Eleven portraits (in folio volume of blue morocco)

(1) Portrait, signed "Faithfully yours   Charles Dickens," from a miniature by Margaret Gillies.

(2) Etching, in outline, by R. Graves of Dickens (Aet. 27) from the painting by D. Maclise (1839).

(3) "Boz" by "Phiz."

(4) Etching by L. H. Baker.

(5) Etching by R. Graves of Dickens (Aet. 47) from the painting by W. P. Frith.

(6) Etching by J. Brown from photograph by Watkins, signed, "Charles Dickens."

(7) Etching by D. J. Pound from photograph by Maynall.

(8) Colored print, folio size.

(9) Etching by L. H. Baker from photograph by Mason, signed, "Charles Dickens 1870."

(10) Etching by C. H. Jeens of Dickens reading *The Chimes* at Forster's chambers, 2 December 1844, from the sketch by Maclise.

C38
"Sairy Gamp and Betsey Prig." Mounted on large plate paper.

C39
"Dickens' Characters in Color by Pailthorpe." Illustrated border with portrait of Dickens on large paper, 20″ by 15″.

C40
Four pictorial front covers to musical compositions based on *The Chimes*.
Includes: "The Chimes Galop." London: S. A. Chappell. "Jullien's Chimes Quadrilles." London: Jullien. "The Chimes Quadrilles from a Goblin Story." London: H. Tolkien. "The Chimes Polka."

C41
Portrait engraved with color with remarque portrait of the artist, Alfred Count D'Orsay, 17″ by 26¼″, dated 16 December 1841. Framed together with second portrait engraved with color with remarque portrait of E. Stodart and Dickens's holograph letter to Miss Kelly making arrangement for a rehearsal of the amateur theatricals.

C42
"Boz and His Creations." Grizaille oil on canvas by W. H. Beard, 21½″ by 26½″. New York, 1870.

C43
Dickens in his study. Engraved steel, 18″ by 23¼″, by Samuel Hollyer. Washington, D.C., 1875.

DICKENSIANA

1 : BOOKS FROM DICKENS'S LIBRARY

All volumes listed in this section have Dickens's bookplate and library sales slip.

D1

THE HISTORY OF SIR CHARLES GRANDISON; IN A SERIES OF LETTERS. BY MR. SAMUEL RICHARDSON. IN SEVEN VOLUMES. A NEW EDITION, WITH THE LAST CORRECTIONS BY THE AUTHOR. London: T. Payne. 1810.

12°. Seven volumes in original leather binding.

D2

ELEGANT EXTRACTS: BEING A COPIOUS SELECTION OF INSTRUCTIVE, MORAL, AND ENTERTAINING PASSAGES, FROM THE MOST EMINENT BRITISH POETS. Vol. I. Book I.II. DEVOTIONAL AND MORAL. London: Sharpe and Hailes. 1812.

8°. In original tan marbled boards, spine renewed.

D3

THE BEAUTIES OF ENGLAND AND WALES: OR, ORIGINAL DELINEATIONS, TOPOGRAPHICAL, HISTORICAL, AND DESCRIPTIVE, OF EACH COUNTY. EMBELLISHED WITH ENGRAVINGS. London: J. Harris. 1801–1818.

8°. Nineteen volumes in twenty-six; in original old diced Russia, rebacked.

D4

SIX MONTHS IN THE WEST INDIES, IN 1825. BY HENRY NELSON COLERIDGE. THIRD EDITION. London: John Murray. MDCCCXXXII.

8°. In three-fourths contemporary red morocco with marbled paper boards and marbled edges.

D5

LIFE AMONG THE GIANTS; OR, THE CAPTIVE IN PATAGONIA. London: Henry Vizetelly and Clarke Beeton & Co. [n.d.].

8°. In original orange paper boards with cloth spine. With Dickens's autograph on front end paper.

D6

ENCYCLOPEDIA AMERICANA. A POPULAR DICTIONARY OF ARTS, SCIENCES, LITERATURE, HISTORY, POLITICS AND BIOGRAPHY. Philadelphia: Lea & Blanchard. 1842.

8°. Four volumes (I, II, VI, XI) in original full old calf.

D7

SIR GUY DE GUY: A STIRRING ROMAUNT. BY BATTLEBRAIN [pseud. of George F. Halse]. ILLUSTRATED BY PHIZ. London, New York: Routledge, Warne, and Routledge. MDCCCLXIV.

8°. In original red cloth with gilt lettering and illustration.

D8

THE TOWN; ITS MEMORABLE CHARACTERS AND EVENTS. BY LEIGH HUNT. ST. PAUL'S TO ST. JAMES'S. WITH FORTY-FIVE ILLUSTRA- TIONS. London: Smith, Elder and Co. 1848.

8°. Two volumes in original polished calf with marbled end papers and marbled edges.

D9

THE LIVING AUTHORS OF ENGLAND. BY THOMAS POWELL. New York: D. Appleton & Co. Philadelphia: Geo. S. Appleton. 1849.

8°. In original embossed green cloth; top cover loose. Attached ALS of Dickens to Lewis Gaylord Clark and of John Chapman to Dickens concerning Powell's forgeries.

D10

THE ILIAD OF HOMER, TRANSLATED BY ALEXANDER POPE. London: Ingram, Cooke, and Co. 1853.

8°. Two volumes bound in one, in full red morocco elaborately tooled.

D11

LIVES OF THE QUEENS OF ENGLAND, FROM THE NORMAN CON- QUEST. BY AGNES STRICKLAND. FOURTH EDITION. EMBELLISHED WITH PORTRAITS OF EVERY QUEEN. IN EIGHT VOLUMES. London: Henry Colburn's Successors, Hurst and Blackett. 1854.

8°. Eight volumes in original green cloth with gilt decoration. Title page of vol. I signed, "Charles Dickens 7th Feby 1861."

D12

AFTER DARK. BY WILKIE COLLINS. London: Smith, Elder and Co. 1856.

8°. Two volumes in original green cloth.

Presentation copy from Collins to Dickens. "Ellery Queen Collection"

D13

THE MARVELLOUS ADVENTURES AND RARE CONCEITS OF MASTER TYLL OWLGLASS. NEWLY COLLECTED, CHRONICLED AND SET FORTH, IN OUR ENGLISH TONGUE, BY KENNETH R. H. MAC KENZIE, AND ADORNED WITH MANY DIVERTING AND CUNNING DEVICES BY ALFRED CROWQUILL. London: Trübner & Co. 1860.

8°. In original red cloth with elaborate gilt design. Inscribed, "Charles Dickens Esq. with the Editor's best Compliments. Nov. 9, 1859."

D14

PERSONAL HISTORY OF LORD BACON. FROM UNPUBLISHED PAPERS. BY WILLIAM HEPWORTH DIXON OF THE INNER TEMPLE. London: John Murray. 1861.

8°. In original wine-colored cloth; top cover loose. Inscribed, "Charles Dickens, Esq. from the author."

D15

CHARLES LAMB: A MEMOIR. BY BARRY CORNWALL. London: Edward Moxon & Co. 1866.

8°. In original brown cloth with gilt design and yellow end papers.

D16

THE AUTO-BIOGRAPHY OF GOETHE. TRANSLATED FROM THE GERMAN BY JOHN OXENFORD, ESQ. London: Bell and Daldy. 1867.

8°. Two volumes in half polished calf and marbled paper boards and end papers; edges marbled.

D17

POEMS FROM THE GREEK MYTHOLOGY: AND MISCELLANEOUS POEMS. BY EDMUND OLLIER. London: John Camden Hotten. 1867.

16°. In original green cloth with brown end papers.

D18

EARLY AND LATE PAPERS HITHERTO UNCOLLECTED. BY WILLIAM MAKEPEACE THACKERAY. Boston: Ticknor and Fields. 1867.

8°. In original green cloth with brown end papers.

Pp. 95-121, "Dickens in France."

See also B557(5) *Household Words* from Dickens's library.

2 : S O N G S — M U S I C

D19

The Ivy Green, Written by Charles Dickens Esqr. Composed by Henry Russell. London: Leoni Lee, Music Seller to Her Majesty, Queen Victoria. [n.d.].

D20

The Ivy Green—A Ballad—The Words Written by Boz. Composed and respectfully Dedicated to Lynde M. Walter Esq. of Boston by Henry Russell. New York: Hewitt & Jaques. 1838. Fifth edition.

D21

There's a Charm in Spring, Ballad, Sung by Mr. Braham, in The Village Coquettes, Performed at the St. James' Theatre. Words by Charles Dickens; Music by John Hullah. New York: Firth & Hall. [n.d.].

D22

The Wery Last Obserwations of Weller, Senior. To Boz, on His Departure from London. Written and sung by J. M. Field, Esq. at the dinner given to Dickens in Boston, 1 February 1842. "Adapted to an old air with symphonies and accompaniments by James G. Maeder." Boston: W. H. Oakes. 1842.

D23

Pickwick Galop. By J. W. Turner. Boston: Oliver Ditson & Co. 1867. Instrumental music dedicated to Dickens.

D24

Peggoty the Wanderer   A ballad from David Copperfield Addressed to Emily. Music by J. W. Etherington. Boston: Oliver Ditson. New York: J. E. Gould & Co. New Orleans: Tyler & Hewitt. Mobile: F. Bromberg. [n.d.].

D25

The Chimes Quadrille. Composed for the *Musical Bouquet,* Most respectfully Inscribed to Charles Dickens, Esqr. Hoxton: J. Bingley. London: W. Strange. [n.d.].

D26

The Stars Their Early Vigils Keep, Song. As Sung at the Complimentary Dinner To Charles Dickens Esq. Written by Dr. O. W. Holmes to the favourite Scotch Air Gramachree, with Symphonies & Accompaniments. By E. L. White. Boston: Henry Prentiss. [n.d.]. In paper wrapper with Maclise portrait of Dickens surrounded by colored illumination.

D27

We're Dickens People   Words by Eleanor Whitmee Watson Set to Music by Gertrude Watson. Hull: From all Music Dealers and the Composer. [n.d.].

D28

Pickwick Galop. By J. W. Turner. Boston. [n.d.].

D29(1-10)

Ten songs based on Dickens's work.

1) "Good Night, Little Blossom" from *David Copperfield.* Words by Geo. W. Birdseye; music by M. Keller. Boston: Oliver Ditson & Co. 1868. Autographed "Charles Dickens."

2) "Little Blossom." Ballad by Stephen Glover. New York: Firth, Pond & Co. [n.d.].

3) "Dora: or, My Child-wife's Farewell." Ballad from *David Copperfield.* Written by George Linley. Composed by Gerald Stanley. London: Jullien & Co. [n.d.].

4) "Agnes: or, I Have Loved You All My Life." Ballard from *David Copperfield.* Written by George Vere Irving, Esq. Composed by Gerald Stanley. London: Jullien & Co. [n.d.].

5) "Clara." Ballad from *David Copperfield.* Written and composed by George Linley. London: Cramer, Beale & Co. [n.d.].

6) "What Are the Wild Waves Saying?" Duet on an incident in *Dombey And Son.* By Joseph Edwards Carpenter. Music by Stephen Glover. London: Robert Cocks & Co. [n.d.].

7) "What Are the Wild Waves Saying?" Duett [sic] between Paul and Florence in *Dombey And Son.* Music by Stephen Glover. New York: Wm. Hall & Son. [n.d.].

8) "Little Dorrit's Polka." Composed by Jules Normann. W. H. Montgomery's Dance Music. [n.p.]: In *Musical Bouquet.* [n.d.].

9) "The Chimes Quadrille." Composed for the *Musical Bouquet*. London: W. Strange. Hoxton: J. Bingley. [n.d.].

10) "Charles Dickens' Last Song, 'Autumn Leaves'." Music by Lesta Vese. [n.p.]: Louis Tripp. 1870.

D30

ALICIA OR THE MAGIC FISHBONE. AN OPERETTA FOR TREBLE VOICES BASED ON A STORY BY CHARLES DICKENS. LIBRETTO BY MARGARET ROSE. MUSIC BY THOMAS F. DUNHILL. London: Edward Arnold & Co. 1938.

8°. In original blue wrapper.

3 : CRITIQUES

D31

"Oliver Twist." In THE CHRISTIAN EXAMINER AND GENERAL RE-VIEW. Boston: James Munroe and Company. London: Wiley and Putnam. 1840.

8°. In three-fourths contemporary morocco with green marbled paper boards.

Vol. XXVII (Third Series, Vol. IX), pp. 161–174.

D32

"Humorists—Dickens and Thackeray." In ECLECTIC REVIEW. March 1849 (taken from ENGLISH REVIEW).

Pp. 370–379, extracted from magazine.

D33

"Humorists, Dickens and Thackeray." In LITTELL'S LIVING AGE, XXI. Boston: April–June 1849.

8°. In original dark brown embossed cloth. Also includes a review of *Dombey and Son*.

D34

LECTURES ON SUBJECTS CONNECTED WITH LITERATURE AND LIFE. BY EDWIN P. WHIPPLE. Boston: Ticknor, Reed, and Fields. MDCCCL.

12°. In original embossed brown cloth with yellow end papers. Advertising leaflet of four pages, dated 1 October 1849.

Second edition.

Lecture 2: "Novels and Novelists—Charles Dickens."

D35

"Charles Dickens and David Copperfield." ECLECTIC REVIEW. February 1851.

Pp. 247–258 extracted from magazine. From *Fraser's Magazine*.

D36

"A Letter from Hop-O-My-Thumb to Charles Dickens, Esq. Upon 'Frauds on the Fairies,' 'Whole Hogs,' Etc." [By George Cruikshank]. London: D. Bogue. [1854].

8°. Pamphlet of eight pages. See A147.

D37

"Charles Dickens." AMERICAN THEOLOGICAL REVIEW. January 1859.

Pp. 22-46 extracted from magazine.

D38

"The Genius of Dickens." In THE ATLANTIC MONTHLY. May 1867.

8°. In original buff wrapper.

D39

MODERN MEN OF LETTERS HONESTLY CRITICISED. BY J. HAIN FRISWELL. London: Hodder and Stoughton. MDCCCLXX.

8°. In original rust cloth decorated in gilt and black, with black end papers.

Dedication copy inscribed, "To Mr. Van de Weyer with the best wishes of the Author. Decr. 1870."

Chap. 1, "Charles Dickens."

D40

"Oliver Twist." By Edwin P. Whipple. In THE ATLANTIC MONTHLY. October 1876.

8°. In original orange wrapper.

D41

PHILOSOPHY OF CHARLES DICKENS. BY THE HON. ALBERT S. G. CANNING. London: Smith, Elder & Co. 1880.

8°. In original purple cloth.

D42

"Dickens as Dramatist." In LITTELL'S LIVING AGE. 19 August 1882.

8°. In original buff wrapper.

D43

THE HUMOUR AND PATHOS OF CHARLES DICKENS. WITH ILLUS-TRATIONS OF HIS MASTERY OF THE TERRIBLE AND THE PICTURES-QUE. SELECTED BY CHARLES KENT. London: Chapman and Hall, Limited. 1884.

8°. In original green cloth decorated in gilt and black with yellow end papers; uncut.

D44

STUDIEN UBER DIE ANFANGE VON DICKENS. BY DR. SIEGFRIED BENIGNUS. Esslingen: Wilh. Langguth. 1895.

8°. In grey wrapper.

D45

"Old Lamps for New Ones." By James MacArthur. THE BOOKMAN. November 1897.

Pp. 189–195 extracted from the magazine.

D46

CHARLES DICKENS A CRITICAL STUDY. BY GEORGE GISSING. New York: Dodd, Mead and Company. 1898.

8°. In original grey paper boards printed in black, red, and gold.

First edition.

D47

CHARLES DICKENS A CRITICAL STUDY. BY GEORGE GISSING. London, Glasgow, Dublin: Blackie & Son, Limited. 1898.

8°. In red cloth. (Victorian Era Series)

D48

"Charles Dickens." By Andrew Lang. THE FORTNIGHTLY REVIEW. December 1898.

Pp. 944-960 extracted from magazine.

D49

CHARLES DICKENS: HIS LIFE AND WORK. COURSE VII: BOOK-LOVERS READING CLUB. TALKS AND LECTURES BY ANDREW LANG, AMELIA E. BARR, AND JAMES L. HUGHES. EDITORIAL NOTES BY PROFESSOR T. M. PARROTT. Philadelphia: Press of The Booklovers Library. 1901.

8°. In brown wrapper with red seal of the club.

D50

CHARLES DICKENS A CRITICAL STUDY. BY GEORGE GISSING. WITH TOPOGRAPHICAL ILLUSTRATIONS BY F. G. KITTON. London: Gresham Publishing Company. [1902].

8°. In original red cloth with gilt lettering and decoration with grey end papers. (Imperial Edition)

D51

CHARLES DICKENS A CRITICAL STUDY. BY G. K. CHESTERTON. New York: Dodd, Mead & Company. 1906.

8°. In red cloth printed in gold.

First edition.

D52

STUDIES IN DICKENS EDITED FOR THE CHAUTAUQUA HOME READING SERIES BY MABELL S. C. SMITH. Chautauqua, New York: Chautauqua Press. 1910.

8°. In red cloth with black lettering and decoration.

D53

CHARLES DICKENS AND THE LAW. BY THOMAS ALEXANDER FYFE. London: Chapman & Hall, Limited. Edinburgh: William Hodge & Company. 1910.

8°. In original blue cloth.

D54

PHASES OF DICKENS THE MAN, HIS MESSAGE, AND HIS MISSION. BY J. CUMING WALTERS. London: Chapman and Hall, Ltd. 1911.

8°. In original olive green cloth with gilt lettering.

D55

CHARLES DICKENS AND HIS GIRL HEROINES. BY BELLE MOSES. New York, London: D. Appleton and Company. 1911.

8°. In original dark red cloth with white lettering.

D56

THE BOOKMAN. DICKENS NUMBERS. London: Hodder and Stoughton. 1901, 1908, 1910, 1912.

4°. Four numbers bound in one volume. In dark green cloth.

Ex libris William Glyde Wilkins.

D57

"The Obviousness of Dickens." By Samuel McChord Crothers. THE CENTURY MAGAZINE. February 1912.

Pp. 560-574 extracted from the magazine.

D58

THE CHARLES DICKENS ORIGINALS. BY EDWIN PUGH. New York: Charles Scribner's Sons. 1912.

8°. In original rough red cloth with gilt lettering.

D59

DICKENS STUDIES IN SIX NOVELS. BY THE HON. ALBERT S. G. CANNING. London, Leipsic: T. Fisher Unwin. 1912.

8°. In rust cloth with gilt lettering and decoration.

D60

IN DICKENS STREET. BY W. R. THOMSON. Glasgow: John Smith & Son, Ltd. London: Chapman & Hall, Ltd. 1912.

8°. In moss green cloth with gilt lettering.

D61

Three articles excised from periodicals: "Chronicle and Comment" from THE BOOKMAN. February 1912. "Charles Dickens as a Husband" by Lyndon Orr reprinted from THE BOOKMAN. March 1906. "In the Heart of Dickens Land. Some Pictures for Christmas-Time" by A. S. Hartrick, A.R.W.S. from THE PALL MALL MAGAZINE.

D62

"Dickens and Christmas." By G. K. Chesterton. In EVERYMAN. Christmas Number, 5 December 1913.

4°. In original white wrapper with portrait of Dickens.

D63

CHARLES DICKENS SOCIAL REFORMER THE SOCIAL TEACHINGS OF ENGLAND'S GREAT NOVELIST. BY W. WALTER CROTCH. London: Chapman & Hall, Ltd. 1913.

8°. In red cloth with gilt lettering.

D64

CHARLES DICKENS. BY ALGERNON CHARLES SWINBURNE. London: Chatto & Windus. 1913.

8°. In dark blue cloth with gilt lettering.

D65

CHARLES DICKENS IN CHANCERY. BY E. T. JAQUES. London: Longmans, Green and Co. 1914.

8°. In original peach-colored wrapper.

D66

"Dickens and Social Reform." In THE RICE INSTITUTE PAMPHLET. Houston, Texas: January 1916.

8°. In grey wrapper, as issued.

D67

THE PAGEANT OF DICKENS. BY W. WALTER CROTCH. London: Chapman & Hall, Ltd. 1916.

8°. In red cloth with gilt lettering. Second, revised edition.

D68

THE SOUL OF DICKENS. BY W. WALTER CROTCH. London: Chapman & Hall, Ltd. 1916.

8°. In red cloth.

D69

THE SECRET OF DICKENS. BY W. WALTER CROTCH. London: Chapman & Hall, Ltd. 1919.

8°. In red cloth with gilt lettering.

D70

DICKENS, READE, AND COLLINS SENSATION NOVELISTS A STUDY IN THE CONDITIONS AND THEORIES OF NOVEL WRITING IN VICTORIAN ENGLAND. BY WALTER C. PHILLIPS. New York: Columbia University Press. 1919.

8°. In green cloth. (Columbia University Studies in English and Comparative Literature)

D71

CHARLES DICKENS AND OTHER "SPIRITS OF THE AGE" DISCUSSED AND ANALYSED. BY ELIZABETH BARRETT BROWNING. London: Printed for Thomas J. Wise by Richard Clay and Sons, Ltd. 1919.

8°. Pamphlet reprinting a letter concerning R. H. Horne's *The New Spirit Of The Age*. One of 30 copies privately printed.

D72

THE TOUCHSTONE OF DICKENS. BY W. WALTER CROTCH. London: Chapman & Hall, Ltd. 1920.

8°. In red cloth with gilt lettering.

D73

CHARLES DICKENS FIFTY YEARS AFTER. GILBERT K. CHESTERTON. [London]: Privately printed by Clement Shorter. 1920.

4°. In original blue-grey stiff wrapper. No. 8 of 25 privately printed copies. Autographed "Clement Shorter."

D74

CRITICAL STUDIES OF THE WORKS OF CHARLES DICKENS. BY GEORGE GISSING. New York: Greenberg, Inc. 1924.

8°. In brown paper boards with cloth spine.

No. 630 of 1500 copies.

D75

CHARLES DICKENS A CRITICAL STUDY. BY G. K. CHESTERTON. New York: Dodd, Mead & Company. 1926.

8°. In red cloth with gilt lettering.

D76

CHARLES DICKENS' HEROINES AND WOMEN-FOLK; SOME THOUGHTS CONCERNING THEM. A LECTURE. BY CHARLES F. RIDEAL. London: The Roxburghe Press. [n.d.].

12°. In original dark green cloth with gilt lettering and decoration.

D77

CHARLES DICKENS AS A LEGAL HISTORIAN. BY WILLIAM S. HOLDS-WORTH. New Haven, Conn.: Yale University Press. 1928.

8°. In red cloth with tan spine and leather label.

D78

LEIGH HUNT AND CHARLES DICKENS THE SKIMPOLE CARICATURE. BY LUTHER A. BREWER. Cedar Rapids, Iowa: 1930.

8°. In beige paper boards with cloth spine. Limited to 300 privately printed copies.

D79

DICKENS. BY OSBERT SITWELL. London: Chatto & Windus. 1932.

8°. In cream-colored paper boards illustrated in brown. (Dolphin Books)

D80

CHARLES DICKENS HIS LIFE AND WORK. BY STEPHEN LEACOCK.
Garden City, New York: Doubleday, Doran and Company, Inc. 1934.

8°. In original tangerine cloth with cream end papers.

D81

DICKENS THE MAN AND THE BOOK. BY RALPH STRAUS. London,
Edinburgh, etc.: Thomas Nelson and Sons, Ltd. 1936.

8°. In original green cloth with gilt lettering.

D82

MEDICINE IN THE SHAKESPEAREAN PLAYS AND DICKENS' DOC-
TORS. BY HERMAN POMERANZ, M.D. New York: Powell Publications.
1936.

8°. In original dark blue cloth with gilt lettering.

D83

THE FACTS ABOUT *A CHRISTMAS CAROL*. BY E. ALLEN OSBORNE.
London: Printed for the author by The Bradley Press. 1937.

8°. In bright red cloth with green leather label. No. 4 of 55 copies privately
printed on Noggin hand-made paper.

D84

CHARLES DICKENS THE PROGRESS OF A RADICAL. BY T. A. JACK-
SON. New York: International Publications. 1938.

8°. In original pink cloth. A Marxist study.

D85

THE LAWYERS OF DICKENS AND THEIR CLERKS. BY ROBERT D.
NEELY. Boston: The Christopher Publishing House. 1938.

8°. In original red cloth with gilt lettering.

Second edition.

D86

DOCTORS, NURSES AND DICKENS. BY ROBERT D. NEELY. Boston:
The Christopher Publishing House. 1939.

8°. In original black cloth with gilt lettering.

D87

DICKENS' WORKS IN GERMANY 1837-1937. BY ELLIS N. GUMMER.
Oxford: Clarendon Press. 1940.

8°. In dark blue cloth with seal of the University Press.

D88

"The Tale of Two Cities." By William Sterling Battis. Reprinted from THE
PLATFORM. Chicago: [n.d.].

4:WORKS ASSOCIATED WITH OR
RELATED TO DICKENS

D89

THE HISTORY AND ANTIQUITIES OF ROCHESTER. Rochester: Printed by W. Wildash. 1817.

8°. In half brown calf and marbled paper boards. Front cover lacking.

D90

"To C. Dickens, Esq. on His Departure for America." By Thomas Hood. In THE NEW MONTHLY MAGAZINE. February 1842.

8°. In original wrapper.

D91

"Welcome to Charles Dickens. The Boz Ball." New York: 1842.

8°. Leaflet with copy of invitation, dated 14 February 1842.

D92

"Dickens's AMERICAN NOTES." In THE WESTMINSTER REVIEW. February 1843.

8°. In original white wrapper, back lacking.

D93

LETTER TO A LADY IN FRANCE OR THE SUPPOSED FAILURE OF A NATIONAL BANK, THE SUPPOSED DELINQUENCY OF THE NATIONAL GOVERNMENT, THE DEBTS OF THE SEVERAL STATES, AND REPUDIATION; WITH ANSWERS TO ENQUIRIES CONCERNING THE BOOKS OF CAPT. MARRYAT AND MR. DICKENS. BY THOMAS G. CARY. Boston: Benjamin H. Greene. 1844.

8°. Lacking cover.

Second edition.

D94

TRAGEDIES; TO WHICH ARE ADDED A FEW SONNETS AND VERSES. BY T. N. TALFOURD. London: Edward Moxon. MDCCCXLIV.

12°. In original red marbled paper boards with half navy-blue calf, red marbled end papers, edges marbled.

Includes "To Charles Dickens on His 'Oliver Twist'."

D95

THE BOOK OF BALLADS. EDITED BY BON GAULTIER. ILLUSTRATED BY ALFRED CROWQUILL. London: Wm. S. Orr and Co. 1845.

16°. Rebound in full brown levant by Zaehnsdorf; original cloth cover included.

D96

THE BATTLE OF LONDON LIFE; OR, BOZ AND HIS SECRETARY. BY MORNA. WITH SIX DESIGNS ON STONE BY GEORGE SALA. London: George Reirce. 1849.

8°. In original stiff green wrapper.

D97

"Vaulting Ambition of Mr. Dickens." In THE MAN IN THE MOON. June 1849.

24°. In original white printed wrapper, as issued.

D98

THE IMMORTAL; A DRAMATIC ROMANCE AND OTHER POEMS. BY JAMES NACK. New York: Stringer and Townsend. 1850.

12°. In original embossed dark green cloth with yellow end papers.

Includes "Dedicatory Lines to Charles Dickens, Esq."

D99

"To Charles Dickens" by Walter Savage Landor. In THE INTERNATIONAL MONTHLY MAGAZINE. December 1850.

8°. In original buff wrapper.

D100

DICKENS'S DICTIONARY OF PARIS. [n.p. 1856.]

16°. In original blue cloth decorated with red and black. Blue end papers with advertising.

D101

OLD STYLES'S. BY HENRY SPICER, ESQ. London: Bosworth & Harrison. MDCCCLIX.

8°. In original purple cloth with gilt lettering and yellow end papers.

Dedicated to Dickens.

D102

Advertising leaflet announcing Dickens's readings 1 and 14 May 1866, at St. James's Hall.

D103

"Charles Dickens" and "A Welcome to Dickens," by F. J. Parmenter. In HARPER'S WEEKLY. A JOURNAL OF CIVILIZATION. New York: 30 November 1867.

D104

AN EPISTLE TO "BOZ" ALIAS CHARLES DICKENS. BY ZEDEKIAH COMITATUS, M.P.E.C. Skaggadduhunk: Scantlewood, Timberlake & Co., Printers to the North River Society. 1867.

12°. Pamphlet of twelve pages. A scurrilous attack on Dickens in verse form.

D105

Printed notice certifying that although Dickens was suffering from "a Neuralgic Affection of the right foot," he would give his scheduled reading. Signed "Fordyce Barker, M.D." [April 1868?].

D106

INFELICIA. BY ADAH ISAACS MENKEN. London, Paris, New York: 1869.

12°. In original green cloth with gilt lettering and brown end papers.

Dedicated to Dickens.

D107

"A Man of the Crowd to Charles Dickens," by E. J. Milliken. In THE GEN-TLEMAN'S MAGAZINE. August 1870.

8°. In original wrapper.

Also "Charles Dickens. In Memoriam" by Blanchard Jerrold, pp. 228-241.

D108

"Charles Dickens." In ECLECTIC REVIEW. 1870.

Articles written at the time of Dickens's death for *Fraser's Magazine, St. Paul's,* and *Macmillan's Magazine.*

D109

"The Death of Charles Dickens." ECLECTIC REVIEW. August 1870.

Article copied from *The Saturday Review;* pp. 217-224 extracted from magazine.

D110

"Four Months with Charles Dickens. During his First Visit to America (in 1842). By His Secretary." Part I. THE ATLANTIC MONTHLY. October 1870.

Pp. 476-482 extracted from magazine.

D111

"The Voice of Christmas Past." HARPER'S NEW MONTHLY MAGAZINE. January 1871.

Pp. 187-190 extracted from magazine.

D112

"Charles Dickens." BLACKWOOD'S EDINBURGH MAGAZINE. June 1871.

Pp. 673-695 extracted from magazine. (Also reprint of this article in *Eclectic Review,* September 1871.)

D113

POEMS. BY BRET HARTE. Boston: James R. Osgood and Company, Late Ticknor & Fields, and Fields, Osgood & Co. 1871.

12°. In original green cloth with brown end papers.

Includes "Dickens in Camp."

D114

THE DICKENS DICTIONARY. A KEY TO THE CHARACTERS AND PRINCIPAL INCIDENTS IN THE TALES OF CHARLES DICKENS. BY GILBERT A. PIERCE. WITH ADDITIONS BY WILLIAM A. WHEELER. Boston: James R. Osgood and Company (Late Ticknor & Fields, and Fields, Osgood & Co). 1872.

8°. In original embossed green cloth with brown end papers.

D115

"Dickens in Relation to Criticism," by George Henry Lewes. ECLECTIC REVIEW. April 1872.

Pp. 445-453 extracted from magazine. Taken from *Fortnightly Review*.

D116

DICKENS'S LONDON: OR, LONDON IN THE WORKS OF CHARLES DICKENS. BY T. EDGAR PEMBERTON. London: Samuel Tinsley. 1876.

8°. In original dark green embossed cloth decorated in gilt and black.

D117

"The Shadow on Dickens's Life," by Edwin P. Whipple. THE ATLANTIC MONTHLY. August 1877.

Pp. 117-122 extracted from magazine.

D118

CHARLES DICKENS, SKETCHES IN ACROSTICS. London: Privately printed. 1879.

8°. Pamphlet in original stiff blue wrapper.

D119

DICKENS'S DICTIONARY OF LONDON, 1879. London: *All the Year Round* Office. New York: Macmillan & Co. 1879.

8°. In original grey wrapper.

D120

THE LIFE OF CHARLES JAMES MATHEWS, CHIEFLY AUTOBIO-GRAPHICAL, WITH SELECTIONS FROM HIS CORRESPONDENCE AND SPEECHES. EDITED BY CHARLES DICKENS [Jr.]. New York: Harper & Brothers. 1879.

4°. No. 71, Franklin Square Library.

D121

TEARS AND LAUGHTER. THE CHARLES DICKENS PARLOR ALBUM OF ILLUSTRATIONS. SELECTED CHRONOLOGICALLY ARRANGED ACCORDING TO THEIR ORIGINAL PUBLICATION. New York: G. W. Carleton & Co. MDCCCLXXIX.

8°. In original rust cloth decorated in gilt and black with cream end papers.

D122

"The Letters of Charles Dickens." In THE NATION. 4 December 1879.

4°. As issued. Weekly publication of Harper and Brothers.

Includes review of the two volumes of letters edited by Dickens's sister-in-law and his eldest daughter.

D123

"Letters of Charles Dickens." In APPLETON'S JOURNAL. January 1880.

8°. In original peach-colored wrapper, as issued.

Includes review of the two volumes of letters edited by Dickens's sister-in-law and his eldest daughter.

D124

"The Letters of Charles Dickens." In SCRIBNER'S MONTHLY ILLUS-TRATED MAGAZINE. January 1880.

8°. In original violet wrapper, as issued.

Includes review of the two volumes of letters edited by Dickens's sister-in-law and his eldest daughter.

D125(1)

"The Letters of Charles Dickens," by William Minto. In LITTELL'S LIVING AGE. 3 January 1880.

8°. In original buff wrapper, as issued.

D125(2)

"The Letters of Charles Dickens," by William Minto. In THE ECLECTIC MAGAZINE. February 1880.

8°. In original green wrapper, as issued.

Includes article from *Littell's Living Age*.

D126

"The Homes and Haunts of Charles Dickens," by A. H. Wall. THE ILLUS-TRATED SPORTING AND DRAMATIC NEWS. 10, 17 January 1880.

Pp. 406-409, 10 January; pp. 434-436, 17 January extracted from magazines.

D127

"Recent Biography, etc.: The Letters of Charles Dickens," by Eugene L. Didier. In THE NORTH AMERICAN REVIEW. March 1880.

8°. In original pink wrapper, as issued.

D128

THE DICKENS DICTIONARY A KEY TO THE CHARACTERS AND PRINCIPAL INCIDENTS IN THE TALES OF CHARLES DICKENS. BY GILBERT A. PIERCE. Boston: Houghton, Osgood and Company. Cambridge: The Riverside Press. 1880.

8°. In green cloth with black end papers.

D129
IN KENT WITH CHARLES DICKENS. BY THOMAS FROST. London: Tinsley Brothers. 1880.

8°. In blue cloth with gilt lettering.

D130
"In and Out of London with Dickens. 'Spendid Strolling'." LONDON MAGAZINE. 1881.

Pp. 32-45 extracted from magazine.

D131
DICKENS'S DICTIONARY OF LONDON, 1881. (THIRD YEAR) AN UNCONVENTIONAL HANDBOOK. London: *All the Year Round* Office. 1881.

8°. In original printed grey wrapper.

D132
" 'Phiz' and 'Boz'." LITTELL'S LIVING AGE. 28 October 1882.

Pp. 254-256 extracted from magazine. Taken from *The Spectator*.

D133(1)
THE CHARLES DICKENS BIRTHDAY BOOK. COMPILED AND EDITED BY HIS ELDEST DAUGHTER. WITH FIVE ILLUSTRATIONS BY HIS YOUNGEST DAUGHTER. New York: Thomas Whittaker. [1882].

8°. In olive green cloth printed in brown and gold, edges gilt.

D133(2)
A second copy with date of publication, 1882, on title page.

D134
THE CHARLES DICKENS BIRTHDAY BOOK. COMPILED AND EDITED BY HIS ELDEST DAUGHTER. WITH FIVE ILLUSTRATIONS BY HIS YOUNGEST DAUGHTER. London: Chapman and Hall, Limited. Philadelphia: J. P. [sic] Lippincott & Co. 1882.

8°. In grey cloth printed with brown, blue and gold.

First edition, with uncorrected title page.

D135
DICKENS BIRTHDAY BOOK. WITH 12 COLOURED ILLUSTRATIONS. London, Paris, New York: Raphael Tuck & Sons, Ltd. [n.d.].

8°. In blue cloth with gilt lettering and design.

D136
ABOUT ENGLAND WITH DICKENS. BY ALFRED RIMMER. London: Chatto and Windus. 1883.

8°. In original olive drab cloth decorated in gilt and black.

D137

DICKENS'S DICTIONARY OF THE THAMES, FROM ITS SOURCE TO THE NORE. London: Macmillan & Co. 1883.

16°. In original olive drab cloth decorated in black and red; pale green end papers with advertising matter.

D138

RECREATIONS OF A LITERARY MAN OR DOES WRITING PAY? BY PERCY FITZGERALD. London: Chatto and Windus. 1883.

8°. In original olive green cloth decorated in dark red and gilt.

D139

LIFE AND LABOURS OF HABLOT KNIGHT BROWNE. "PHIZ." BY DAVID CROAL THOMSON. WITH ONE HUNDRED AND THIRTY IL-LUSTRATIONS. London: Chapman and Hall, Limited. 1884.

4°. In original mustard colored cloth with yellow end papers. No. 15 of 250 copies.

D140

PERSONAL TRAITS OF BRITISH AUTHORS. EDITED BY EDWARD T. MASON. New York: Charles Scribner's Sons. 1885.

8°. In original wine colored cloth.

D141

LITERARY LANDMARKS OF LONDON. BY LAURENCE HUTTON. Boston: James R. Osgood and Company. 1885.

8°. In olive green cloth decorated in red with black lettering.

D142

"Souvenir of Dickens Carnival in Aid of the Women's Educational and Industrial Union." Boston: 17 February 1885.

4°. Pamphlet in green wrapper.

D143

LONDON RAMBLES "EN ZIGZAG," WITH CHARLES DICKENS. BY ROBERT ALLBUT. A NEW EDITION, WITH ILLUSTRATIONS. London: S. Drewett. [1886].

8°. In tan cloth with portrait of Dickens and advertisements for "Woods' Family Hotel, Furnival's Inn, Holborn."

D144(1)

LONDON AND COUNTRY RAMBLES WITH CHARLES DICKENS. BY ROBERT ALLBUT. REVISED EDITION, WITH ILLUSTRATIONS. London: Sheppard & St. John. [1886].

8°. In brown cloth printed in gold, edges gilt.

D144(2)

A second copy in original red cloth with gilt lettering and decoration; floral end papers; edges gilt.

D145(1)
THE BOOK FANCIER. OR THE ROMANCE OF BOOK COLLECTING. BY PERCY FITZGERALD. London: Sampson Low, Martson, Searle, & Rivington. 1887.

8°. In original wine-colored cloth with leather spine.

Includes "Grangerising and Dickensiana."

D145(2)
A second copy in dark blue cloth.

D146
"Readings from Dickens," by His Son Charles Dickens. Brooklyn, New York: Academy of Music. 26 October 1887.

8°. Program of the reading.

D147
"Programme of the Charles Dickens Bazaar in aid of the Fund for the Restoration of St. Peter's Church, Saffron Hill, at the Holborn Town Hall, on Wednesday, Thursday, & Friday, June 27th, 28th, & 29th, 1888. To be Opened by Her Royal Highness Princess Henry of Battenberg (Princess Beatrice)."

8°. Printed lengthwise. In original wrapper printed in grey.

Excerpts from Dickens's text together with illustrations by various artists.

D148
OF MANY MEN. BY T. C. EVANS. New York: The American News Company. 1888.

8°. In original bright blue cloth with gilt lettering.

Presentation copy from the author, dated "Hawk's Lodge West Milford N.Y. Aug. 3ᵈ 1894."

D149
A sheet of forty-one decal transfers of Dickens characters, in color. [c. 1890].

D150
"Dickens and 'Punch'," by F. G. Kitton. In THE ENGLISH ILLUSTRATED MAGAZINE. August 1891.

8°. In original pale green wrapper.

D151(1)
A WEEK'S TRAMP IN DICKENS-LAND. TOGETHER WITH PERSONAL REMINISCENCES OF THE 'INIMITABLE BOZ.' BY WILLIAM R. HUGHES. London: Chapman & Hall, Limited. 1891.

8°. In green cloth printed in gold with dark green end papers.

D151(2)
A second copy in original grey cloth with half black leather; white end papers; top edge gilt. London: Chapman & Hall, Limited. Boston: Estes and Lauriat. 1891.

D152(1)
DICKENS'S DICTIONARY OF THE THAMES, FROM ITS SOURCE TO
THE NORE. 1891. AN UNCONVENTIONAL HANDBOOK. WITH MAPS.
EDITED BY CHARLES DICKENS, JR. London: J. Smith. 1891.
8°. In drab-green cloth printed in black and red.

D152(2)
A copy of the 1896 edition; as D152(1).

D153
DICKENS' DICTIONARY OF LONDON. London: E. J. Larby. [n.d.].
8°. In flexible tan cloth. With "Preface to the New Edition."

D154
PICKWICKIAN MANNERS AND CUSTOMS. BY PERCY FITZGERALD.
London: The Roxburghe Press, Limited. [n.d.].
8°. In brick-red cloth.

D155
"Charles Dickens in Paris," by George Augustus Sala. In PHILMAY'S IL-
LUSTRATED WINTER ANNUAL. London: Walter Haddon's Central Publishing & Advertising Offices. 1892.
8°. In stiff white wrapper printed in black and red.

D156
THROUGH THE YEAR WITH DICKENS COMPILED BY HIS ELDEST
DAUGHTER. Boston: DeWolfe, Fiske & Co. [n.d.].
8°. In original embossed green suede with gilt lettering; edges gilt.

D157
CROSS CURRENTS. A NOVEL. BY MARY ANGELA DICKENS. New
York: D. Appleton and Company. 1892.
8°. In original blue cloth decorated in dark blue with gilt lettering; figured
blue end papers.

D158
"Disappearing Dickensland," by Charles Dickens [the younger]. NORTH
AMERICAN REVIEW. June 1893.
Pp. 670-684 extracted from magazine.

D159
"A Famous Illustrator of Dickens," by George Holme. MUNSEY'S MAGA-
ZINE. October 1893.
Pp. 37-44 extracted from magazine. [Frederick Barnard]

D160
"Charles Dickens," by A. D. Hurd. MUNSEY'S MAGAZINE. March 1894.
Pp. 647–660 extracted from magazine.

D161

BOZLAND DICKENS' PLACES AND PEOPLE. BY PERCY FITZGERALD.
London: Downey & Co. 1895.

8°. In blue cloth.

D162

"Glimpses of Charles Dickens," I, II, by Charles Dickens the younger. NORTH
AMERICAN REVIEW. May, June 1895.

Pp. 525—537, 677—684 extracted from magazines.

D163

LITTLE JOURNEYS TO THE HOMES OF GOOD MEN AND GREAT: BY
ELBERT HUBBARD: CHARLES DICKENS. New York, London: G. P.
Putnam's Sons. New Rochelle, New York: The Knickerbocker Press. September 1895.

8°. Pamphlet with outer leaf as wrapper.

D164

"Notes on Some Dickens Places and People," by Charles Dickens the younger.
In PALL MALL MAGAZINE. July 1896.

8°. In original stiff white wrapper printed in red and green.

D165

IN JAIL WITH CHARLES DICKENS. BY ALFRED TRUMBLE. New York:
Francis P. Harper. 1896.

8°. In original light green cloth with green decoration and gilt lettering; top
edge gilt.

D166

GREAT THINKERS AND WORKERS. SELECTED AND EDITED BY
ROBERT COCHRANE. London, Edinburgh: W. & R. Chambers, Limited.
[1896?].

8°. In original brown cloth with brown and gilt decoration and decorative
end papers.

Prize book from Leicester School Board to Albert Robinson, dated Jan. 1896.

D167

AN INDEX TO *PICKWICK*. BY C. M. NEALE. London: J. Hitchcock, for
the author. 1897.

8°. In original green paper boards with cloth spine.

D168

ABOUT ENGLAND WITH DICKENS. BY ALFRED RIMMER. A NEW
EDITION, WITH FIFTY-EIGHT ILLUSTRATIONS. London: Chatto &
Windus. 1899.

8°. In blue cloth printed in black and gold.

D169

MY LITERARY LIFE. BY MRS. LYNN LINTON. London: Hodder and Stoughton. 1899.

8°. In yellow cloth with red lettering.

Chapter II, "Landor, Dickens, Thackeray."

D170

"The Writing of Pickwick, I." THE BOOK BUYER. October 1900.

Pp. 189—194 extracted from magazine.

D171(1)

DICKENS AS AN EDUCATOR. BY JAMES L. HUGHES. New York: D. Appleton and Company. 1901.

8°. In original flexible red leather.

Presentation copy to Georgina Hogarth.

D171(2)

A copy of the regular edition in original dark grey cloth decorated in red and black with grey-blue end papers.

Presentation copy from the author to Henry F. Dickens, inscribed "Toronto December 1st 1900. 'Let us do justice and honor to the nature of a child. Dickens'."

D172

"Dramatisations of Dickens," by Paul Wilstach. THE BOOKMAN. September 1901.

Pp. 52—62 extracted from magazine.

D173

"Characters from Dickens as Impersonated by Mr. Bransby Williams." THE SKETCH. 10 September—19 October 1902.

Photographs extracted from magazines.

D174

DICKENS' LONDON. BY FRANCIS MILTOUN. Boston: L. C. Page & Company. MDCCCCIII.

8°. In original grey cloth with gilt and red decoration and gilt lettering.

D175

THE REAL DICKENS LAND WITH AN OUTLINE OF DICKENS'S LIFE. BY H. SNOWDEN WARD AND CATHARINE WEEK BARNES WARD. London: Chapman & Hall, Limited. 1904.

8°. In original red cloth with gilt decoration and lettering.

D176
THE GREAT FOLK OF OLD MARYLEBONE. WRITTEN BY MRS. BAILLIE SAUNDERS. WITH ILLUSTRATIONS BY THE AUTHOR AND A MAP. London: Henry J. Glaisher. 1904.

8°. In original blue cloth with white spine.

D177
SYNOPSES OF DICKENS'S NOVELS. BY J. WALKER McSPADDEN. New York: Thomas Y. Crowell & Co. [1904].

12°. In original green cloth with white lettering.

D178
"The Dickens Fellowship. Birthday Celebration . . . The President's Address." 8 February 1904.

8°. Leaflet with speech of Sir Henry Fielding Dickens, autographed.

D179
"The Convict's Tribute to Charles Dickens." By Helen Brinckman. 1904.

Leaflet in stiff white wrapper.

With presentation note from author to Mr. Miller, dated 16 Dec. 1904.

D180
"Christmas in Dickensland a Reverie." By J. W. T. Ley. London: Office of *The Dickensian*. 1905.

12°. Leaflet of twelve pages in stiff red wrapper.

D181
"George Alfred Williams A New Illustrator of Dickens." In THE INTERNATIONAL STUDIO. December 1905.

8°. In original green wrapper.

D182
"The Old Familiar Faces New Drawings by Reginald Birch Illustrating Scenes in the Lives of Some of Dickens' Greatest Characters." In THE READER. July 1906.

16°. In original illustrated white wrapper.

D183
THE DICKENS CONCORDANCE. BY MARY WILLIAMS. London: Francis Griffiths. 1907.

8°. In original dark green cloth.

D184
SUPPRESSED PLATES WOOD ENGRAVINGS, &C. BY GEORGE SOMES LAYARD. London: Adam and Charles Black. 1907.

8°. In original olive green cloth with gilt decoration and lettering.

Chapter IV, "Dickens' Cancelled Plates."

D185

"Dickens and 'Father Christmas' A Yule-Tide Appeal for the Babes of Famine Street." THE NINETEENTH CENTURY. December 1907.

Pp. 1014-1029 extracted from magazine.

D186

ABOUT DICKENS BEING A FEW ESSAYS ON THEMES SUGGESTED BY THE NOVELS. BY HENRY LEFFMANN. Philadelphia: Published by the Author. 1908.

8°. In brown paper boards and cloth spine.

D187

"Charles Dickens in Picture and Story." In THE BOOK NEWS MONTHLY. November 1908.

8°. In original yellow wrapper printed in brown.

D188

SYNOPSES OF DICKENS'S NOVELS. BY J. WALKER McSPADDEN. New York: Thomas Y. Crowell Company. [1909].

8°. In red cloth printed in gold.

D189

A DICKENS DICTIONARY. BY ALEX J. PHILIP. London: George Routledge & Sons, Limited. New York: E. P. Dutton & Co. 1909.

8°. In original red cloth.

D190

"The Topical Pickwick." THE BOOKMAN. April 1910.

Pp. 113–115 extracted from magazine.

D191

DICKENS AND THE DRAMA. BY S. J. ADAIR FITZ-GERALD. New York: Charles Scribner's Sons. 1910.

8°. In original red cloth.

D192

RAMBLES WITH AN AMERICAN. BY CHRISTIAN TEARLE. New York: Duffield & Company. 1910.

8°. In original red cloth with gilt lettering and decoration.

D193

"Dickens's Children Four Drawings," by Jessie Willcox Smith. In SCRIBNER'S MAGAZINE. December 1910.

8°. In original illustrated white wrapper.

D194

"The Charles Dickens Testimonial. Have You Bought Your Dickens Stamps?" In THE STRAND MAGAZINE. December 1910.

8°. Wrapper lacking.

D195

GAD'S HILL PLACE AND CHARLES DICKENS. BY EDWIN HARRIS. ILLUSTRATED. Rochester: Edwin Harris & Sons. 1910.

8°. In original red paper boards.

Inscribed: "Original Edition of 150 copies sold by Edwin Harris to Arthur G. Fuller of Groton, Mass., U.S.A. Eastgate, Rochester. 8h Feb. 1912."

D196

THE DICKENS COUNTRY. BY FREDERIC G. KITTON. London: Adam and Charles Black. 1911.

8°. In original dark green cloth with gilt lettering and decoration.

D197

"A Mystery of Dickens," by Andrew Lang. BLACKWOOD'S MAGAZINE. May 1911.

Pp. 670-681 extracted from magazine.

D198

"Why I Shall Buy the Dickens Stamp," by Andrew Lang. In THE CONNOISSEUR. March 1911.

8°. In original white illustrated wrapper.

D199

"The Dickens Centenary and Some New Appreciations." In CURRENT LITERATURE. June 1911.

8°. In original white wrapper.

D200

CHARLES DICKENS CENTENARY FESTIVAL. DICKENSIANA. EDITED BY EADE MONTEFIORE. London: For Robert Arthur. [1911].

8°. In original red wrapper with white label.

D201

DICKENS'S HONEYMOON AND WHERE HE SPENT IT. BY ALEX. J. PHILIP. London: Chapman & Hall, Ltd. Gravesend: Bryant & Backstraw, Ltd. 1912.

8°. In original green wrapper.

D202

DICKENS'S CHILDREN. TEN DRAWINGS BY JESSIE WILLCOX SMITH. New York: Charles Scribner's Sons. MCMXII.

4°. In original olive drab cloth with colored illustration and gilt lettering.

D203

THE DICKENS SOUVENIR OF 1912.´EDITED BY DION CLAYTON CAL-
THROP AND MAX PEMBERTON. London: The *Daily Telegraph* Centenary
Fund by Chapman and Hall, Limited. 1912.

4°. In original red cloth with gilt lettering and flowered end papers.

D204

THE ANCESTRY OF CATHERINE THOMSON HOGARTH THE WIFE
OF CHARLES DICKENS, NOVELIST. BY JOHN CHRISTIE. Edinburgh:
William J. Hay. MCMXII.

8°. Leaflet in original brown wrapper.

One of 250 copies privately printed.

D205

FROM DAY TO DAY WITH DICKENS. COMPILED BY MARY E. SALIS-
BURY. New York: Barse & Hopkins. 1912.

8°. In original green cloth with decoration and lettering in gilt and white.

D206

JOHN FORSTER AND HIS FRIENDSHIPS. BY RICHARD RENTON. London: Chapman and Hall, Ltd. 1912.

8°. In dark blue cloth.

D207

FAMOUS HOUSES AND LITERARY SHRINES OF LONDON. BY A. ST.
JOHN ADCOCK. London: J. M. Dent & Sons, Ltd. New York: E. P. Dutton
& Co. 1912.

8°. In original red cloth with gilt lettering and decoration.

D208

"Dickens in America Fifty Years Ago," by Joseph Jackson. THE WORLD'S
WORK. January 1912.

Pp. 283–294 extracted from magazine.

D209

"My Father and His Friends," by Alfred Tennyson Dickens. COSMOPOLITAN
MAGAZINE. January 1912.

Pp. 148–159 extracted from magazine.

D210

"Dickens Characters in Real Life," by Harold Begbie. THE CENTURY
MAGAZINE. January 1912.

Pp. 323–338 extracted from magazine. "Old Friends from Dickens," four illustrations by S. J. Woolf.

D211
"Dickens in America," by Charles Randall Hart. WILLIAMS LITERARY MONTHLY. February 1912.

Pp. 259–267 extracted from magazine.

D212
"A Costume Pageant of Leading Dickens Characters." In THE STRAND MAGAZINE. February 1912.

8°.

D213
"Charles Dickens: A Tribute," by Agnes Lee. In THE NORTH AMERICAN REVIEW. February 1912.

8°.

D214
"A Centenary Meeting," by H.W.N. In THE LIVING AGE. 9 March 1912.

8°. In original buff wrapper.

D215
"Dickens' Vital Hold on the Imagination (with illustrations)." In CURRENT LITERATURE. March 1912.

8°. In original orange wrapper.

D216
"The Loves of Charles Dickens." In THE AMERICAN REVIEW OF RE-VIEWS. March 1912.

8°. In original white wrapper with blue lettering.

D217
"The Grandchildren of Charles Dickens Who Will Benefit by the Centenary Fund." In THE STRAND MAGAZINE. March 1912.

8°. Wrapper lacking.

D218
THE CONNOISSEUR. Dickens Centenary Exhibition Number. April 1912.

8°. In original illustrated white wrapper.

D219
"Official Guide and Souvenir of Grand Dickens Bazaar and Industrial Ex-hibition." Tooting Congregational Church. May 1912.

8°. In original brown wrapper.

D220

WHO'S WHO IN DICKENS. COMPILED BY THOMAS ALEXANDER FYFE. London, New York, Toronto: Hodder and Stoughton. 1913.

8°. In original brown cloth.

Second edition.

D221

THE DICKENS YEAR BOOK. COMPILED BY LOIS E. PRENTISS AND GERTRUDE C. SPAULDING. ILLUSTRATIONS BY DAN SAYRE GROES-BECK. Chicago: A. C. McClurg & Co. 1913.

8°. In original brown paper boards with colored illustration and brown lettering.

D222

MY SKETCHES FROM DICKENS. BY BRANSBY WILLIAMS. London: Chapman & Hall, Ltd. 1913.

8°. In original orange and white wrapper. Stamped "Presentation copy."

D223

CHARLES DICKENS AN APPRECIATION. BY CHARLES DUDLEY WARNER. Newark, New Jersey: The Carteret Book Club. 1913.

12°. In original ivory paper boards with paper labels.

D224

"The Sportsmen of Dickens," by W. Walter Crotch. WINDSOR MAGAZINE. March 1913.

Pp. 549–559 extracted from magazine.

D225

"A Christmas Carol by Charles Dickens Retold in Pictures," by Arthur I. Keller. In THE LADIES' HOME JOURNAL. December 1913.

4°. In original orange wrapper illustrated in color.

D226

A DICKENS PILGRIMAGE. London: John Murray. 1914.

8°. In grey cloth printed in dark blue. (The Times Series)

D227

A DICKENS PILGRIMAGE. New York: E. P. Dutton and Company. 1914.

8°. In original red cloth. (The Times Series)

D228

THE DICKENS DICTIONARY A KEY TO THE PLOTS AND CHARAC-TERS IN THE TALES OF CHARLES DICKENS WITH COPIOUS IN-DEXES AND BIBLIOGRAPHY. BY GILBERT A. PIERCE. WITH ADDI-TIONS OF WLLIAM A. WHEELER. A NEW AND REVISED EDITION ILLUSTRATED WITH ETCHINGS. Boston and New York: Houghton Mifflin Company. 1914.

8°. In original wine colored cloth.

D229

WEEK-ENDS IN DICKENS LAND. A HANDBOOK FOR THE RAMBLER. BY DUNCAN MOUL. London: St. Bride's Press. [n.d.].

8°. In original white paper boards. (A Bijou Handbook for the Cyclist and Rambler with Map)

D230

"A Dickens Fireside Fantasy," by Stephen Leacock. In THE BOOKMAN. April 1915.

8°. In original yellow wrapper.

D231(1)

IN DICKENS'S LONDON. BY F. HOPKINSON SMITH. ILLUSTRATED WITH CHARCOAL DRAWINGS BY THE AUTHOR. New York: Charles Scribner's Sons. MCMXVI.

Large 8°. In green cloth printed in gold and light green. (Also portfolio of sketches, see C28)

D231(2)

A second copy in light green paper boards with white cloth spine, lettering and decoration in green.

D232

MY DICKENS FRIENDS. BY FRANK SPEAIGHT. New York: James B. Pond. 1916.

8°. In purple cloth.

A collection of verses about Dickens's characters.

D233

A collection of forty pieces: programs, advertisements for lectures and readings from Dickens's works. 1884–1916.

D234

DICKENSIAN INNS & TAVERNS. BY B. W. MATZ. London: Cecil Palmer. 1922.

8°. In original blue cloth.

D235

DICKENSIAN INNS & TAVERNS. BY B. W. MATZ. New York: Charles Scribner's Sons. 1922.

8°. In blue cloth.

Ex libris Henry Alexander.

D236

MEMORIES OF A HOSTESS. A CHRONICLE OF EMINENT FRIEND-SHIPS DRAWN CHIEFLY FROM THE DIARIES OF MRS. JAMES T. FIELDS. BY M. A. DE WOLFE HOWE. Boston: The Atlantic Monthly Press. 1922.

8°. In original olive drab boards with cloth spine and paper label. Chapter V, "With Dickens in America."

D237

"Charles Dickens," by G. K. Chesterton. In THE LIVING AGE. February 1922.

8°. In original orange wrapper.

Address by Chesterton to the Dickens Fellowship on his election to the Presidency.

D238

A REVERIE. BY HOWARD DUFFIELD. New York. 1922.

8°. Leaflet, privately printed, in original cream wrapper.

Inscribed "To William J. Stone from his friend, Howard Duffield. Dec. 22 '22," with accompanying letter.

D239(1)

DICKENS IN CAMP. BY BRET HARTE. San Francisco: John Howell. 1922.

12°. In grey paper boards with buff cloth spine.

No. 70 of 350 copies, privately printed.

D239(2)

A second copy, no. 303, in grey-green paper boards varying slightly from D239(1).

Presentation copy from John Howell to Clark Prescott Bissett.

D240

DICKENS IN CAMP. BY BRET HARTE. San Francisco: Printed by John Henry Nash from MS. at Mills College. MDCCCCXXIII.

4°. In stiff floral wrapper.

Facsimile edition, mounted with red ruled border.

D241

A DICKENS ATLAS INCLUDING TWELVE WALKS IN LONDON WITH CHARLES DICKENS. BY ALBERT A. HOPKINS AND NEWBURY FROST READ. New York: Hatton Garden Press. London: Spurr and Swift. MCMXXIII.

4°. In portfolio of brown paper boards with cloth spine.

Ex libris George Barr McCutcheon.

D242

DICKENS'S OWN STORY   SIDE-LIGHTS ON HIS LIFE AND PER-
SONALITY. BY SIR WILLIAM ROBERTSON NICOLL. London: Chapman
and Hall, Ltd. 1923.

8°. In original green cloth with gilt lettering.

D243

DICKENS IN CARTOON AND CARICATURE. COMPILED BY WILLIAM
GLYDE WILKINS. EDITED WITH INTRODUCTON BY B. W. MATZ.
Boston: For Members of the Bibliophile Society. MCMXXIV.

8°. In brown paper boards with leather spine.

D244(1)

THE DICKENS ENCYCLOPEDIA. BY ARTHUR L. HAYWARD. London:
George Routledge and Sons, Ltd. New York: E. P. Dutton & Co. 1924.

8°. In original red cloth.

D244(2)

A binding variant in green cloth with gilt lettering.

D245

THE LONDON OF CHARLES DICKENS. BY E. BERESFORD CHANCEL-
LOR. London: Grant Richards, Ltd. MDCCCXXIV.

8°. In original bright blue cloth with gilt lettering.

D246

CHARACTER SKETCHES FROM DICKENS. COMPILED WITH FORE-
WORD BY B. W. MATZ. WITH INTRODUCTION BY KATE PERUGINI.
ILLUSTRATED BY HAROLD COPPING. London, Paris, New York: Raphael
Tuck & Sons, Ltd. 1924.

4°. In full natural calf.

No. 39 of 1,000 copies of the edition de luxe.

D247

THE ENGLAND OF DICKENS. BY WALTER DEXTER. Philadelphia: J. B.
Lippincott Company. [1925].

8°. In original navy blue cloth with gilt lettering.

D248

THE LONDON OF DICKENS. BY WALTER DEXTER. New York: E. P.
Dutton. 1925.

8°. In dark red cloth with tan spine and paper labels.

D249

THE CHARM OF LONDON   AN ANTHOLOGY   COMPILED BY ALFRED H. HYATT WITH 12 ILLUSTRATIONS BY YOSHIO MARKIN. London: Chatto & Windus. 1925.

8°. In original moss-green cloth with red lettering and decoration.

D250

UNDER A DICKENS ROOFTREE. By S.N.E. London: Spottiswoode, Ballantyne & Company, Ltd. 1925.

8°. In original yellow wrapper. [description of 48 Doughty Street]

D251

THE OXFORD BOOK OF ENGLISH PROSE. CHOSEN AND EDITED BY SIR ARTHUR QUILLER-COUCH. Oxford: Clarendon Press. 1925.

16°. In original navy blue cloth with gilt lettering and decoration.

D252

"Dickens Patent Block Calendar." London: Raphael Tuck & Sons, Ltd. 1926.

D253

THE EDINBURGH RELATIVES AND FRIENDS OF DICKENS. BY W. FORBES GRAY. London: The Dickens Fellowship. [c. 1926].

8°. Pamphlet reprinted from *The Dickensian,* September and December 1926.

D254

THE DAYS OF DICKENS. BY ARTHUR L. HAYWARD. New York: E. P. Dutton & Company. London: George Routledge & Sons, Ltd. 1926.

8°. In purple cloth with gilt lettering.

D255

THE ACTOR IN DICKENS. BY J. B. VAN AMERONGEN. New York: D. Appleton and Co. MCMXXVII.

8°. In original red cloth.

D256

MR. PICKWICK'S PILGRIMAGES. BY WALTER DEXTER. ILLUSTRATED FROM THE ORIGINAL DRAWINGS BY "PHIZ," AND PHOTOGRAPHS BY THE AUTHOR. Philadelphia: J. B. Lippincott Company. 1927.

8°. In original dark blue cloth.

D257

"To Meet Charles Dickens," by Harry Furniss. THE STRAND MAGAZINE. December 1927.

Pp. 537—543 extracted from magazine.

D258

THIS SIDE IDOLATRY A NOVEL BASED ON THE LIFE OF CHARLES DICKENS. BY C. E. BECHHOFER-ROBERTS ("EPHESIAN"). Indianapolis: The Bobbs-Merrill Company. 1928.

8°. In original light blue cloth with paper labels.

First edition.

D259

THIS SIDE IDOLATRY A NOVEL. BY EPHESIAN (C. E. BECHHOFER-ROBERTS). London: Mills & Boon, Limited. 1928.

8°. In original brown cloth with orange lettering and decoration.

D260

DICKENS IN LONDON. FORTY-SEVEN DRAWINGS WITH DESCRIP-TIVE NOTES BY ARTHUR MORELAND. WITH AN INTRODUCTION BY FRANK S. JOHNSON. London: Cecil Palmer. MCMXXVIII.

4°. In original brown cloth with tan spine.

D261

A DICKENS DICTIONARY. BY ALEX. J. PHILIP. 2ND EDITION, REVISED AND GREATLY ENLARGED. BY ALEX. J. PHILIP . . . AND LIEUT.-COL. W. LAURENCE GADD. Gravesend: "The Librarian." London: Simpkin Marshall, Ltd. Leipzig: G. Hedler. 1928.

8°. In original blue cloth.

D262

"The Dickens Calendar." New York: George Sully & Co. 1928.

D263

"The Dickens Calendar." New York: George Sully & Co. 1929.

D264

BOOKS AND THE MAN. BY JOHN T. WINTERICH. New York: Greenberg. 1929.

8°. In original black cloth with gilt lettering.

D265

QUOTATIONS AND REFERENCES IN CHARLES DICKENS. BY JAMES S. STEVENS. Boston: The Christopher Publishing House. 1929.

8°. In original light blue cloth with gilt lettering.

D266

"Scenes from 'Oliver Twist'," by Sarah Agnes Wallace. In EDUCATION. April 1930.

D267

DICKENS AND RELIGION. BY W. KENT. London: Watts & Co. 1930.
8°. In original blue cloth.

D268

A HUNDRED YEARS OF PUBLISHING BEING THE STORY OF CHAP-
MAN & HALL, LTD. BY ARTHUR WAUGH. London: Chapman and Hall.
1930.
8°. In original dark blue cloth.

D269

PENNY PLAIN TWO PENCE COLOURED A HISTORY OF THE
JUVENILE DRAMA. BY A. E. WILSON. WITH A FOREWORD BY
CHARLES B. COCHRAN AND EIGHTY-THREE ILLUSTRATIONS. London, Bombay, Sydney: George G. Harrap & Co., Ltd. 1932.
4°. In red cloth.

D270

"Three Woodcuts for HARD TIMES BY CHARLES DICKENS," by V.
Favorsky. In THE LONDON MERCURY. July 1932.
8°. In original orange wrapper, as issued.

D271

"A Study in Contrast: The Broken Friendship of Dickens and Thackeray," by
Henry Sayre Scribner. In SCHOLASTIC, THE NATIONAL HIGH SCHOOL
WEEKLY. 3 February 1934.
4°. In original white wrapper illustrated in blue and black.

D272

THE DUMMY LIBRARY OF CHARLES DICKENS AT GAD'S HILL PLACE
RECOLLECTIONS OF A PILGRIMAGE AS NARRATED BY CHARLES
RUBENS TO J. CHISTIAN BAY [n.p.] MDCCCCXXXIV.
12°. Pamphlet in original blue wrapper with white paper label.

No. 69 of 300 copies, privately printed. Inscribed "To Mr. Harry B. Smith,
with the compliments of Charles Rubens 1/19/34."

D273

AN ENQUIRY INTO THE NATURE OF CERTAIN NINETEENTH CEN-
TURY PAMPHLETS. BY JOHN CARTER & GRAHAM POLLARD. London:
Constable & Co., Ltd. New York: Charles Scribner's Sons. 1934.
8°. In original red cloth.

Includes "To Be Read at Dusk."

D274

ANGLO-AMERICAN FIRST EDITIONS 1826–1900 EAST TO WEST. BY I. R. BRUSSEL. WITH AN INTRODUCTION BY GRAHAM POLLARD. London: Constable & Co., Ltd. New York: R. R. Bowker Co. 1935.

8°. In grey mottled paper boards and ivory paper spine.

D275

"Andrew Lang on Dickens" and "A Few Interesting Dickens Illustrations." Excised from LITERATURE & BOOKS. [n.d.].

D276

A HANDBOOK TO PICKWICK PAPERS. BY LOGAN CLENDENING. New York, London: Alfred A. Knopf. 1936.

8°. In original grey paper boards with gilt illustration and orange cloth spine.

D277

EARLY VICTORIAN DRAMA (1830–1870). BY ERNEST REYNOLDS. Cambridge: W. Heffer & Sons, Ltd. 1936.

8°. In original blue cloth.

D278

WHEN VICTORIA BEGAN TO REIGN. A CORONATION YEAR SCRAP-BOOK MADE BY MARGARET LAMBERT. London: Faber & Faber, Ltd. 1936.

8°. In original lavender cloth, with lettering in silver on green.

D279

"Over the Garden Wall," dramatized by Daisy Melville Vance from NICHOLAS NICKLEBY. In SCHOLASTIC, THE AMERICAN HIGH SCHOOL WEEKLY. 30 January 1937.

8°. In white pictorial wrapper.

D280

"Le Jour de Gloire. Pièce en trois actes et onze tableaux dont un prologue." In LA PETITE ILLUSTRATION. 27 Février 1937.

As presented 23 December 1936 at the Théatre National de L'Odéon.

D281

GREATEST SHOW ON EARTH   AS PERFORMED FOR OVER A CEN-TURY AT ASTLEY'S. . . . BY M. WILLSON DISHER. London: G. Bell and Sons, Ltd. 1937.

8°. In bright red cloth decorated with silver lettering and design.

D282

THE HISTORY OF THE ENGLISH NOVEL. FROM THE BRONTES TO MEREDITH: ROMANTICISM IN THE ENGLISH NOVEL. BY ERNEST A. BAKER. London: H. F. & G. Witherby, Ltd. 1937.

8°. In original olive green cloth with gilt lettering and decoration.

D283
THE NONESUCH DICKENS. RETROSPECTUS AND PROSPECTUS. London: The Nonesuch Press. 1937.

8°. In bright blue cloth.

D284
VICTORIAN PANORAMA. WITH A COMMENTARY BY PETER QUENNELL. London: B. T. Batsford, Ltd. 1937.

8°. In original blue cloth with gilt lettering and printed end papers.

D285
VICTORIAN STREET BALLADS. EDITED BY W. HENDERSON. London: Country Life, Ltd. 1937.

8°. In original green and red paper boards with dark grey cloth spine and pink paper labels.

D286
GEORGIAN ADVENTURE. BY DOUGLAS JERROLD. London: Collins. 1937.

8°. In original rough white cloth with orange end papers.

D287
CHRONICLES OF HOLLAND HOUSE 1820–1900. BY THE EARL OF ILCHESTER. London: John Murray. 1937.

8°. In original red cloth with gilt lettering and decoration.

D288
THE LONDON MISCELLANY. A NINETEENTH CENTURY SCRAPBOOK. London, Toronto: William Heinemann, Ltd. 1937.

8°. In original pink cloth with gilt lettering.

D289
TASTE AND FASHION FROM THE FRENCH REVOLUTION UNTIL TODAY. BY JAMES LAVER. London, Toronto, Bombay, Sydney: George G. Harrap & Company, Ltd. 1937.

8°. In original green cloth with gilt lettering.

D290
JANUS WEATHERCOCK. THE LIFE OF THOMAS GRIFFITHS WAINEWRIGHT 1794–1847. BY JONATHAN CURLING. London, Edinburgh, etc.: Thomas Nelson and Sons, Ltd. 1938.

8°. In original red cloth with gilt lettering.

D291

WE ARE OBSERVED   A MIRROR TO ENGLISH CHARACTER. BY W. J. BLYTON. London: John Murray. 1938.

8°. In original blue-green cloth.

Chapter X, "The New Point about Dickens."

D292

BOOKS AND I. BY PAUL LEMPERLY. Cleveland: The Rowfant Club. 1938.

8°. In brown cloth and half buff cloth printed in brown.

D293

ONE PAIR OF HANDS. BY MONICA DICKENS. New York, London: Harper & Brothers. 1939.

8°. In original bright blue cloth decorated in gilt and black, with blue end papers speckled with silver.

D294

"Charles Dickens Tries to Remain Anonymous," by Anne Lyon Haight. In THE COLOPHON   NEW GRAPHIC SERIES NUMBER ONE. New York: MCMXXXIX.

4°. In illustrated paper boards. Authorship of "The Loving Ballad of Lord Bateman."

D295

"Richard Gimbel's Sensational Dickens Discovery." In THE COLLECTOR'S GUIDE. April–June 1939. [Mimeographed quarterly for book dealers and collectors].

D296

LIFE IS SWEET, BROTHER. BY BERNARD DARWIN. London: Collins. 1940.

8°. In rough white cloth with blue lettering. Third impression. Includes "A Little Dickens."

D297

INSIDE THE WHALE AND OTHER ESSAYS. BY GEORGE ORWELL. London: Victor Gollancz, Ltd. 1940.

8°. In black cloth.

Chap. 1, "Charles Dickens."

D298

Dickens Centenary Items: sheet of stamps, menus, invitations, souvenir pamphlets, tickets to special entertainments.

D299

THE DICKENS WORLD. BY HUMPHRY HOUSE. Oxford: University Press. 1941.

8°. In rust cloth.

D300

THE WOUND AND THE BOW. BY EDMUND WILSON. Cambridge, Mass.: Houghton Mifflin Company. 1941.

8°. In blue cloth.

Chap. 1, "Dickens: The Two Scrooges."

D301

ROMANTIC MR. DICKENS A COMEDY-DRAMA IN THREE ACTS. BY H. H. AND MARGUERITE HARPER. Cedar Rapids, Iowa: The Torch Press. MCMXLI.

8°. In blue cloth.

Presentation copy from the authors to Phillip Moeller. One of 100 copies printed for complimentary distribution.

D302

THE MONTH AT GOODSPEED'S. Boston, Mass.: Goodspeed's Book Shop. January-February 1944.

16°. Pamphlet in original cream wrapper with blue lettering and illustration.

Includes "Boz Comes to America."

D303

LETTERS OF THOMAS J. WISE TO JOHN HENRY WRENN. A FURTHER INQUIRY INTO THE GUILT OF CERTAIN NINETEENTH-CENTURY FORGERS. EDITED BY FANNIE E. RATCHFORD. New York: Alfred A. Knopf. 1944.

8°. In original black cloth with gilt lettering and decoration.

D304

EDWARD'S FANCY. BY MONICA DICKENS. New York, London: Harper & Brothers. 1944.

8°. In original buff paper boards with red lettering.

D305

THE STREETS OF LONDON THROUGH THE CENTURIES. BY THOMAS BURKE. London: B. T. Batsford, Ltd. 1941.

8°. In original red cloth.

Second edition.

D306

ONE PAIR OF FEET. BY MONICA DICKENS. New York, London: Harper & Brothers. 1942.

8°. In original blue cloth with red lettering.

D307

A DAY WITH CHARLES DICKENS. BY MAURICE CLARE. New York: Hodder & Stoughton. [n.d.].

8°. In original red flexible leather with gilt lettering and decoration.

D308

A LITERARY MAN'S LONDON. BY CHARLES G. HARPER. Philadelphia: J. B. Lippincott Company. [n.d.].

8°. In original wine-red cloth with gilt lettering.

D309

DICKENS IN YORKSHIRE. BY CHARLES EYRE PASCOE. London: Sir Isaac Pitman & Sons, Ltd. [n.d.].

8°. In original grey paper boards with illustrative paper label and brown lettering.

D310

DICKENS COUNTRY WATER-COLOURS. BY W. BISCOMBE GARDNER AND OTHERS. London: A. & C. Black, Ltd. [n.d.].

8°. In original brown paper boards with colored illustration.

D311

FAMILIAR CHARACTERS FROM THE WORKS OF CHARLES DICKENS. ILLUSTRATED BY H. REYNOLDS. Designed in England; printed in Germany. London: Hildesheimer & Faulkner. New York: Geo. C. Whitney. [n.d.].

12°. In original stiff white paper wrapper.

D312

CHARACTERS FROM DICKENS. DRAWN BY CLAUD LOVAT FRASER. London, Edinburgh: J. C. & E. C. Jack, Ld. [n.d.].

4°. In original yellow paper boards with black watered silk spine and paper labels.

No. 156 of 350 copies. Colored illustrations mounted on pages.

D313

DICKENS PICTURES. London: Ernest Nister. New York: E. P. Dutton & Co. [n.d.].

8°. Folder in original stiff white paper wrapper illustrated in color.

D314

FLOWERS FROM DICKENS. Buffalo, New York: The Hayes Lithographing Co. [n.d.].

4°. In white imitation leather decorated with colored flowers.

D315

POPULAR ENTERTAINMENTS THROUGH THE AGES. BY SAMUEL McKECHNIE. London: Sampson Low, Marston & Co., Ltd. [n.d.].

8°. In original light blue cloth.

D316

THE DICKENS BIRTHDAY BOOK. WITH 6 ILLUSTRATIONS IN COLOUR BY P. FLETCHER WATSON. London, Paris, etc.: Raphael Tuck & Sons, Ltd. [n.d.].

8°. In original brown paper boards with portrait in color.

D317

"Dickens Folk." By Mark Tapley. London: Hodder & Stoughton. [n.d.].

12°. Leaflet in blue paper wrapper. (Old Christmas Series)

D318

"Pearls from Dickens." Buffalo, New York: The Hayes Lithographing Co. [n.d.].

4°. In white paper boards with colored illustration.

D319

"Gems from Dickens." London, Paris, New York: Raphael Tuck & Sons, Ltd. [n.d.].

12°. Leaflet in stiff ivory wrapper with portrait and decoration in color.

D320

"Quotations from Dickens." A card game introducing sixty-six of the principal characters from fifteen books of Charles Dickens. Compiled by C. H. Syman. London: Truslove & Hanson, Ltd. [n.d.].

D321

"Dickens' Doctors." Yonkers, N.Y.: [n.d.].

Advertising pamphlet for "Liquid Peptonoids."

D322

Twelve Christmas cards, "The Charles Dickens Assortment." "Actual scenes of Dickens's life and authentic quotations from his works." [n.d.].

D323

Seventy-one Christmas and New Year Cards, collected by W. Miller, Esq.

D324

"Progressive Whist." Score cards and the game of "Snap," each illustrated with a Dickens character.

D325

Material relating to various Dickens Clubs: membership cards, programs, menus, etc.

BIOGRAPHIES AND BIBLIOGRAPHIES

1 : BIOGRAPHIES

E1

CHARLES DICKENS THE STORY OF HIS LIFE. BY THE AUTHOR OF THE "LIFE OF THACKERAY." [Theodore Taylor] London: John Camden Hotten. [n.d.].

8°. In original green cloth with gilt lettering and brown end papers.

E2

CHARLES DICKENS. THE STORY OF HIS LIFE. BY THE AUTHOR OF THE "LIFE OF THACKERAY." WITH ILLUSTRATIONS AND FAC-SIMILES. New York: Harper & Brothers. 1870.

8°. In three-fourths brown morocco with marbled paper boards and end papers.

E3

PEN PHOTOGRAPHS OF CHARLES DICKENS' READINGS, TAKEN FROM LIFE. BY KATE FIELD, PHOTOGRAPHER. Boston: Loring. 1868.

8°. In original buff wrapper, as issued. (Loring's Tales of the Day)

E4

Notices concerning the death of Dickens reprinted from various periodicals. In THE ECLECTIC MAGAZINE OF FOREIGN LITERATURE, SCIENCE, AND ART. NEW SERIES XII. July—December 1870.

8°. In original half old calf with red marbled paper boards, and brown marbled end papers. Front cover detached.

E5

CHARLES DICKENS WITH ANECDOTES AND RECOLLECTIONS OF HIS LIFE. WRITTEN AND COMPILED BY WILLIAM WATKINS. London: The London Newsvenders' Publishing Company. [c. 1870].

16°. Memorial pamphlet in original yellow wrapper with black-bordered portrait of Dickens.

E6(1)

CHARLES DICKENS. BY GEORGE AUGUSTUS SALA. London: George Routledge & Sons. [1870].

8°. In original stiff orange wrapper.

First edition. Amplified version of article written by Sala for the *Daily Telegraph*, 10 June 1870.

E6(2)

A second copy bound in heavy grey cloth with brown morocco spine.

E7

CHARLES DICKENS: A SKETCH OF HIS LIFE AND WORKS. BY F. B. PERKINS. New York: G. P. Putnam & Sons. 1870.

8°. In original purple cloth with gilt lettering.

E8(1)

LIFE OF CHARLES DICKENS. BY R. SHELTON MACKENZIE. PER-SONAL RECOLLECTIONS AND ANECDOTES;—LETTERS BY 'BOZ,' NEVER BEFORE PUBLISHED;—AND UNCOLLECTED PAPERS IN PROSE AND VERSE. Philadelphia: T. B. Peterson & Brothers. [1870].

8°. In original purple cloth printed in gold, with brown end papers.

Presentation copy from the author. Inscription pasted in: "Andrew C. Craig Esq. from his friend and countryman, the Author. R. Shelton MacKenzie Aug 16, 1870 Philadelphia."

E8(2)

Binding variant in wine-colored cloth.

E8(3)

Binding variant in original green cloth with gilt lettering and brown end papers.

E9(1)

THE BEST OF ALL GOOD COMPANY. EDITED BY BLANCHARD JER-ROLD. A DAY WITH CHARLES DICKENS. London: The Useful Knowledge Company. 1871.

8°. In original yellow paper wrapper.

With copies of Dickens's letters to Douglas Jerrold and reprints of articles published at the time of Dickens's death.

E9(2)

A second copy of the original issue bound in red cloth with wine-colored end papers, yellow wrapper included.

E10

THE BEST OF ALL GOOD COMPANY. BY BLANCHARD JERROLD. FIRST SERIES. ILLUSTRATED. Boston: Shepard & Gill. 1874.

8°. In original green cloth with gilt decoration; white end papers over brown papers.

E11

PEN PHOTOGRAPHS OF CHARLES DICKENS'S READINGS. TAKEN FROM LIFE. BY KATE FIELD. NEW AND ENLARGED EDITION, WITH ILLUSTRATIONS. Boston: James R. Osgood and Company, Late Ticknor & Fields, and Fields, Osgood, & Co. 1871.

8°. In original green cloth with brown end papers.

E12

THE LIFE OF CHARLES DICKENS. BY JOHN FORSTER. THIRD EDI-TION. London: Chapman and Hall. 1871.

8°. Three volumes in green polished calf, richly gilt.

E13

A set of three volumes of the 1872 [1873, 1874] edition in half dark green levant morocco and green cloth with red marbled end papers.

E14(1)

THE LIFE OF CHARLES DICKENS. BY JOHN FORSTER. Philadelphia: J. B. Lippincott & Co. 1871–1874.

8°. Three volumes in purple cloth with gilt portrait, with brown end papers.

E14(2)

A second set of three volumes as E14(1) except that vol. I is dated 1872.

E15

THE LIFE OF CHARLES DICKENS. BY JOHN FORSTER. WITH 500 PORTRAITS, FACSIMILES, AND OTHER ILLUSTRATIONS. COL-LECTED, ARRANGED, AND ANNOTATED BY B. W. MATZ. London: Chapman and Hall, Limited. 1911.

8°. Two volumes in original blue cloth with gilt decoration and lettering. (Memorial Edition)

E16

THE LIFE OF CHARLES DICKENS. BY JOHN FORSTER. EDITED AND ANNOTATED WITH AN INTRODUCTION BY J. W. T. LEY. London: Cecil Palmer. 1928.

4°. In original dark blue cloth.

E17

THE LIFE AND WRITINGS OF CHARLES DICKENS: A WOMAN'S MEMORIAL VOLUME. BY PHEBE A. HANAFORD. Boston: B. B. Russell. 1871.

8°. In original purple cloth with gilt lettering, pale pink end papers.

E18

CHARLES DICKENS SOME NOTES ON HIS LIFE AND WRITINGS, WITH EIGHT PORTRAITS, THIRTY-SEVEN ILLUSTRATIONS AND FACSIMILES OF HIS HANDWRITING AND AUTOGRAPHS. London: Chapman and Hall, Limited. [c. 1872].

8°. In green paper wrapper.

E19

ANECDOTE BIOGRAPHIES OF THACKERAY AND DICKENS. EDITED BY RICHARD HENRY STODDARD. New York: Scribner, Armstrong, and Company. 1875.

8°. In original beige cloth with elaborate decoration in gilt and black. (Bric-A-Brac Series)

E20

RECOLLECTIONS OF WRITERS. BY CHARLES AND MARY COWDEN CLARKE. New York: Charles Scribner's Sons. 1878.

8°. In original blue-grey cloth.

"Charles Dickens and His Letters," pp. 295–341.

E21

A SHORT LIFE OF CHARLES DICKENS. WITH SELECTIONS FROM HIS LETTERS. BY CHARLES H. JONES. New York: D. Appleton and Company. 1880.

12°. In original black cloth with black morocco spine.

E22(1)

DICKENS. BY ADOLPHUS WILLIAM WARD. London: Macmillan and Co. 1882.

8°. In original red cloth with black end papers.

First edition, first issue. Imprint on verso of title page: "Charles Dickens and Evans, Crystal Palace Press."

E22(2)

Variant issue in tan cloth with paper label.

E23

DICKENS. BY ADOLPHUS WILLIAM WARD. London: Macmillan and Co. 1901.

8°. In original tan cloth with dark blue lettering.

E24

THE YOUTH AND MIDDLE AGE OF CHARLES DICKENS. BY JAMES PAYN (FROM CHAMBER'S JOURNAL). 1883.

4°. Original issue with blue paper wrapper, bound in half dark green morocco with green marbled boards and end papers. Front cover detached. One of 50 copies printed.

E25

CHARLES DICKENS AS I KNEW HIM. THE STORY OF THE READING TOURS IN GREAT BRITAIN (1866–1870). BY GEORGE DOLBY. London: T. Fisher Unwin. 1885.

8°. In half olive green levant with blue marbled paper boards and end papers.

E26

LIFE OF CHARLES DICKENS. BY FRANK T. MARZIALS. London: Walter Scott. 1887.

8°. In original dark blue cloth.

E27

THE CHILDHOOD AND YOUTH OF CHARLES DICKENS. BY ROBERT LANGTON. Manchester: Published by the author. 1883.

4°. In original green cloth with gilt lettering and black rule border; dark grey end papers. (Subscribers' Edition)

Presentation copy inscribed, "Mr. C. W. Sutton with the writer's compliments and thanks. Robert Langton, Nov. 22nd 1883."

E28

THE CHILDHOOD AND YOUTH OF CHARLES DICKENS. BY ROBERT LANGTON. London: Hutchinson & Co. 1891.

8°. In original tan cloth with gilt lettering and decoration; flowered end papers. (Edition de Luxe)

No. 49 of 300 copies on large hand-made paper with proofs of illustrations on India paper.

E29

THE CHILDHOOD AND YOUTH OF CHARLES DICKENS. BY ROBERT LANGTON. London: Hutchinson & Co. 1912.

8°. In original green cloth with gilt lettering.

E30

CHARLES DICKENS AND THE STAGE. BY T. EDGAR PEMBERTON. London: George Redway. 1888.

8°. In original green cloth with dark grey end papers.

E31

CHARLES DICKENS BY HIS ELDEST DAUGHTER [Mamie Dickens]. London: Cassell and Company, Limited. 1885.

8°. In original grey cloth decorated in black and red with yellow end papers.

E32

CHARLES DICKENS BY HIS ELDEST DAUGHTER   FIFTH EDITION. London, Paris, Melbourne: Cassell and Company, Limited. 1894.

8°. In blue cloth decorated in black and red. (The World's Workers)

E33

L'INIMITABLE BOZ ÉTUDE HISTORIQUE ET ANECDOTIQUE SUR LA VIE ET L'OEUVRE DE CHARLES DICKENS. PAR ROBERT DU PONTAVICE DE HEUSSEY. Paris: Maison Quantin Compagnie Générale d'Impression et d'Édition. 1889.

8°. In original orange paper wrapper.

One of 25 copies printed on Japanese paper.

E34

THE CHILDHOOD AND YOUTH OF CHARLES DICKENS. BY ROBERT LANGTON. Boston: Dana Estes & Co. [1890].

8°. In green cloth printed in gold.

E35

THE CHILDHOOD AND YOUTH OF CHARLES DICKENS. BY ROBERT LANGTON. London: Hutchinson & Co. 1891.

4°. In original brown cloth printed in gold, with floral end papers.

No. 89 of 300 copies, Edition de Luxe, on hand-made paper with proofs of illustrations on India paper.

E36

"Landor, Dickens, Thackeray," Mrs. E. Lynn Linton. In THE BOOKMAN. April 1896.

8°. In original drab paper wrapper printed in black and red.

E37

MY FATHER AS I RECALL HIM. BY MAMIE DICKENS. London: The Roxburghe Press. [1896].

8°. Presentation copy in red cloth with gilt lettering and decoration. Inscribed: "Dear Lizzie With much love and best wishes for all from Georgina Hogarth Christmas 1896."

E38(1)

MY FATHER AS I RECALL HIM. BY MAMIE DICKENS. New York: E. P. Dutton & Co. [1897].

8°. In original green cloth printed in gold, with brown end papers.

E38(2)

MY FATHER AS I RECALL HIM. BY MAMIE DICKENS. New York: E. P. Dutton & Company. 1897.

8°. In original dark red cloth with gilt lettering and white end papers.

E39(1)

DICKENS AND HIS ILLUSTRATORS. BY FREDERIC G. KITTON. WITH TWENTY-TWO PORTRAITS AND FACSIMILES OF SEVENTY ORIGINAL DRAWNGS NOW REPRODUCED FOR THE FIRST TIME. London: George Redway. 1899.

4°. In half blue morocco, top edge gilt.

E39(2)

A second copy in original green cloth.

E40

DICKENS AND HIS ILLUSTRATORS. BY FREDERIC G. KITTON. London: George Redway. 1899.

4°. In original green cloth.

Second edition.

E41(1)

LIFE OF CHARLES DICKENS. BY FRANK T. MARZIALS. WITH A BIOGRAPHY OF DICKENS BY SIR LESLIE STEPHENS. Philadelphia: John D. Morris and Company. [c. 1900].

8°. In dark red contemporary morocco with marbled paper boards and end papers.

One of 1,000 copies, De Luxe Edition.

E41(2)

A second copy bound as E41(1) in variant state. Verso of title page differs: "Edition de Luxe" in Gothic type without rules in purple ink. In E41(1) this appears in larger white letters with rules and in blue ink.

E42

CHARLES DICKENS: HIS LIFE AND WORK. Philadelphia: The Book-Lovers' Library. [1901].

8°. In original brown wrapper. (Handbook to accompany reading course)

E43

FORSTER'S LIFE OF DICKENS ABRIDGED AND REVISED BY GEORGE GISSING. London: Chapman and Hall, Ltd. 1903.

8°. In blue cloth with gilt lettering.

E44

CHARLES DICKENS. BY G. K. CHESTERTON AND F. G. KITTON. WITH NUMEROUS ILLUSTRATIONS. London: Hodder and Stoughton. 1903.

4°. In stiff boards covered with red cloth. (The Bookman Booklets)

E45

CHARLES DICKENS. BY G. K. CHESTERTON. London: Methuen & Co. 1906.

8°. In green cloth.

Second edition.

E46

CHARLES DICKENS HIS LIFE, WRITINGS, AND PERSONALITY. BY FREDERIC G. KITTON. WITH NUMEROUS ILLUSTRATIONS. London, Edinburgh: T. C. & E. C. Jack. 1902.

8°. In original red cloth with gilt lettering.

E47

CHARLES DICKENS HIS LIFE, WRITINGS, AND PERSONALITY. BY FREDERIC G. KITTON. London, Edinburgh: T. C. & E. C. Jack. [c. 1908].

8°. In original blue cloth decorated with gilt figures from Dickens's novels.

E48

CHARLES DICKENS HIS LIFE, WRITINGS, AND PERSONALITY. BY FREDERIC G. KITTON. New York: D. Appleton and Company. 1908.

8°. In original blue cloth decorated with gilt figures from Dickens's novels, as E47 with added dedication and altered title page.

E49

CHARLES DICKENS. BY G. K. CHESTERTON. London: Methuen & Co. 1906.

8°. In green cloth.

Second edition.

E50

DICKENS. BY W. TEIGNMOUTH SHORE. London: George Bell & Sons. 1904.

8°. In original green cloth on stiff paper. (Bell's Miniature Series of Great Writers)

E51

THE LIFE OF CHARLES DICKENS AS REVEALED IN HIS WRITINGS. BY PERCY FITZGERALD. London: Chatto & Windus. 1905.

8°. Two volumes in original green cloth.

First edition.

E52

THE PHILOSOPHY OF DICKENS A STUDY OF HIS LIFE AND TEACHING AS A SOCIAL REFORMER. BY MRS. BAILLIE-SAUNDERS. London: Henry J. Glaisher. 1905.

8°. In red cloth and black end papers.

E53

CHARLES DICKENS THE APOSTLE OF THE PEOPLE. BY EDWIN PUGH. London: The New Age Press. 1908.

8°. In original brown wrapper; edges trimmed.

E54

CHARLES DICKENS AND HIS FRIENDS. BY W. TEIGNMOUTH SHORE. WITH NUMEROUS ILLUSTRATIONS. London, New York, Toronto, Melbourne: Cassell and Company, Ltd. 1909.

8°. In wine-red cloth with gilt lettering.

E55

THE CHILDHOOD AND YOUTH OF CHARLES DICKENS WITH RETROSPECTIVE NOTES AND ELUCIDATIONS FROM HIS BOOKS AND LETTERS. BY ROBERT LANGTON. London: Hutchinson & Co. 1912.

8°. In original olive green cloth with gilt lettering.

E56

THE FEBRUARY 1912 BOOKMAN DICKENS CENTENARY NUMBER WITH PRESENTATION PLATE PORTRAIT. London: Hodder & Stoughton. 1912.

4°. In paper wrapper with portrait of Dickens.

E57(1)

A CHILD'S JOURNEY WITH DICKENS. BY KATE DOUGLAS WIGGIN. Boston, New York: Houghton Mifflin Company. [1912].

12°. In brown paper boards with green cloth spine.

E57(2)

A second, presentation copy, inscribed: "To Rose deVaux Ronyer [?] From the author Kate Douglas Wiggin. I was the 'child' & this my first 'journey' into the world."

E58

CHARLES DICKENS AND MUSIC. BY JAMES T. LIGHTWOOD. London: Charles H. Kelly. 1912.

8°. In original brown cloth with gilt lettering and decoration.

First edition.

E59

DICKENS' HONEYMOON AND WHERE HE SPENT IT. BY ALEX J. PHILIP. London: Chapman & Hall, Ltd. Gravesend: Bryant & Rackstraw, Ltd. 1912.

8°. In green wrapper.

E60

CHARLES DICKENS THE MAN AND HIS WORK. BY EDWIN PERCY WHIPPLE. Boston, New York: Houghton Mifflin Company. MDCCCCXII.

8°. Two volumes in dark green paper boards.

No. 209 of 550 sets printed.

E61

MEMORIES OF CHARLES DICKENS. BY PERCY FITZGERALD. Bristol: J. W. Arrowsmith, Ltd. London: Simpkin, Marshall, Hamilton, Kent & Co., Limited. [1913].

4°. In dark red cloth with gilt lettering.

E62

PHIZ AND DICKENS AS THEY APPEARED TO EDGAR BROWNE. WITH ORIGINAL ILLUSTRATIONS BY HABLOT K. BROWNE. London: James Nisbet & Co., Limited. 1913.

4°. In original white cloth decorated in green and gilt.

E63

CHARLES DICKENS. BY ALBERT KEIM AND LUIS LUMET. TRANSLATED FROM THE FRENCH BY FREDERIC TABER COOPER. New York: Frederick A. Stokes Company. 1914.

8°. In original brown cloth.

E64

PHIZ AND DICKENS AS THEY APPEAED TO EDGAR BROWNE WITH ORIGINAL ILLUSTRATIONS BY HABLOT K. BROWNE. New York: Dodd, Mead & Company. 1914.

8°. In blue cloth.

E65

CHARLES DICKENS   A BOOKMAN EXTRA NUMBER. London: Hodder & Stoughton. 1914.

4°. In flexible cloth with colored portrait of Dickens.

E66

DICKENS AND TALFOURD WITH AN ADDRESS & THREE UNPUBLISHED LETTERS TO TALFOURD, THE FATHER OF THE FIRST COPYRIGHT ACT WHICH PUT AN END TO THE PIRACY OF DICKENS' WRITINGS. BY CUMBERLAND CLARK. London: Chiswick Press. 1917.

8°. In original red cloth. Privately printed.

E67

CHARLES DICKENS. BY RICHARD BURTON. Indianapolis: The Bobbs-Merrill Company. 1919.

8°. In green cloth.

E68(1)

THE DICKENS CIRCLE A NARRATIVE OF THE NOVELIST'S FRIENDSHIPS. BY J. W. T. LEY. New York: E. P. Dutton & Company. [1919].

8°. In red cloth printed in gold.

E68(2)

A variant issue. No address given for publisher; no date. "Printed in Great Britain by Richard Clay & Sons, Limited. Brunswick St., Stamford St., S.E. 1, and Bungay, Suffolk."

E69

CHARLES DICKENS FIFTY YEARS AFTER. BY GILBERT K. CHESTER-TON. [London]: Clement Shorter. June 1920.

4°. Pamphlet in original stiff blue wrapper.

One of 25 copies privately printed.

E70

MR. DICKENS GOES TO THE PLAY. BY ALEXANDER WOOLLCOTT. London, New York: G. P. Putnam's Sons, The Knickerbocker Press. 1922.

8°. In blue paper boards with brown cloth spine.

Inscribed: "AMB & WSB from A.W. and Charles Dickens [the younger] 10/20/22."

E71

DICKENS THE IMMORTAL. BY EDWARD BASIL LUPTON. Kansas City: Alfred Fowler. 1923.

8°. In tan paper boards with cloth spine.

E72

INDEX TO THE UNIQUE COPY OF THE LIFE OF CHARLES DICKENS, 1812–1870, BY JOHN FORSTER. CHAPMAN & HALL, 1873. EXTRA ILLUSTRATED WITH UPWARDS OF 2,100 ENGRAVINGS, PORTRAITS, AUTOGRAPH LETTERS, THEATRICAL PLAYBILLS, ETC. NOW THE PROPERTY OF GEORGE GREGORY. Bath [Eng.]. 1925.

4°. In red cloth.

E73

CHARLES DICKENS AND OTHER VICTORIANS. BY SIR ARTHUR QUILLER-COUCH. Cambridge: University Press. 1925.

8°. In dark blue cloth.

E74

CHARLES DICKENS AND OTHER VICTORIANS. BY SIR ARTHUR QUILLER-COUCH. New York, London: G. P. Putnam's Sons. 1925.

8°. In original blue paper boards and blue cloth spine.

E75

CHARLES DICKENS SHORTHAND WRITER   THE 'PRENTICE DAYS' OF A MASTER CRAFTSMAN. BY WILLIAM J. CARLTON. London: Cecil Palmer. 1926.

8°. In blue cloth.

First edition.

E76

DICKENS DAYS IN BOSTON   A RECORD OF DAILY EVENTS. BY EDWARD F. PAYNE. Boston, New York: Houghton Mifflin Company. Cambridge: The Riverside Press. 1927.

8°. In red cloth with green end papers.

E77

DICKENS: A PORTRAIT IN PENCIL. BY RALPH STRAUS. London: Victor Gollancz Ltd. 1928.

8°. In orange cloth.

E78

MEMORIES OF MY FATHER. BY SIR HENRY F. DICKENS. London: Victor Gollancz, Ltd. 1928.

8°. In original blue cloth.

E79

NEW YEAR'S EVE FROLIC   TWELFTH NIGHT FESTIVITIES. RECOLLECTIONS OF CHARLES DICKENS BY HIS DAUGHTER MAMIE DICKENS. New York: Harmon & Irwin, Inc. 1928.

8°. In mottled paper boards with paper label.

Edition of 350 copies, privately printed.

E80

CHARLES DICKENS   A BIOGRAPHY FROM NEW SOURCES. BY RALPH STRAUS. New York: Cosmopolitan Book Corporation. MCMXXVIII.

8°. In original red cloth with paper labels and white end papers illustrated with characters from Dickens's novels.

E81

THE CHARITY OF CHARLES DICKENS   HIS INTEREST IN THE HOME FOR FALLEN WOMEN AND A HISTORY OF THE STRANGE CASE OF CAROLINE MAYNARD THOMPSON. BY EDWARD F. PAYNE AND HENRY H. HARPER. Boston: For the Bibliophile Society. MCMXXIX.

8°. In full brown morocco printed in gold.

E82

THE CHARITY OF CHARLES DICKENS. BY EDWARD F. PAYNE AND HENRY H. HARPER. Cedar Rapids: Privately printed for Charles E. Goodspeed. MCMXXIX.

8°. In ivory paper boards.

One of 100 copies printed for Mr. Goodspeed at The Torch Press.

E83

THE ROMANCE OF CHARLES DICKENS AND MARIA BEADNELL WINTER. BY EDWARD F. PAYNE AND HENRY H. HARPER. Boston: The Bibliophile Society. MCMXXIX.

8°. In full natural calf with gilt lettering.

E84

THE MAN CHARLES DICKENS A VICTORIAN PORTRAIT. BY EDWARD WAGENKNECHT. Boston, New York: Houghton, Mifflin Company. Cambridge: The Riverside Press. 1929.

8°. In red cloth.

E85

GREEN LEAVES: NEW CHAPTERS IN THE LIFE OF CHARLES DICKENS. BY JOHN HARRISON STONEHOUSE. London: Henry Sotheran, Ltd. 1931.

12°. Five parts in original green wrappers. Also extra copy of No. 1 without price, issued as advertisement from the Piccadilly Fountain Press for Henry Sotheran, Ltd.

First edition. Presentation copy from the author inscribed, "Miss Perkins, with kind regard from J. H. Stonehouse June 26 1931."

E86

GREEN LEAVES NEW CHAPTERS IN THE LIFE OF CHARLES DICKENS. BY JOHN HARRISON STONEHOUSE. REVISED AND ENLARGED EDITION WITH 10 ILLUSTRATIONS. London: The Picadilly Fountain Press. 1931.

4°. In original blue-grey paper boards with paper label, pages unopened.

No. 74 of 535 copies, signed by the author.

E87

DICKENS. BY BERNARD DARWIN. New York: The Macmillan Company. 1933.

12°. In red cloth. (Great Lives)

E88

THE GREATEST PAGES OF CHARLES DICKENS. BY STEPHEN LEACOCK. Garden City, N.Y.: Doubleday Doran and Company, Inc. 1934.

8°. In original bright green cloth.

E89

DICKENS. BY ANDRÉ MAUROIS. TRANSLATED BY HAMISH MILES. London, New York: Harper & Brothers. 1935.

8°. In wine-colored cloth.

First edition.

E90

THE SENTIMENTAL JOURNEY A LIFE OF CHARLES DICKENS. BY HUGH KINGSMILL. New York: William Morrow and Company. 1935.

8°. In blue cloth.

E91

THE LIFE OF CHARLES DICKENS. BY THOMAS WRIGHT. New York: Charles Scribner's Sons. 1936.

8°. In original bright blue cloth.

E92

ENGLISH INNS AND ROAD-HOUSES. BY GEORGE LONG, F.R.G.S. London: T. Werner Laurie, Ltd. 1937.

8°. In original blue cloth.

E93

DICKENS AND HIS AGE AN ESSAY BY O. F. CHRISTIE, M.A. London: Heath Cranton, Limited. 1939.

8°. In lavender cloth.

E94

DICKENS AND DAUGHTER. BY GLADYS STOREY. London: Frederick Muller, Ltd. 1939.

8°. In original dark blue cloth.

E95

INTRODUCING CHARLES DICKENS. BY MAY LAMBERTON BECKER. ILLUSTRATIONS BY OSCAR OGG. New York: Dodd, Mead & Company. 1940.

8°. In green cloth.

E96

CHARLES DICKENS. BY UNA POPE-HENNESSY. New York: Howell, Soskin, Inc. [1946].

8°. In dark blue cloth with gilt lettering.

E97

DICKENS HIS CHARACTER, COMEDY, AND CAREER. BY HESKETH PEARSON. New York: Harper & Brothers. [1949].

8°. In original red cloth.

First edition.

E98

CHARLES DICKENS HIS TRAGEDY AND TRIUMPH. BY EDGAR JOHNSON. New York: Simon and Schuster. 1952.

8°. Two volumes in original grey cloth with red labels.

Presentation copy inscribed, "For Edwin Bachman with gratitude Edgar Johnson 24 October 1952."

E99

THE HEART OF CHARLES DICKENS. AS REVEALED IN HIS LETTERS TO ANGELA BURDETT-COUTTS. SELECTED AND EDITED . . . WITH A CRITICAL AND BIOGRAPHICAL INTRODUCTION BY EDGAR JOHNSON. New York: Duell, Sloan and Pearce. Boston: Little, Brown and Company. 1952.

8°. In turquoise cloth.

E100

DICKENS & ELLEN TERNAN. Berkeley, Los Angeles: University of California Press. 1952.

8°. In original pink cloth.

E101

THE STORY OF THE LIFE OF THE WORLD'S FAVOURITE AUTHOR. BY WALTER DEXTER. London: The Dickens Fellowship. [n.d.].

8°. In original stiff orange wrapper.

E102

LA VIE ANECDOTIQUE ET PITTORESQUE DES GRANDS ECRIVAINS. CHARLES DICKENS. 43 PORTRAITS ET GRAVURES. Paris: Société des Editions Louis-Michaud. [n.d.].

8°. In original tan wrapper printed in brown and green; back lacking.

2 : BIBLIOGRAPHIES

E103(1)

CATALOGUE OF THE BEAUTIFUL COLLECTION OF MODERN PICTURES, WATER-COLOUR DRAWINGS, AND OBJECTS OF ART, OF CHARLES DICKENS DECEASED. [London, 1870].

8°. In grey-green paper boards with brown cloth spine.

First edition. The Christie sale, 9 July 1870, with clipping from the *Daily Telegraph* for Monday, 11 July 1870, "Relics of Charles Dickens" by G. A. Sala.

E103(2)

A second copy in original blue wrapper.

E104(1)

DICKENS MEMENTO WITH INTRODUCTION BY FRANCIS PHILLIMORE AND "HINTS TO DICKENS COLLECTORS" BY JOHN F. DEXTER CATALOGUE WITH PURCHASERS' NAMES & PRICES REALISED. London: Field & Tuer, The Leadenhall Press; E. C. Simpkin, Marshall & Co.; Hamilton, Adams & Co. New York: Scribner & Welford. [1870].

4°. In brown cloth.

First edition. Relating to the Christie sale, 9 July 1870; first publication of Dexter's *Hints to Dickens Collectors*.

E104(2)

A second copy in marbled paper boards with blue cloth spine and tips.

E105

BIBLIOGRAPHY OF THE WRITINGS OF CHARLES DICKENS. BY JAMES COOK. London: Frank Kerslake. Paisley: J. & J. Cook. MDCCCLXXIX.

8°. In original grey paper wrapper with cloth spine.

E106(1)

THE BIBLIOGRAPHY OF DICKENS. (From 1834 to 1880). [Manchester: 1881].

8°. In grey wrapper.

By Richard Herne Shepherd.

E106(2)

A second copy bound in half brown crushed levant with mottled paper boards and end papers. Top edge gilt.

E107

HANDBOOK OF THE DYCE AND FORSTER COLLECTIONS IN THE SOUTH KENSINGTON MUSEUM. WITH ENGRAVINGS AND FAC-SIMILES. London: For the Committee of Council on Education by Chapman and Hall, Limited. [1880].

8°. In original grey paper wrapper; front detached.

E108

HINTS TO COLLECTORS OF ORIGINAL EDITIONS OF THE WORKS OF CHARLES DICKENS. BY CHARLES PLUMPTRE JOHNSON. London: George Redway. 1885.

8°. In white vellum.

E109

DICKENSIANA A BIBLIOGRAPHY OF THE LITERATURE RELATING TO CHARLES DICKENS AND HIS WRITINGS. COMPILED BY FRED. G. KITTON. London: George Redway. 1886.

8°. In original green cloth with brown end papers.

E110

THE HISTORY OF PICKWICK AN ACCOUNT OF ITS CHARACTERS, LOCALITIES, ALLUSIONS AND ILLUSTRATIONS WITH A BIBLI-OGRAPHY. BY PERCY FITZGERALD. London: Chapman and Hall, Limited. 1891.

8°. In green cloth with dark green end papers.

E111

THE NOVELS OF CHARLES DICKENS A BIBLIOGRAPHY AND SKETCH. BY FREDERIC G. KITTON. London: Elliot Stock. 1897.

8°. In original olive green cloth with gilt lettering. (The Book-Lover's Library)

E112

GLIMPSES OF CHARLES DICKENS AND CATALOGUE OF DICKENS
LITERATURE IN LIBRARY OF E. S. WILLIAMSON ILLUSTRATIONS
AND FACSIMILES. Toronto: The Bryant Press. 1898.

8°. In embossed white paper wrapper with portrait of Dickens.
No. 129 of 250 copies.

E113

DICKENS AND HIS ILLUSTRATORS. BY FREDERIC G. KITTON. WITH
TWENTY-TWO PORTRAITS AND FACSIMILES OF SEVENTY ORIGINAL
DRAWINGS NOW REPRODUCED FOR THE FIRST TIME. London: George
Redway. 1899.

4°. In green cloth with gilt lettering.

Second edition.

E114(1)

THE MINOR WRITINGS OF CHARLES DICKENS A BIBLIOGRAPHY
AND SKETCH. BY FREDERIC G. KITTON. London: Elliot Stock. 1900.

8°. In olive green cloth.

E114(2)

THE MINOR WRITINGS OF CHARLES DICKENS A BIBLIOGRAPHY
AND SKETCH. BY FREDERIC G. KITTON. New York: A. C. Armstrong &
Son. London: Elliot Stock. [1900].

8°. In olive green cloth with gilt lettering and decoration.

E115

THE DICKENS EXHIBITION ORGANIZED BY THE DICKENS FELLOW-
SHIP. COMPILED AND EDITED BY F. G. KITTON. London: The Dickens
Fellowship. [1903].

8°. In original pale green stiff wrapper.

E116

BIBLIOGRAPHY OF THE WRITINGS OF CHARLES DICKENS. EDITED
BY J. C. THOMSON. Warwick: J. Thomson. New York: G. E. Stechert. 1904.

4°. In original blue-grey paper boards with paper label.

E117

THE PICKWICK EXHIBITION HELD AT THE NEW DUDLEY GAL-
LERY UNDER THE AUSPICES OF THE DICKENS FELLOWSHIP.
COMPILED AND EDITED BY B. W. MATZ AND J. W. T. LEY. WITH AN
APPRECIATION OF "THE PICKWICK PAPERS" BY PERCY FITZGERALD.
London: The Dickens Fellowship. 1907.

8°. In green paper wrapper with design for original wrapper of *Pickwick
Papers*.

E118

THE THIRD DICKENS EXHIBITION AT THE NEW DUDLEY GAL-
LERIES. London: 1909.

8°. In original grey paper wrapper. Catalogue of exhibits with an introduction by Percy Fitzgerald.

E119(1)

FIRST AND EARLY AMERICAN EDITIONS OF THE WORKS OF
CHARLES DICKENS. BY WILLIAM GLYDE WILKINS. Cedar Rapids,
Iowa: Privately printed. 1910.

8°. In green paper boards with brown cloth spine.

One of 200 copies.

E119(2)

A binding variant in grey paper boards with brown cloth spine.

E120(1)

VICTORIA & ALBERT MUSEUM GUIDES DICKENS EXHIBITION
MARCH TO OCTOBER, 1912. London: His Majesty's Stationery Office. 1912.

8°. Pamphlet in original grey wrapper.

E120(2)

A second copy in blue wrapper.

E121

AN EXHIBITION OF BOOKS: PRINTS: DRAWINGS MANUSCRIPTS &
LETTERS COMMEMORATIVE OF THE CENTENARY OF CHARLES
DICKENS. St. Louis: The Franklin Club. MDCCCCXII.

8°. In half brown leather with dark grey paper boards.

One of three large paper copies.

E122

CATALOGUE OF AN EXHIBITION OF THE WORKS OF CHARLES
DICKENS WITH AN INTRODUCTION BY ROYAL CORTISSOZ. New
York: The Grolier Club. 1913.

8°. In greyish paper boards with red label.

E123(1)

THE FIRST EDITIONS OF THE WRITINGS OF CHARLES DICKENS
AND THEIR VALUES A BIBLIOGRAPHY. BY JOHN C. ECKEL. London:
Chapman & Hall, Ltd. 1913.

4°. In half vellum with light brown cloth.

E123(2)

A second copy in light brown cloth.

E124

A CATALOGUE OF THE WRITINGS OF CHARLES DICKENS IN THE LIBRARY OF HARRY ELKINS WIDENER. BY A. S. W. ROSENBACH. Philadelphia: Privately printed. MDCCCCXVII.

4°. In dark blue cloth.

E125

THE LIBRARY OF WILLIAM ANDREWS CLARK, JR. THE POST-HUMOUS PAPERS OF THE PICKWICK CLUB BY CHARLES DICKENS THE DOUGLAS-AUSTIN COPY NOW IN THE POSSESSION OF WILLIAM ANDREWS CLARK, JR. A BIBLIOGRAPHICAL DESCRIPTION. San Francisco: John Henry Nash. 1920.

4°. In grey paper boards with green cloth spine and paper label.

E126

THE LIBRARY OF WILLIAM ANDREWS CLARK, JR. CRUIKSHANK AND DICKENS COLLATED AND COMPILED BY ROBERT ERNEST COWAN AND WILLIAM ANDREWS CLARK, JR. San Francisco: John Henry Nash. 1921.

4°. Two volumes in grey paper boards with green cloth spine and paper label.

E127

GEORGE CRUIKSHANK A CATALOGUE RAISONNÉ. BY ALBERT M. COHN. London: Office of "The Bookman's Journal." 1924.

4°. In original brown cloth.

No. 348 of 500 numbered copies.

E128

THE RENOWNED COLLECTION OF FIRST EDITIONS OF CHARLES DICKENS AND WILLIAM MAKEPEACE THACKERAY. FORMED BY GEORGE BARR McCUTCHEON. New York: American Art Association, Inc. [1926].

8°. In original white wrapper.

E129

THE RENOWNED COLLECTION OF THE WORKS OF CHARLES DICKENS FORMED BY THOMAS HATTON. New York: American Art Association, Inc. [1927].

8°. Bound with original white wrapper in flexible blue morocco.

E130

THE POSTHUMOUS PAPERS OF THE PICKWICK CLUB SOME NEW BIBLIOGRAPHICAL DISCOVERIES. BY GEORGE W. DAVIS. London: Marks & Co. [1928].

8°. In stiff green paper wrapper.

E131

PRIME PICKWICKS IN PARTS CENSUS WITH COMPLETE COLLA-
TION COMPARISON AND COMMENT. BY JOHN C. ECKEL. New York:
Edgar H. Wells & Co., Inc. London: Charles J. Sawyer, Ltd. 1928.

8°. In original green cloth with design by Seymour.

E132

CHARLES DICKENS HIS LIFE AS TRACED BY HIS WORKS. BY CORTES
W. CAVANAUGH. EARLY AMERICAN EDITIONS OF THE WORKS OF
CHARLES DICKENS. BY HERMAN LEROY EDGAR AND R. W. G. VAIL.
New York: The New York Public Library. 1929.

8°. In grey paper wrapper.

E133

THE DICKENS ADVERTISER A COLLECTION OF THE ADVERTISE-
MENTS IN THE ORIGINAL PARTS OF NOVELS BY CHARLES DICK-
ENS. EDITED BY BERNARD DARWIN. London: Elkin Mathews & Marrot.
1930.

8°. In blue cloth.

E134

A CHOICE OF BOOKS OLD AND NEW: THE CHARLES DICKENS
NUMBER, COMPRISING FIRST EDITIONS OF HIS WORKS, AUTO-
GRAPH LETTERS BY HIM AND HIS CIRCLE. London: Henry Sotheran,
Ltd. [1931].

8°. Lacking wrapper.

E135

THE FIRST EDITIONS OF THE WRITINGS OF CHARLES DICKENS
THEIR POINTS AND VALUES A BIBLIOGRAPHY BY JOHN C. ECKEL
REVISED AND ENLARGED WITH ILLUSTRATIONS AND FACSIMILES.
New York: Maurice Inman, Inc. London: Maggs Bros. 1932.

4°. In three-fourths dark blue morocco with light blue cloth.

No. 86 of 250 copies printed.

E136(1)

A BIBLIOGRAPHY OF THE PERIODICAL WORKS OF CHARLES DICK-
ENS BIBLIOGRAPHICAL ANALYTICAL AND STATISTICAL BY
THOMAS HATTON AND ARTHUR H. CLEAVER WITH 31 ILLUSTRA-
TIONS AND FACSIMILES. London: Chapman & Hall, Ltd. 1933.

8°. In green cloth.

Edition limited to 750 copies.

E136(2)

A binding variant in original tan cloth.

E137

DICKENS POSITIVELY THE FIRST APPEARANCE A CENTENARY REVIEW WITH A BIBLIOGRAPHY OF SKETCHES BY BOZ. BY F. J. HARVEY DARTON. London: The Argonaut Press. 1933.

8°. In moss-green paper boards and cloth spine with paper label.

E138

THE SENTIMENTAL JOURNEY A LIFE OF CHARLES DICKENS. BY HUGH KINGSMILL. New York: William Morrow and Company. 1935.

8°. In original blue cloth.

E139

CATALOGUE OF THE LIBRARY OF CHARLES DICKENS FROM GADS-HILL REPRINTED FROM SOTHERAN'S 'PRICE CURRENT OF LITERATURE' NOS. CLXXIV AND CLXXV. EDITED BY J. H. STONEHOUSE. London: Piccadilly Fountain Press. 1935.

8°. In brown cloth with paper label. Reprint of the catalogues of the libraries of Dickens and Thackeray.

E140

A CENTENARY BIBLIOGRAPHY OF THE PICKWICK PAPERS. BY W. MILLER AND E. H. STRANGE. London: The Argonaut Press. 1936.

8°. In original green cloth with gilt lettering.

E141

A COLLECTION OF THE FIRST EDITIONS OF THE WORKS OF CHARLES DICKENS AUTOGRAPH LETTERS PERSONAL RELICS AND DICKENSIANA. London: Chas. J. Sawyer, Ltd. 1936.

8°. In original white wrapper.

E142

A DICKENS LIBRARY EXHIBITION CATALOGUE OF THE SAWYER COLLECTION OF THE WORKS OF CHARLES DICKENS COMPRISING MANUSCRIPTS, AUTOGRAPH LETTERS, PRESENTATION COPIES, THE ISSUES IN ORIGINAL PARTS, DICKENSIANA, ETC. Letchworth, Herts.: Privately printed. 1936.

4°. In original green paper boards with portrait of Dickens.

E143

BOOKS FOR THE READER AND COLLECTOR. London: Charles J. Sawyer, Ltd. 1937.

8°. Catalogue in original yellow wrapper with many Dickens items.

E144

"Special Bibliography: The Stage Versions of Dickens' Novels." In three parts in BULLETIN OF BIBLIOGRAPHY, Sept.–Dec., 1936, Jan.–April, 1937, May–Aug., 1937.

8°. Three separate numbers in blue wrappers, as issued.

E145

CATALOGUE OF A FURTHER PORTION OF THE WELL-KNOWN LI-
BRARY THE PROPERTY OF THE COMTE DE SUZANNET . . . THE
CELEBRATED COLLECTION OF MATERIALS CONCERNING CHARLES
DICKENS. London: Sotheby & Co. 1938.

E146

A REMARKABLE DICKENS COLLECTION COMPRISING ORIGINAL
MANUSCRIPTS PRESENTATION COPIES A COMPLETE SET OF THE
ISSUES IN ORIGINAL PARTS BOUND COPIES OF FIRST EDITIONS
DICKENSIANA, ETC. London: Charles J. Sawyer, Ltd. [1938].

8°. In original green wrapper.

E147

RARE BOOKS ORIGINAL DRAWINGS AUTOGRAPH LETTERS AND
MANUSCRIPTS COLLECTED BY THE LATE A. EDWARD NEWTON
REMOVED FROM HIS HOME OAK KNOLL DAYLESFORD, PA. FOR
PUBLIC SALE. New York: Parke-Bernet Galleries, Inc. 1941.

8°. In lavender paper boards with purple lettering, illustrative end papers.
Part one: A-B.

E148

"A Catalogue of Interesting Books." London: P. J. & A. E. Dobell. 1940.

8°. Leaflet in original white wrapper. Includes "A Collection of Dickensiana,
from the Library of the late Sir Henry and Lady Dickens."

E149

THE DISTINGUISHED COLLECTION OF FIRST EDITIONS—AUTO-
GRAPHS MANUSCRIPTS—ORIGINAL DRAWINGS BY AND RELATING
TO CHARLES DICKENS FORMED BY LEWIS A. HIRD. New York: Parke-
Bernet Galleries, Inc. 1953.

8°. Pamphlet in original buff wrapper.

E150

COLLATION OF THE FAMOUS LAPHAM-WALLACE PICKWICK. New
York: Harry F. Marks. [n.d.].

4°. Pamphlet with outer sheet as wrapper.

No. 77 of 250 copies.

E151

AMERICAN AND ENGLISH LITERATURE. FIRST EDITIONS MANU-
SCRIPTS AUTOGRAPH LETTERS. SELECTIONS FROM THE LIBRARY
OF THE LATE DR. SAMUEL WYLLIS BANDLER OF NEW YORK CITY.
PART II. New York: Charles S. Boesen. [n.d.].

8°. In reddish-brown paper wrapper.

E152

Catalogue of the Dickens Collection of John S. Barnet. Typewritten list of
titles and prices.

INDEX

Entries are arranged under five headings:

   I : Charles Dickens
  II : Artists, Engravers, Illustrators
 III : Binders, Printers, Publishers
 IV : Collectors
  V : General

Parodists, adaptors, translators are entered under V, but the peculiar titles of their works are subsumed in the original title entries under I. Relatively unimportant Dickensiana is excluded from the index.

I. CHARLES DICKENS

Books from his library: B149(2), B557(5), D1-18; books presented by: B16(1) B25(1,2), B237(1), B258(1), B476(2), B489(3), B499(1), B501, B570, B611, B671
Books written or edited by:
Account of "Not So Bad as We Seem": B657(1,2)
Address Delivered at the Birmingham and Midland Institute: B613
All the Year Round: A117, A121, A130, B250(1-3), B444-447, B449, B452, B454, B457-458, B574(1-3), B577, B582, B594
American Note Never Intended for General Circulation: B648
American Notes: A20-21, A30, B476(1-3)-488
Another Round of Stories by the Christmas Fire: B441

Barnaby Rudge: A16, A103, A171-172, A187(1), B162-169, B171, B173, B175, B179-180, B692
Battle of Life: B417(1-16)-424
Bleak House: A89, A173-177, B236(1-6)-246

Child's Dream of a Star: B573, B588(1-2)-589
Child's History of England: A88-89, B499(1,2)-502
Chimes: A36, B385(1-9)-401, C37, C40
Christmas Books: B430(1,2)
Christmas Carol: A180-181, B356(1-10)-384, B683(1), D83
Christmas Stories: B429, B431, B438, B460, B470
Complete Poems: B540(1-3)
Cousin-Seeker of Berlin: B670
Cricket on the Hearth: B368, B402(1-12)-416, B434, B469, B682a, B692
Curious Dance Round a Curious Tree: B465

Daily News: A36, A38, B490, B594
Daily Remembrancer, 1838-1841: A151
David Copperfield: A64, A187(1), B220(1-5)-235, B683(5), B707
Dickens v. Barabbas: B651(1,2)
Doctor Marigold's Prescriptions: B446, B454-456, B466, B683(3,4)
Dombey and Son: A56, B173, B194(1-5)-219, B682

Edwin Drood: See Mystery of Edwin Drood
Enlightened Clergyman: A121, B582
Evenings of a Working Man: A32, B606-607(1,2)
Extraordinary Gazette: B549-550(1,2)

Five Christmas Novels: B433

II. ARTISTS, ENGRAVERS, ILLUSTRATORS

Note: Reference is made to certain works illustrated by a person not mentioned in the notes.

Aldin, Cecil: B31, B34, B75
Ardizonne, Edward: B265(1,2), B723

Bacon, John H.: B725
Baker, L. H.: C37
Barnard, Frederick: B252, B516, B725, C5, C7, C9-10, C15, C19, C21, C24-25, C31-32
Bedford, F. D.: B587
Blaikie, F. M. B.: B146
Block, T.: B17
Bonner: B59(1-4)
Brock, Charles E.: B51
Brown, J.: C37
Brown, Hablot Knight (Phiz): A89, A157, B13(1-3), B24(3), B26-27, B29, B42, B46, B49, B125(1,2), B127, B134-135, B152-153(1,2), B162, B170-171, B173, B181(1-4), B182(1,2)-183, B189, B196, B205-207, B221, B224-225, B239, B244, B473, B527(2), B528, C1-2, C4, C14, C18, C25, C36-37, D139, D256, E62, E64
Brundage, Frances: B218
Burn, Gerald M.: C33
Buss, Robert William: B13(1,2), B15(3), B16(1), B29, B37, B49

Cattermole, George: A9, A16, A213, B152-153(1,2), B162
Clarke, J. Clayton (Kyd): A187(1,2), B172, C8(1,2)
Coburn, F. S.: B410
Coffin, Ernest: B300(1,2)
Copping, Harold: B218, B725, B730, D246
Crane, Walter: A193
Crowdy, Wallace L.: C27
Crowquill, Alfred: See Forrester, Alfred H.
Cruikshank, George: A136, A139, A147, A185-186, B4(1,2), B9-21, B88, B91(1,2)-92, B96, B98(4), B101, B104-106, B666(1-3)-668, C18, C36, D36, E127

Dalziel Brothers: A118, A168
Dalziel, E. G.: A166, A168, C25
Darley, Felix O. C.: B214, B230(2), B245(2), B434, B625, C6, C11-12
Daugherty, James: B168
Doyle, Richard: B385(1-9)-386(1-3), B402(1-12), B417(1-16)

Egg, Augustus L.: A194
Eytinge, S., Jr.: B231, B512, B684

Fildes, Luke: B276(1-8)-277(1,2), C18, C36
Forrester, Alfred Henry (Crowquill): B19, B40, B58-59(1-4), D95
Fraser, C. Lovat: C29, D312
Fraser, F. A.: C25
French, H.: C25
Frith, William Powell: A203, C37
Frost, A. B.: B50(1,2), B484, C25

Gibson, C. D.: C16
Gihon, W. F.: B224
Gilbert, Sir John: B24(3), B44, C6
Gillies, Margaret: C37

III. BINDERS, PRINTERS, PUBLISHERS

Abbott, William: B645
Alden, Beardsley & Co.: B566(1-3)-567
Alden, John B.: B692
Allen, Josiah Jr.: B613
Allen, W. H., & Co.: B296(1-3), B538(1,2)-539(1,2)
Allman, Thomas: B397
Altemus, Henry: B369, B729
American Art Association: E128-129
Anderson, John R.: B191(2), B245(2)
Appleton, D., and Company: B117, B280, B533, B583(1,2), D55, E21, E48
Appleyard, E.: B44
Arakelyan Press: B596
Argonaut Press: E137, E140
Armstrong, A. C., & Son: E114(2)
Arrowsmith, J. W.: E61
Associated Newspapers: B520
Atlantic Monthly Press: B372

Bain, A. W., and Co.: B83(2)
Baker & Taylor: B73(1), B368, B462
Baker, Walter, & Co.: B412, B734
Barker, Arthur: B521
Barnes, A. S., & Co.: B687
Barth, W.: B396
Belford, Clarke & Company: B263
Bell & Daldy: B668
Bell, George, and Sons: E50
Bentley, Richard: B86, B93, B498, B525(1-3), B548(1,2), B550(1,2), B554, B599(1-4)-600, B603
Bentley, Samuel: B526
Berwick Press: B71
Blackie & Son: D47
Blackwood, William, & Sons: B664
Bobbs-Merrill: E67
Boeson, Charles S.: E151
Bogue, David: A147, B667
Bonner, R.: B575
Bradbury & Evans: B97(1,2)-98(1-4), B194(1-5)-195(1,2), B202, B211, B220(1-5), B222, B225, B236(1-6)-237(1-3), B247(1-7)-248, B361, B402(1-12), B417(1-16), B425(1-7), B445, B469, B489(1-3), B499(1,2), B503(1,2), B681-682
Bradbury and Guild: B196
Bradley Press: D83
Brady, F. A.: B560
Brentano's: B13(1)
British Art Company: C33
Bryant & Rackstraw: E59
Bryant Press: E112
Buchanan, James: C34
Buck and Wooton: B614
Bunce & Brother: B564
Burgess, Stringer: B199
Burt, A. L.: B133

Caldwell, H. M.: B435
Cambridge University Press: B303
Carey & Hart: B362(1,2), B608, B625

265

IV. COLLECTORS

NOTE: *In addition to Mr. Halstead VanderPoel, principal collectors represented are George A. Aiken, Edwin Bachmann, T. E. Hanley, and Mrs. Miriam Lutcher Stark. Individual items from these collectors are not indexed here.*

Baillie, William Elliot: B539(1)
Bandler, Samuel Wyllis: E151
Barnet, John S.: A150, B350, E152
Bement, Clarence S.: B603
Clark, William Andrew, Jr.: E125-126
Cosens, Frederick William: A157
Crummer, Mrs. LeRoy: B259, B270
Daly, Augustine: B603
DeGolyer, E.: B599(3)
DeSuzannet, Comte: A1, B659, E145
Deverell, John Croft: B527(2)
DuBois, Loren Griswold: B41(2)
Eckel, John: E123(1,2), E131, E135
Field, Eugene: B1
Fields, James T.: B365(2), B585, B626(1,2)
Fitzgerald, Percy: B13(2), B30, B65, B67, B69, D138, D145(1,2), D154, D161, E51, E61, E110, E117-118
Follett, Fred I.: B182(2)
Goodwin, H. T.: B30
Hatton, Thomas: A214, B677(2), E129, E136(1,2)
Hird, Lewis A.: E149
Kern, Jerome: B525(2)
Lowther, Marcus: B69
McCutcheon, George Barr: A156, B77, B516, B573, B647, D241, E128
Newton, A. Edward: B372, E147
Parsons, E. A.: B271, B371(1)
Rich, Waldo Leon: B298
Ross, Barnaby: B455, B510
Sawyer, Charles J.: B651(1,2), E131, E141-143, E146
Senff, Gustavia A.: B600
Skillicorne, William Nash: B87(1)
Smith, Harry Bache: B550(1), B639, B659, D272
Starrett, Vincent: B279, B283-284, B289-290, B292(2)-283, B297(1,2), B300(2)-301(1,2), B306(1,2)-307, B308(2), B310, B313-317(1,2), B319, B323, B348-355
Ulizio, B. George: B356(4), B489(1)
Webster, Baron Dickinson: B298
Widener, Harry Elkins: E124
Widener, Joseph: B603
Wilkins, William Glyde: B9, B18, B99, B129, B157-158, B166, B185, B388(1), B420, B623, D56, D243, E119(1,2)
Williamson, E. S.: E112
Wise, Thomas J.: A81, B470(2), B558, B657(1,2)-658, D71, D303
Wrenn, John Henry: B470(2), B658, D303

V: GENERAL

Wilson, Edmund: D300
Wise, Thomas James: A81, B657(1)
Woods, George B.: B320
Woollcott, Alexander: E70
World Telegram (New York): B518
Wright, Thomas: E91

Yeats-Brown, Timothy: B649